London,
Gun Manufacturer.

W.A.BECKWITH
Gun Maker

AUSPICIO   SENATUS ANGLIÆ
REGIS ET
To the Hon.ble East India Comp.y
Skinner Street
LONDON

LANG'S
PATENT

WESTLEY RICHARDS

327

PATENT

PATENT

J. ERSKINE & C.o

NEWTON STEWART

N.o 3

JEFFERIES
PATENT

W. GREENER
PATENT

THE BRITISH SHOTGUN 1850-1870

A Sandringham Bouquet from The Illustrated London News

THE BRITISH SHOTGUN

VOLUME ONE 1850-1870

I. M. Crudgington
and
D. J. Baker

BARRIE & JENKINS
COMMUNICA - EUROPA

First published in 1979 by
Barrie and Jenkins Ltd
24 Highbury Crescent, London N5 1RX

ISBN 0 214 20493 6

To Carol and Lynne for their forbearance

Printed at the Shenval Press, London and Harlow

Foreword

This is the first volume of a work that I have anxiously awaited since I first met Ian Crudgington eight years ago, and I have felt the lack of it for even longer. Considering the amount published on shooting and firearms in general, there is surprisingly little precise and accessible information on the evolution of the breech loading sporting gun. As a cataloguer, I have a special interest in being able to identify and date examples, but the history of sporting guns reveals a richness of ingenuity and skills that deserves a wide appreciation. The development of breech loading in the nineteenth century is significant in social, military and technical history. Though the principle was evolved abroad and British gunmakers accepted the innovation somewhat reluctantly, they eventually raised it, in the form of the sporting gun, to an excellence that sets the standard still. The breech loading shotgun, therefore, has a valid place in our national heritage.

As the need for this book is clear to my mind, so are the qualifications of its authors. Both became interested in firearms at an early age, but the vital quality that they share is unrelenting curiosity: the desire to know precisely. This means that they have no inclination to serve us warmed-over legends. Instead, they have drawn on original sources of every type and have carefully compared, where possible, documentary evidence with surviving guns. Hopefully, the identification provided by this book will bring to light some of the untraced specimens. The authors acknowledge the probability that not every question has been asked, let alone answered, but this is part of their continuing quest and one in which the reader may share.

The individual qualities of the authors are equally significant. Ian Crudgington is a Past Master of the Worshipful Company of Gunmakers and his long practical experience as a gunmaker has sharpened his appreciation of the problems and skills of his craft brethren. He is, however, relieved by time from the need to assess the work of competitors, a relevant factor in the writings of most insiders. In fact, few people in the trade appear to have taken any interest in gunmaking history and fewer still can have realised that they were making it. In consequence, gunmakers' records are all too often lost, incomplete or imprecise, but there are vital oral traditions and hereditary techniques to which Ian Crudgington has had privileged access.

David Baker is an amateur in the best sense. His interest in firearms is wide and motivated by the values he perceives in them rather than the price put upon them by others. His enthusiasm extends where possible to using the guns he studies in the sporting field. This has given him an unusually sensitive feeling for the practicality and popularity of different designs. Professionally, David Baker is a pharmacist and this scientific discipline shows in his scrupulous approach to physical and written evidence.

The complementary nature of the authors' talents is not only fruitful, but apt: for the successful emergence of the modern breech loader also hinges on a partnership, the coming together of a sound gun and an efficient cartridge.

Christopher Brunker

Christie's
London
March 1978

Daw headstamp   *Eley headstamp*

Daw cap

Contents

Introduction

One of the most fascinating parts of the story of British gunmaking is the evolution, in the last half of the nineteenth century, of the sporting shotgun. When we, the authors, first discussed this project, we envisaged covering the period in a single volume. However, on second thoughts, we realised that the mass of invention was such that this was not possible, certainly in a volume of manageable dimensions. We therefore decided to divide the period at 1870, so that the first part deals primarily with the pin and centre fire hammer guns, while the second is overwhelmingly concerned with the hammerless guns.

It is surprising that a full description of this fascinating era has not been attempted earlier. The upheavals caused by two world wars and a severe depression have had no small part to play in this delayed recognition. As a result of this, those who could have told something of this story from memory have long been in their graves, and we have been forced to reconstruct as much as is possible from the written records of the period. Prominent among these are the records of the Patent Office but much valuable material has also been obtained from *The Field* in particular, *Land and Water* and other periodicals in general. This research has shown many curious errors in the writings of both J. H. Walsh and W. W. Greener, whose books on the period have long been regarded as the standard works of reference. The most glaring of these errors was to omit to remark on the true origins of the famous Lancaster Base Fire gun, and then to quote a false date for its introduction.

Having said this, the authors are all too well aware of the limitations of their own knowledge, particularly in regard to the human element involved, and would welcome any further information, however brief, in the hope that a future edition may be more complete.

This volume could never have been produced without the co-operation and generous assistance of a great many people to whom we offer our sincere thanks.

We are especially grateful to Her Majesty the Queen for graciously granting us permission to consult the Royal Photographic Archives at Windsor, to examine and photograph the royal sporting guns at Sandringham, and to reproduce those on pages 55, 57, 66, 134, 135, 185 and 186.

We are indebted to all those who have supplied information, photographs, permission to photograph, suggestions and, perhaps most important of all, encouragement.

John Amber; Avon County Library, Bath; D. H. L. Back; Larry Baer; Roger Barlow; A. C. Bedford, Proof Master, London Proof House; Birmingham Reference Library; Bodleian Library, Oxford; John Bogg; Boss & Co Ltd; Roger Booth; British Patent Office, especially the staff of the printing and sale branch, St Mary Cray, and the foreign patent department; C. E. Brunker: Messrs Christie Manson & Woods Ltd; Cambridge University Library; R. Chapman; Jean-Rene Clergeau; Leo Cullinan; Daily Telegraph Information Service; Deutsches Waffen Journal; Miss Dimond: Assistant Librarian, Windsor Castle; The late Mark Dinely; A. Fletcher: Messrs Fletcher & Son, Gloucester; French Patent Office; T. N. and R. N. Gallyon: Messrs Gallyon & Son Ltd, Cambridge; G. T. Garwood; Gastinne Renette Ltd; Roy Grainger: *The Field*; The Guardians of the Birmingham Proof House; The Master, Wardens and Court of Assistants of the Worshipful Company of Gunmakers of the City of London; Keith Haddrell; P. Harvey; Haseltine, Lake & Co; Col L. J. Hill: Messrs Webley & Scott Ltd, Birmingham; Bob Hinman; Messrs Holland & Holland Ltd; I. M. I. (Kynoch) Ltd; Interarmco Ltd; Islington Library; T. V. Jackson; D. B. Jeffrey: Messrs C. Jeffrey & Son Ltd, Dorchester; N. Johnson; A. N. Kennard; A. Lawrie: Messrs Churchill Ltd; Roger Lees, Proof Master, Birmingham Proof House; G. E. Lewis: Messrs G. E. Lewis & Son, Birmingham; D. A. Masters: Messrs Churchill Ltd; Peter McGowan; Sir Philip Moore; Naval Historical Library; W. Keith Neal; The Newspaper Library (Colindale); D. Nie: Weller and Dufty Ltd; Oxford Reference Library; Camille Passot; D. Powell: Messrs Wm Powell & Son Ltd, Birmingham; Reading Library; Regimental Librarian, Coldstream Guards; Frank Richards; Llewellyn Robins; Emil Rosner; Jan Shrader; A. Sinclair: Messrs John Dickson & Son Ltd, Edinburgh; Forrest Smith; E. L. Stone; Swindon Reference Library; P. Towler: Messrs Darlow, Norwich.

We would thank all those friends and acquaintances made during our gun collecting careers who, by their kindness and willingness to share their knowledge, have fired our imaginations and prompted this deeper study of our subject.

Finally, a very special thank you from us both to Lynne, who not only gave valuable help in all aspects connected with the writing of this book, but also, in the most chaotic of conditions and from wretched writing on any material to hand, typed the manuscript so expertly.

10

Photograph Acknowledgements

The photographs used to illustrate this book are the work of many photographers using a variety of instruments.

They were taken over a number of years, some, of necessity, in conditions less than ideal, with the result that the end product has inevitably suffered. By using a faster film to compensate for poor light, a grainy print is often produced.

The majority of the authors' photographs were taken on 35mm Ilford Pan F film for the half tones, and Kodak 2556 for the line drawings. Where no acknowledgement is given the print can be assumed to be the work of the authors.

We would thank the following in particular:
Roger Barlow: illustrations on page 143, Birmingham Reference Library: 50, John Bogg: 117, Carey Keates: 80 (top), 134, 151, Christie Manson and Woods Ltd: 14, 12, 108 (bottom), 118, 125 (bottom), 173, Elizabeth Johnston: 55, 57 (bottom), 135, 186, Ron Lucking: 100, Peter McGowan: 29, W. Keith Neal: 18, 20, 48, 75 (bottom), 89 (bottom), 95, 102 (bottom), 118, 147 (top), 151, 190, Camille Passot: 19, Forrest Smith: 30, 97, 132, 180 (top), 192 (top), Weller and Dufty Ltd: 25 (top)

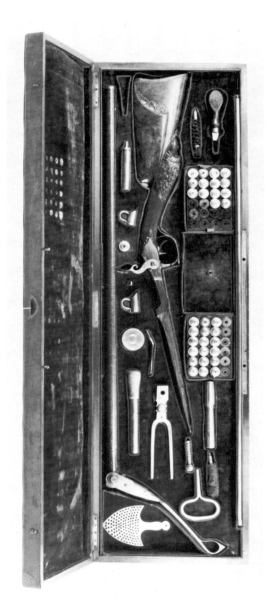

Pauly shotgun in case with tools and accessories to make cartridges

Chapter One

THE ORIGINS

While it is true that there have been breech loading guns almost as long as there have been guns, certainly examples are known which date back to the 14th century, and these could be argued to be the ancestors of the British breech loading shotgun, yet the direct line of evolution really began in the early years of the 19th century with the work of the Reverend Alexander John Forsyth, which culminated in his patent No. 3032 of 1807. In this he described how he had succeeded in using a group of chemicals which ignite when struck to fire a charge of common gunpowder in a muzzle loading gun. This patent was tested in the courts on at least five occasions and held to be a master patent but though Forsyth's vigorous defence of it was undoubtedly sound commercial sense, it had the unfortunate effect of restricting the development in Great Britain. When general use came to be made of the invention, first by licence and ultimately on the expiry of the patent, it was extensively used in place of a flint lock to fire muzzle loading weapons of all sorts. However, while Forsyth's patent was valid only in Great Britain, news of his invention travelled overseas and it is in France that a series of important steps were taken. Why this turbulent period of French history should have produced this surge of invention is beyond the scope of this work. Ultimately it was to result not only in the breech loading shotgun, but was to be largely responsible for the use of the elongated rifle bullet which expanded on firing to fit the bore of a muzzle loading rifle, known today as the Minie bullet after one of its inventors. But the Minie appeared nearly four decades on from the Forsyth.

Only five years after the latter's patent there appeared in Paris a gun which is arguably second only to Forsyth's invention as one of the most important developments in the whole history of firearms.

The inventor of this was Samuel Johannes Pauly, a Swiss artillery man, who had seen active service in Napoleon's army. Pauly was a man of an inventive nature whose first interest was dirigible ballooning. However on 29 September 1812 he obtained a French patent, No. 843, for the breech loading system for which he is now remembered. To exploit his invention commercially, he formed an association with the Parisian gunmaker, Prelat, whose premises were at 4 Rue des Trois Frères. The exact nature of this business relationship is unknown and is now obscured by Pauly's fame, which has meant that there was kudos to be gained by linking one's name to his. So it is recorded that a Prussian by the name of Johann Nikolaus von

Dreyse, who was later to achieve fame by his own gun invention, was 'employed by Pauly as a lock-maker'.

The gun on which its inventor's fame rests is, to the majority of present day British shotgun users, strange in that the barrels are fixed in relation to the stock and it is the breech that pivots to load the gun. Conversely, it would have been thought less unusual at the date of its production when the muzzle loader with its fixed barrels was the normal sporting gun.

Pauly shotgun

The breech block is pivoted on trunnions on either side of the barrel breeches and the gun opens by lifting this block up, by means of the long tail-like lever which is in fact a continuation of the block proper. When closed the lever lies along the hand of the stock and is retained by a catch on the front of the comb. The ammunition that this gun used was uncannily like a modern cartridge, being composed of a metal head and a paper tube with the percussion powder in a recess in the head. This paper tube would have been largely destroyed on firing and the brass base did not act as a gas seal, thus a certain amount of gases and corrosive residue were allowed to enter the lock mechanism.

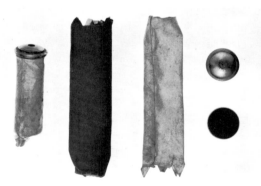

Pauly cartridges

Another feature with which Pauly pointed the way very far ahead of his time was that his gun had an internal striking mechanism built on a trigger plate action. The very elegant 'hammers' are but cocking levers.

While we were preparing this book, a particularly fine specimen of a

14

Pauly gun passed through a well-known London auction room. Of great interest are the contents of the case, for from these we can glimpse the effort that a pioneering user of a Pauly had to expend before he could use his gun. Contained in the case are a supply of turned brass heads and cut papers with which to roll fresh tubes on the dowel former provided. In addition to the case, the sportsman, or more likely a trusted servant, had to prepare the pellets of detonating compound to reprime the heads of the home made cases. The mould for these is the object something like a playing card spade with holes in it situated in the left of the case.

In retrospect it would appear that this gun was too far ahead of its time and we. must regard many of the subsequent 'improvements' made to it as retrograde steps.

The fall of Paris on 5 April 1814 to the Allied Armies appears to have prompted Pauly to move to London, and here on 4 August he obtained a British patent, No. 3833, for a version of his gun with compressed air ignition. Whether he thought this superior to his original method is not, as far as we are aware, recorded but it is the authors' opinion that it was more likely an attempt to circumvent Forsyth's patent. In either event it was a commercial failure and no contemporary mention, beyond the patent specification, exists and the very few guns that survive would all seem to be prototypes.

Pauly then abandoned firearms, reverted to dirigible balloons and succeeded in interesting his fellow Swiss, the successful London gunmaker Durs Egg, in the scheme to build a 90ft long fish-shaped conveyance which was called *The Dolphin*. It was, however, never completed; as is so often the way of such things, it proved more costly to build than originally anticipated, a sum of £10,000 is mentioned as being spent on it, and equally important, sometime in 1815 its inventor died.

On the departure of Pauly from Paris his business had been carried on by a certain Henri Roux, who continued to build Pauly type guns. In Deane's *Manual of Firearms* there is a mention that M. Roux 'made the slight improvement to this (Pauly) system by substituting the capsule for the fulminate of mercury in powder in the rosettes affixed to the cartridge: But in this also the same defect of a constantly primed cartridge existed'. This, of course, brought the Pauly gun even closer to the modern shotgun, but despite this, and M. Roux's efforts to popularise it by writing a small book on it (*Fusils de Chasse,* published in Paris in 1822), it remained too far ahead of its time. Deane gives one important clue as to this, expressing the apprehension felt at the use of a constantly primed cartridge. This fear remains to this day among those unfamiliar with firearms.

The copper cap, as we now would call Deane's 'capsule', is another of the crucial stages in the evolution of the modern shotgun but the real inventor remains a mystery. There is a delightful passage in a small book published in 1906 by the ammunition makers F. Joyce & Co, to mark the centenary of percussion ignition, that neatly sums up the problem.

It is a question most difficult to determine, that of the identity of the true and first inventor of the percussion cap. Reliable authorities attribute the discovery to Mr Joshua Shaw, in America; to Colonel Vergnaud, in France, and to practically every well-known gunmaker at that time established in England. Mr Durs Egg, it is asserted, made the first cap out of a penny piece, Mr Joshua Shaw made it out of a steel disc, Mr Purdey out of the ferrule of an old umbrella, and Colonel Hawker entertained a strong conviction that he himself made it out of his own head.

So it was that Roux's business successor, Eugène Pichereau, bowed to popular opinion and took the retrograde step of adopting the nipple and copper cap, so producing what in modern parlance is a capping breech loader. M. Pichereau was in turn succeeded by M. Lefaucheux.

Lefaucheux-made gun of Pichereau type

This was Casimir Lefaucheux whose influence was to loom large in the subsequent history of the breech loading shotguns, indeed his name was, for a considerable time, synonymous with breech loading. He continued to build breech loaders of what we may call the Pauly/Pichereau type and took out a series of French patents in the 1830s to cover breech loaders of his own design.

While he claims that the inspirations for these comes from Pauly, the guns, we think, of 'Lefaucheux' were essentially different in that he adopted the established method of revealing the open ends of the breeches which required the muzzles to pivot down. By having the fulcrum some two or three inches from the action face he produced a mechanism which was to be used on the overwhelming majority of sporting guns made in Europe for the rest of the nineteenth century and what is indeed still regarded by many as 'a conventional sporting gun'.

Initially the cartridge used in this gun was fired by an external percussion cap placed on a nipple fixed to the barrel of the gun as in the Pichereau modification of the Pauly. But in 1836 Lefaucheux patented a crude pinfire cartridge in which the powder charge was ignited by a pellet of percussion compound which lay at one side of the inside of the head of the cartridge. Upon this pellet bore a rod or pin which transversed the head of the

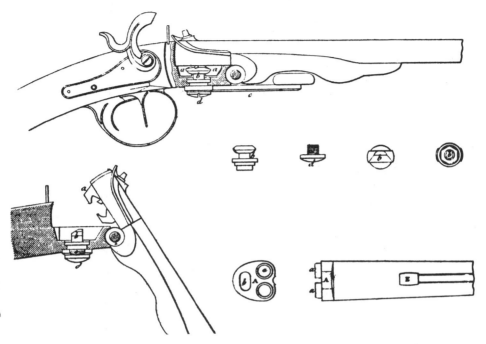

Lefaucheux's French patent of 1834

cartridge and continued out through a hole in the side of the head. This pin was designed to be struck by a hammer or cock on the gun of very similar form to that used on the earlier capping breech loader Lefaucheux guns. From the sparse details in the patent drawings this cartridge would appear to have been far from gas tight, but it evidently was acceptable in practice and guns were made in at least token quantities until the invention eleven years later of more satisfactory ammunition.

As will happen many times in our story, the evolution of the Lefaucheux gun poses questions that we regret cannot now be answered. We have no direct knowledge of why M. Casimir Lefaucheux adopted the pivot open breech action in the first place after Pauly type guns had been produced for 20 or so years previously, or why he chose the pinfire type of cartridge or for what reason the double bite action, shown in the 1834 patent as well to the rear of the barrels, was abandoned in favour of a single bite much nearer the pivot. This was to become a major and valid point of criticism when guns of this design came into common use in England a couple of decades later.

This perhaps gives the impression that the development of the breech loader was the prerogative of a single establishment in Paris. This was not so and it is an indication of the growing popularity of breech loading shotguns in France that from the mid-1820s onwards there was a steady stream of designs produced and patented both for guns to fire special cartridges or simply for improved cartridges.

Throughout our story, and indeed the whole of man's mechanical progress, it is a sure guide to the usefulness of an idea if other inventors seek to improve it, or makers, other than the original inventor, attempt to or actually copy it.

While not quite strictly fulfilling these criteria, but nevertheless a pointer to the acceptance of the Pauly system of breech loading by a proportion of French sportsmen, is a French patent, in the name of Clement Pottet, No. 3930 of 12 March 1829.

The importance of this specification lies in the fact that the drawing shows a species of centre fire cartridge in which a percussion cap is placed on a central nipple and we thus have the essential feature of untold millions of cartridges used since.

Steel reloadable cartridge case with nipple in base for copper cap, marked E. M. Reilly & Co.

Pottet patent of 1829

This eventually evolved into reloadable chamber pieces, in either steel or brass, which were used and continued in modified forms particularly for sportsmen visiting out of the way places where cartridge cases were not readily obtainable.

Also included in this specification are what appear to be modifications of a Pauly type action and a cartridge more like the Pauly in that it used loose priming powder pressed into a central depression in the head of the cartridge.

But much more interesting is that Pottet tells us in his specification that he had been 'Contremaitre' or overseer for Pauly and that a problem of the latter's gun was that it had a tendency to fire the second barrel by a flash from the first carrying across the breech.

Building on the success and publicity of the Pauly/Roux gun, another breech loader became popular in France. It was the invention of a certain M. Robert, whom some accounts claim to have been a Parisian dentist, but

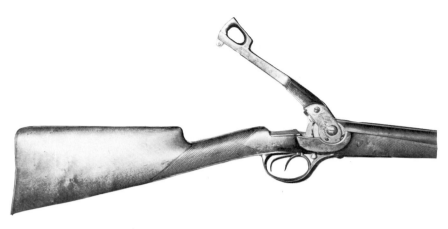

Robert gun

more recent work would suggest that he was in fact a gunmaker. His gun had the great virtue of being very simple. Naturally it was protected by a French patent, and in Great Britain it was patented by an agent, A. Demondion, No. 6137. On 13 July 1831 he obtained a massive patent covering not only the military version of this gun and a bayonet but also machinery to make both gun and cartridge. Robert, like Pauly, made attempts to interest the military authorities in France in his invention but without success.

As a sporting gun the Robert enjoyed considerable success and the patent had no less than 39 'Certificats d'addition', according to one account, to cover modifications. It is far beyond our scope to attempt a detailed description of them all.

Like the Pauly, the Robert has its barrel or barrels fixed in relation to the stock like a muzzle loader and the breech block pivots open on trunnions set on either side of the breech. The rear of the breech block is formed as a lever which lies back in a channel cut in the hand of the stock, to catch in a guard in the front of the comb. By releasing this catch and pulling up on the ring the breech is opened. The leverage so obtained is used to cock the locks. These are of cunningly simple design and consist of only three parts in addition to the necessary pivots and fixing. Combined as one part are what, in a conventional lock, would be tumbler and mainspring, while the sear is formed as part of the trigger blade, the final part being a trigger/sear spring. The spring/tumbler arrangement can best be described as a V with its point towards the muzzle of the gun and the lower limb shorter than the upper and fixed to the trigger plate. The upper limb of the V is, at its rear end, thickened and curved up to produce the actual striking part, the 'head of the hammer' and just behind this is the notch that is the bent of the sear. The action is cocked by projections towards the rear of the bottom of the breech block which bear down on the spring as the block is opened. When the head of the spring is lowered sufficiently the bent engages with the nose formed on the trigger blade which is held forwards by a spring fixed behind it on the trigger plate. The hammer spring, as it is called in the Demondion patent, is made to serve yet another function. A stud is made on the lower part of the head which, when the lock is cocked, projects through a slot in the bottom of the action to announce the fact.

The cartridge that this gun fired was ultimately the reason for its failure and certainly seems to have been the weak point in the design. A variety of case materials were used, none of the forms, we believe, were totally gas tight. From the rear of the cartridge, as it lay in the gun in line with the axis of the bore, projected a 'tail' which was a tube of soft metal filled with detonating compound. When the gun was closed the bottom of the breech block formed an anvil against which the tube was struck by the rising hammer when the lock was released. These cartridges were thus rather delicate and dangerous things to carry.

A further unsatisfactory feature of the Robert was that, again like a muzzle-loader, the gun was built without a metal action bar in the sense we understand it today. Instead the various parts were let into the stock which was thus weakened in the region of the breech and surviving specimens are very frequently found cracked at this point.

Despite these faults the gun was awarded a Gold Medal at the Paris Exhibition of 1834 and enjoyed wide usage in France at this time.

Another French gun which claims at least brief mention, first because it would appear to have enjoyed a measure of success and second because of its novel cartridge, is the Beringer. It shows the influence of Lefaucheux in

Beringer gun using cartridge as patented no. 4909 of 1848 (French)

that it employs the pivot opening and bolting by a bite on the barrel lump, but differs in using the trigger guard as the underlever. However the real novelty of the design lies in its cartridge, which was of rim fire type with the percussion compound in a rim or belt round the circumference of its base. Another point of resemblance with the pin fire gun, which gives an indication of the wide use of the latter, is that the firing pin necessary for this new cartridge was sited on the barrel and became, in effect, a captive pin fire pin. The cocks were therefore of necessity the same shape as on a pin fire gun, which the whole gun at a glance strongly resembles. We learn from the obituary of William Blanch, son of John Blanch, who was one of the early pioneers of the breech loading system in this country, that in 1855 he 'sent to Paris and purchased of Beringer, for £27 odd one of the new fashioned guns. This he set to work to copy and improve.'

It is an indication of the degree of use and interest in breech loading guns that we should find a patent specification concerned solely with improvements to cartridges. It is a regrettable feature of the requirements of the French patent office of that time that nothing in the way of personal details or even a detailed address of inventors was recorded. As a result all we know of the inventor whose work we now briefly consider is that he was Monsieur Houllier of Paris. Any further particulars are it seems lost in the mists of time.

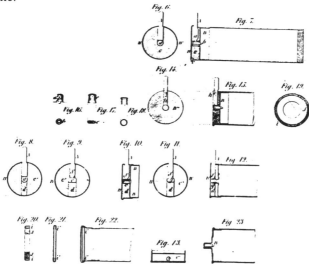

Houllier patent no. 1963 of 1846

The reason for his inclusion in this summary of continental developments is that the cartridge he invented was all but perfectly gas tight. It thus transformed the guns in which it was used and ensured for its inventor a certain place in the history of breech loading firearms.

The cartridges shown in the patent specification drawing have a variety of sites of ignition and we would call them rim, pin and centre fire, thus fitting them for a range of existing guns. However the fine detail of all these cartridges is insignificant beside the fact that all used the essential feature of Houllier's invention – what is known today as a base wad.

This is a thickness of some resilient material that, under the pressure of the firing charge, expands to seal the chamber and, when the pressure returns to atmospheric, contracts to permit the withdrawal from the breech of the spent case. The result of this seemingly simple idea was that, at the date of the publication of the patent with the skills and machinery then available, it was possible to produce a cartridge which was, for practical purposes, gas tight, could be easily removed after firing and, equally important, was relatively cheap to produce. So that, while a fair degree of fit was still needed between gun and cartridge, no longer need gunmakers strive to the impossible goal of a gas tight mechanical joint capable of being repeatedly opened and closed which would continue to function when slightly worn or when fouled by the sticky soot produced by the burning charge. For the ordinary sportsman the convenience, not least on the score of cleanliness, made possible by this improvement would have widened further the appeal of the system of breech loading.

So far in our résumé of breech loading sporting shotguns invented and in use on the continent of Europe prior to 1850 we have noticed only French developments. While it is true to a certain extent that the greatest number of systems were produced in France, sportsmen and gunmakers alike in other parts of Europe were alive to the potential of the breech loading gun.

In the catalogue of the Great Exhibition, the firearms from which are listed in an appendix, as No. 158 in that list we have 'Montigny and Fusnot, Brussels, three infantry guns (Montigny system)'. While we obviously have no absolute way of checking exactly what this was, we are of the opinion that it was a version of the gun that J. H. Walsh in his *The Shotgun and Sporting Rifle,* first published in 1859, referred to as *The Chateauvillier needle gun.*

Now the Chateauvillard patent is British patent No. 12613 of 1849. Walsh describes this as a 'needle gun' which was then a term used to classify any gun fired by what we would term a firing pin, in addition to those in which a long sharp needle penetrated the powder charge or cartridge. While we have been fortunate enough to examine a gun of this type nothing really definite seems to be recorded of the cartridge, which, we assume, was largely consumed when it was discharged and any remnants, in the form of a wad forming the base, were swept out by the next charge fired.

Externally the Montigny/Chateauvillard gun has obvious points of similarity with earlier guns particularly the Robert. The breech is opened by a long lever which lies down the hand of the stock and again terminates in a catch on the forward end of the comb. The novelty of the Chateauvillard gun is that the breech is two plugs which slide back and forth in channels which are rearward continuations of the barrels. The opening lever broadens out to form a stout breech cover on which are pivoted both the breech plugs and twin short levers which connect the cover

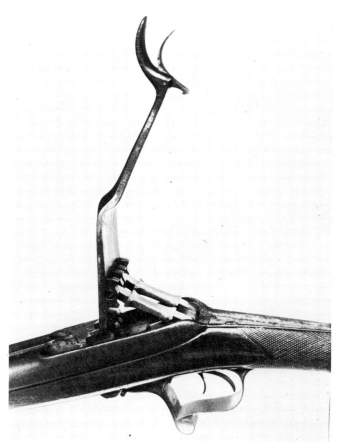

Chateauvillard gun

to the stock and which result in the compound lever or toggle link.

The division between the two breech channels is kept as high as possible to minimise the chance of a double discharge should a cartridge flash back. This small piece of metal and the fact that the breech plugs are of brass are eloquent reminders of the problems of using a breech loading gun not adapted to gas tight cartridges.

A final point about this gun is that the opening and cocking are totally separate. To cock the trigger plate action, the scroll front of the trigger guard has to be pushed forwards.

We have been fortunate enough to find an actual example of this gun, albeit a well worn specimen, in which the script on the barrel rib is just illegible. One word, which may be London, can be made out. If this were so it would suggest that some enterprising gun dealer or maker was importing and retailing these guns. When and in what numbers are questions which are probably now impossible to answer.

A gun which, in its inspiration at least, stems back to Pauly, is that known as the 'Dreyse needle gun'. As we noted earlier, Johann Nikolaus von Dreyse worked for Pauly in Paris as a lockmaker. Evidently he returned to his native Prussia and developed the family of guns we now consider. The essential feature of these was to use a cartridge case which was intended to largely burn with the powder charge. The powder charge was to be ignited by a patch of percussion powder fixed to a wad at the front of the charge and therefore had to be struck by a long sharp firing pin which first had to pierce cartridge case and powder, hence the term needle gun. To fire variations of this ammunition, revolvers, sporting shotguns and a military rifle were produced. The shotgun was very like the Oelkers and Spengler hammerless gun that we describe in our final chapter. More correctly the Belgian gun resembled the von Dreyse for it is certain that that was the direction of the inspiration. The military rifle was a single shot bolt action. However the details of construction of these various forms and the fact that, due to a large gas leak at the rear, they were only marginally serviceable, all pale to insignificance before the fact that, if the von Dreyse did not sow the seeds of the adoption of the breech loading shotgun by British sportsmen, it most surely finely tilled the soil for those seeds. The military rifle was adopted by the Prussian army and used by them with devastating effect in two brief wars with the Danes and the Austrians. The success in battle of this rifle was to spark a rush among the nations of Europe to arm their troops with breech loading rifles for it was realised that no matter how brave or how well trained and led, no army could contend on anything like equal terms with one possessing the overwhelming advantage of fire power that even a weapon as imperfect as the von Dreyse needle gun gave to its users. These developments naturally produced the keenest interest in Great Britain, then an imperial power. The result was to awaken a realisation of the potential of breech loading and, we believe, thus began the train of events which we will attempt to follow through the rest of this book.

Despite all the work and invention that was taking place on the continent of Europe, the development of the breech loading *shotgun* was, it seems, almost totally ignored by the British gun trade. There were only three British patents taken out for breech loaders using self-contained cartridges in this period. The Demondion and Chateauvillard have been previously noted, and in 1840 William Bush obtained patent No. 8513 for a species of needle fire cartridge. But none of these, to the best of the authors' knowledge, was even so much as mentioned in sporting literature of the period and no guns to fire the Bush cartridge appear to have survived. Indeed the only contemporary reference to breech loaders of which we are aware is the warning of Colonel Hawker:

> Let me caution the whole world against using firearms that are opened
> and loaded at the breech end – a horrid ancient invention, revived by
> foreign makers, that is dangerous in the extreme and by which I have

Privately imported continental pinfire

just heard (April 29th 1844) of a man being killed by the very gun that I condemned when in Paris in 1841.

Unfortunately nothing further seems to be known either as to the gun involved or the circumstances surrounding this accident. In fact this quotation would seem to sum up very neatly the opinion of the British gun trade and the majority of sportsmen. In an article published in *Land and Water* in 1872, there is the following account:

> The Lefaucheux of 1836 which was introduced first into this country by Wilkinson and Co of Pall Mall, successors to Henry Nock, the famous gunmaker to George IV, in 1844. Such however was the rabid antipathy displayed by sportsmen to this now widely disseminated form of breech action that they could induce no one to use it, and it was actually sold as a curiosity to a Mr C. D. Scarisbrick.

But despite these views there is some evidence of interest in breech loading in this country, for instance in 1975 a double barrel pin fire gun was auctioned in Birmingham. It was claimed in the catalogue that this gun, originally the property of the Duke of Bedford, was given to him in 1837.

Indeed to ascertain the degree of use of a particular system or style of gun has been one of our greatest problems in preparing this work. Nowhere is it better illustrated than in the question of the extent to which breech loaders were in use prior to 1850. While the gunmaker Joseph Lang in a letter to *The Field* in 1853 claims that they had been in 'general use in France for 10 years', in two books on French sport, *Field Sports of France* by R. O'Connor and *The Sportsman in France* by F. Tolfrey, published in 1846 and 1841 respectively, breech loaders are not even mentioned. The truth, we must assume, lies somewhere between these two extremes.

Casimir Lefaucheux's signature

Chapter Two

THE GREAT EXHIBITION AND ITS AFTERMATH

Having thus briefly sketched the history of the sporting breech loader on the Continent of Europe and noted how little impact had been made by such guns in Great Britain, we must now turn our attention to the Great Exhibition held at the Crystal Palace in Hyde Park from 1 May to 15 October 1851. The stated aim of this exhibition was to 'unite the industry and art of all the nations of the earth'. The exhibition was by all accounts a success both financially and perhaps more importantly in the interchange of ideas which occurred as a result. This was certainly true in the case of firearms, and the Great Exhibition is looked upon as something of a watershed in arms development in Great Britain. It is perhaps instructive at this point to consider the list of sporting and other personal guns exhibited (see appendix). In the main the gun exhibits were of conventional type, mostly very highly finished and some very ornate. But there were all sorts of more or less useful inventions, such as that shown by Davies of Bath, who used the blade of the bayonet as the ramrod for a military musket. A charming and interesting exhibit was Colonel Hawker's in which the grand old warrior, then in his 65th year and still sorely troubled by his wound suffered 42 years before at the Battle of Talavera, had his wildfowling gear, punt guns, new inventions and all, transported from Hampshire and put on show. These however have but little bearing on our present theme. What is important is that makers from the continent exhibited, among them two noted in the previous chapter, namely Montigny of Brussels and Lefaucheux of Paris. Now it is odd that earlier accounts of the introduction of the breech loader to Great Britain have never noted the exhibit No. 158 which must refer to the Montigny gun as described in Chapter 1. But we have all noted No. 1308 and despite the very terse note in the official catalogue this

Lefaucheux gun at the The Great Exhibition of 1851. Drawing from the Illustrated London News

was none other than the pin fire gun and cartridge as previously described and we, with the benefit of hindsight, look upon it as the most important exhibit in the gun section. For many of the six million who paid to enter the Great Exhibition this was their first encounter with the progress made by the continentals in this field. Now it is part of the folklore surrounding the adoption of the breech loading shotgun in Great Britain that the significance of the Lefaucheux exhibit was appreciated by the London gunmaker, Joseph Lang of Cockspur Street. That Lang was a keen, practical sportsman, as well as a gunmaker, lends credence to this tradition, and the fact that he was also an exhibitor at Crystal Palace. But there is a story that a man called E. C. Hodges who later was to become one of the leading London outworker actioners saw the Lefaucheux gun and produced a copy which he sold to Lang. This story has come down through his family and was told to one of the authors (IMC) by Hodges' grandson. If true, and we have no reason to doubt it, this gun made by Hodges was the first modern British breech loader. It is also part of the folklore of the breech loader that, following the Great Exhibition, there was a rush by British sportsmen to adopt the new style of gun. This has not been borne out by our researches. It is an unfortunate fact that the ravages of over a century, which has included two world wars and numerous moves, amalgamations and closures, have left us very few sets of contemporary gunmakers' records. However it would seem that a few really wealthy progressive sportsmen had equipped themselves with various breech loading shotguns of continental manufacture.

Further confirmation of the reticence shown by British sportsmen to adopt the new gun can be inferred from a series of articles which appeared in *The Field* in 1853, *Hints to Young Shooters on Guns* contributed by *Umbra*, in which the breech loading gun is not even mentioned. Also in *The Field* a couple of years later there arose a discussion of how best to prevent sporting guns misfiring in wet weather. Even though this is one of the great points of a breech loader using a self contained cartridge, such guns were again not thought worthy of mention.

Then too there is the evidence of surviving specimens which admittedly must be considered in the realisation that there has been more than ample time for them to be worked to death, particularly as they were built at a time when the requirements of a sound breech loading shotgun were only imperfectly understood. But it is our experience, based on years of collecting, that it is very rare to encounter a British pin fire gun built as a breech loader, converted muzzle loaders excepted, which belongs to the period 1851–57.

They are however not unknown and in general these early pin fire guns followed the French pattern, having a lump brazed in a V slot between the breech ends of the barrel tubes, the front end bearing on a joint or hinge pin, and the rear having a slot to take a holding-down bolt approximately halfway between the joint pin and the standing breech, while the lever working the bolt lay horizontally over the forend, or round the guard when the appearance did not offend the owner's eye.

This method of bolting was mechanically unsound and, when combined with a thin standing breech, exhibited a dangerous weakness, as upon being fired the action bar tended to bend slightly and the standing breech to open.

Early pinfire gun by George Gibbs of Bristol

Purdey pinfire with single grip inert action

Continual repetition of this action caused a permanent gap between the breech face of the barrels and the standing breech which allowed more movement of the cartridge in the chamber when fired and which, in turn, increased the pressure on the standing breech and consequently a break at the angle of the standing breech and the bar of the action was not unknown. This weakness was certainly recognised by J. D. Dougall, who in his book *Shooting Simplified,* published in 1857, writes on page 169: 'How long the jointing at the breech end may continue to withstand the tremendous vibrations of our heavy charges, time alone can shew.'

But despite these valid objections there are clues which suggest that there was an increasing tendency for sportsmen to import breech loading shotguns, particularly from France. For instance, in a letter written to *The Field* early in 1857 a correspondent who signed himself *'G.M.'* claimed that both he and his friends used French made breech loaders and went on to comment favourably on the shooting qualities of these guns.

These remarks should not be taken to imply that the drop down gun as popularised by Monsieur C. Lefaucheux was the only line of development to be followed by those who were striving to improve British breech loaders. In the year after the Great Exhibition closed, Joseph Needham obtained his patent for a needle fire gun. The year was 1852, the date 2 October, the patent No. 184.

This is rather odd in view of the fact that at the Great Exhibition there was an exhibit by W. & J. Needham, No. 218 in the official catalogue (see appendix), which refers to 'double and single guns to load at the breech'. From this we must assume that either this gun or a version of it was in existence and on show before a patent was applied for – a fact that today would preclude the granting of a patent, or that this was a different gun, possibly some species of capping breech loader.

This gun occupies a position remarkable in several respects in the story of the British shotgun, it being at once the first hammerless gun to enjoy any

14 bore Needham cartridge compared with 14 bore centre fire cartridge

wide usage, the only gun using a special cartridge ever to offer any challenge to the card tubed, brass headed Houllier style of ammunition and one of the few types of British shotgun to have barrels that do not pivot down to load. Its inspiration undoubtedly was the Dreyse needle gun but its inventor developed the idea in a rather different way. In large part the degree of success that this gun achieved lay in the fact that it was built under licence by the highly reputable and even then long established firm of John Rigby at that date trading only in Dublin. The prestige that this lent to the design is difficult to assess accurately, but it must have been considerable,

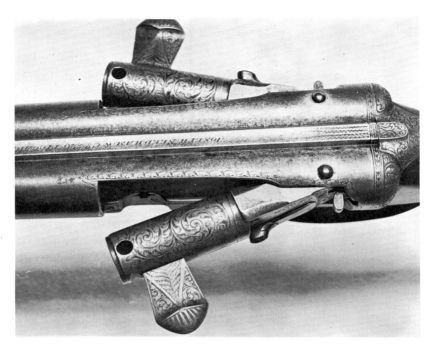

Needham needle fire with locks open

for more guns are encountered bearing the Rigby name than that of the inventor and so it is tempting to speculate that without this patronage by one of the foremost 'names' in the guntrade this gun would be virtually unknown.

Belonging as it does to this early period of the story of the British breech loader when ready-made ammunition for the new guns was not to be had in every small town, one of the points in favour of this needle fire was that it was well within the capabilities of a dextrous sportsman to assemble his own cartridges and to charge them with the loose powder and shot that was freely available. The fact that he thereby saved money as compared with the purchase of pin cartridges was made much of by the proponents of the needle gun.

To open each barrel of this gun the bolt handle, which in the closed position is vertically down, giving a double gun something of the look of a beagle, is grasped and rotated through some 180 degrees to the limit of its travel at which point it is almost vertical. This turns the bolt head on the stout thread and so draws it back far enough for the whole bolt to be swung out sideways. If the bolt so opened had previously been fired this rotation of the head also served to cock the lock. For there are two cams in the inside of the head which act on two projections on the firing needle and force it back against the spiral mainspring as the bolt head is turned. The needle is held cocked by a sear which engages when this needle reaches the rearward limit of its travel. In this position too the safety can be applied by the lever working vertically on the side of the bolt.

The tails of the sears project towards the midline of the gun and are depressed by the trigger blades, thus reversing the action of a conventional gun lock. The backward thrust of the charge is taken primarily on the two substantial vertical rods on which the bolts pivot but in addition the rear ends of the bolts are formed as arcs which abut closely to the standing breeches.

Aside from this lockwork the gun is constructed very much as a muzzle loader. A transverse bolt in the forend holds down the barrels and when this slide is removed the barrels can be lifted at the muzzle end to disengage two hooks from the face of the false breech fitted to the stock.

There is a further mention of guns of this type in the records of the Patent Office. Contained in the provisional specification in the name of Joseph Needham, No. 1760 of 14 July 1864, is an extractor to remove the remains of a cartridge from a needle gun. Since mention is made of a metal head we assume that experiments continued with this gun at least until the date of this specification.

Of the designer of this gun little now seems to be traceable. On his patent he describes himself as 'Joseph Needham of 26 Picadilly in the county of Middlesex, gun manufacturer'. The first Needham recorded at No. 26 was William in 1844 who was presumably the father of our man. Joseph joined the firm some time before 1851 because at the Great Exhibition the style of the firm was W. & J. Needham. There was also a Henry Needham under whose name another firm traded for some 20 years. But since the two concerns joined it is probable that he may have been a relative of Joseph. The only other trace we have found of this firm is that Joseph Needham went bankrupt in 1869. Belonging to the next generation is Joseph Vernon Needham. It is known that he worked for Westley Richards in Birmingham, possibly he was apprenticed there. When he left he traded from a variety of addresses in the Birmingham gun quarter and produced and widely advertised the sidelever gun we shall consider later. Examples of this are also found with the Joseph Needham name and the 26 Piccadilly address, which would suggest a family link between the two concerns. Beyond our present scope is the Needham ejector gun which was a product of Joseph Vernon. His firm was ultimately absorbed by W. W. Greener and the name continued for a considerable period as a brand name for some cheaper guns.

While the Needham was one of the fascinating blind alleys that we shall encounter so frequently during our study, the next gun of this period that we come to consider had a considerable influence on later events, it being the gun now known as the *Lancaster Base Fire* and regarded as pointing the way in which the British shotgun was to develop. This being so it is regrettable that Greener and Walsh in their standard textbooks should tell so little of the story and that so many of the authors who followed them should have been content to take the writings of these two as gospel. Walsh must accept the bulk of the blame for this state of affairs for when he wrote the first edition of *The Shotgun and Sporting Rifle* in 1859 the events in question were of very recent date. But Greener when he wrote the first edition of *The Gun and its Development* a little over 20 years later surely did not have to perpetuate Walsh's inaccuracies.

The myth has grown up that the gun was introduced in 1852, but a close scrutiny of Lancasters records does not bear this out. Every gun of this type that the authors have encountered is boldly marked 'Charles Lancaster's Patent'. But there is no patent registered in Lancaster's name for a gun of this description of any date. But on 29 November 1853 a patent agent by the name of Auguste Edouard Loradoux Bellford took out patent No. 2778 for a variety of guns, one of which is the gun we know as the Lancaster. Part of this patent is a reproduction of the French patent No. 9058 of 1853 granted to Louis Julien Gastinne. The standard introduction to the British patent would suggest that all the inventions contained in it were from a single source and in the British patent No. 2744 of 11 October 1862 obtained by M. Gastinne we find the statement: 'The extractor . . . as in the guns for which letters patent were granted to Auguste Edouard Loradoux Bellford, the 29th day of November 1853, No. 2778 and assigned to Charles William Lancaster of New Bond Street London, the 22nd day of November, 1856.' So that we feel confident that the whole of the contents of the Bellford patent were the inventions of Louis Julien Gastinne.

It was the acquisition of a Lancaster gun at the outset of the collecting career of one of the authors (DJB) which stimulated interest both in this gun and in the whole subject of breech loading shotguns. I well remember

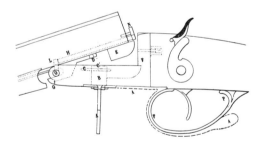

A. Bellford patent no. 2778 of 1853

how fascinated I was with the gun, its smooth action and evident strength, and can now well understand *A Soldier's* remarks in *The Field* of 1858: 'That (the Lancaster) being really the most perfect mechanical movement I ever saw.'

32

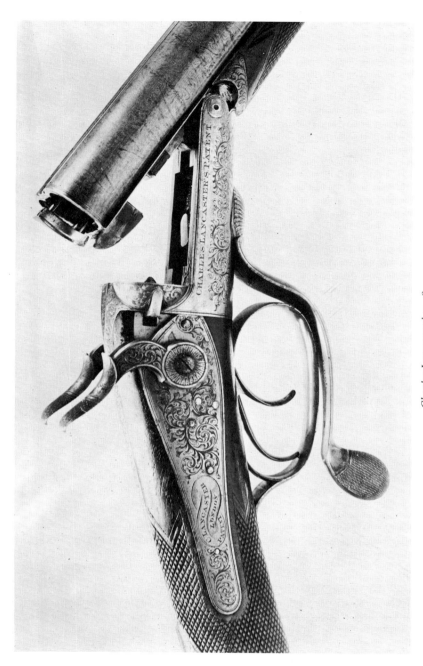

Charles Lancaster base fire gun

The motion has the virtue of being basically simple. The strong underlever, much sturdier on a Lancaster gun than drawn on the patent, turns a large turret in the action bar. This turret carries a stout stud which, when the underlever is turned, acts on a slot cut in the lump and cams the barrels back and forth. This action has considerable leverage and the author records with shame that he used it to resize some of his early 14 bore reloads that he fired in his gun. The actual bolting of this gun, depends on a lug which slides under the standing breech and, on most specimens encountered, on the fact that the angle between the standing breech and the action bar is less than a right angle. However the Bellford patent does not show this feature, neither does the part sectionalised drawing used by Walsh, Greener and their modern followers. This fact could possibly be explained as an engraver's error but for the discovery that a proportion of the earliest Lancaster guns, possibly a very small one, had action faces at right angles to the flats.

One of the less desirable features of the design that the author learned at first hand on using his gun was the fact that if the left hand grasped the gun at the hinge pin as it was closed, a very nasty pinch could be administered, as a piece of flesh was trapped in the hinge. Equally damaging to the gun's reputation is the feeling of looseness experienced when the gun is open and which suggests, particularly to the non-mechanically minded sportsman, that the gun is in some way unsound.

Now Walsh *et al,* illustrate with this gun the Lancaster base fire cartridge which we know only from the sectionalised drawings which, like the gun, are common to the standard books. We have not been able to examine an original, though it is rumoured that odd examples exist. Even Churchill, Atkin, Grant and Lang who are the successors to Charles Lancaster, do not now have an example. There is the sad story that the only one they possessed was stolen by an 'enthusiast'.

The drawing mentioned above shows a cartridge with a very slight rim but a deep copper capsule. The head of the cartridge is devoid of any cap or any other evidence to show how it was fired. We believe it had no headstamp but 'Lancasters' was printed round the body. Beneath the outer capsule was a disc of brass with four flash holes in, the rear face of this was smeared with percussion compound. So that the actual point at which it was struck was not critical and the flash from the priming was communicated to the main charge via the four flash holes.

By modern standards the cartridge is also peculiar in that it lacked a base wad and, as drawn, the wadding over the shot was as thick as that over the powder. The case was not reloadable and the lack of a base wad causes us to wonder what sort of state it was in when it was withdrawn from the gun. A base wad is now considered essential for a satisfactory paper cased cartridge. But contemporary accounts claimed that there was no gas leak, which must mean that the cases were very well made and that they closely fitted the gun chambers, and the soft copper used obturated very

34

effectively. Lancaster's records for this period (1854–61) mention only 12 and 14 bore guns, so we must assume that these were the only sizes of cartridges made.

That this was the only cartridge used in Lancaster guns until the introduction of the Schneider cartridge by George Daw after 1861, we suspect to be less than the whole truth. There is the evidence given by Eleys in the Eleys v Daw law-suit in which Eleys' counsel asserted that they had made centre fire cartridges for Lancaster in 1854, but were unable to produce specimens or other proof of this claim. There is also the advertisement that Lancasters ran in *The Field* and *Land and Water* in the 1860's which read:

> Charles Lancaster Gun Manufacturer: 151, New Bond Street, London. Inventor and maker of the first central fire breech loading gun (1856). Sole proprietor of the Pottet central fire cartridge, introduced by him into England in 1857, lately improved by Colonel Boxer R.A. and adopted as the standard ammunition for the British Army, solicits an inspection of his recent improvements in breech loading guns and rifles.

Now unless both the court evidence and the advertisement were lies of the most brazen sort, we must accept that Lancasters at least experimented with Pottet type cartridges at the same time as they introduced their gun. The fact that both dates are so close might even mean that the original cartridge for the Lancaster gun was the Pottet and it was only when this was found to be prone to misfire due to its very thin anvil that it was abandoned by Lancasters in favour of the cartridge described above. This we admit to be pure conjecture, but it is one of those facts that Walsh in 1859 could so easily have checked.

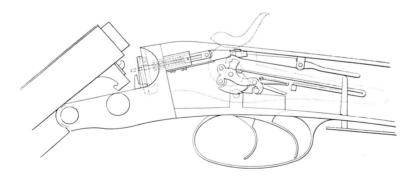

Hammond patent no. 236 of 1859

From the preceding two guns employing cartridges peculiar to themselves and enjoying fairly wide usage, we now turn to a gun that is all but unknown. Indeed the only specimen which has come to our notice is much modified and we cannot be absolutely certain that it originally conformed to the patent specification. The inventor was the Winchester gunmaker, Isaac Hammond, who obtained patent No. 236 dated 26 January 1859 for his creation. This was for a rather complex gun and a cartridge, in a sense intermediate in design between the true needle fire of the Needham and the later Pottet/Schneider. From the patent drawings it can be seen that Hammond proposed both rimmed and rimless forms of his cartridge, but as no mention is made of them in the text of his specification we have no means of knowing what he saw as the relative advantages of the two forms. Curiously he did not propose to use the rim as a means of extracting the spent case. Instead the extractor had a hook or hooks which were to spike into the cartridge which was withdrawn as the gun was opened and the sliding extractor, captive on the breech face, was lifted up.

To fire these special cartridges he used a conventional gun lock either with a cock striking a semi enclosed firing pin or having the cocks simply as cocking levers and a tumbler with a head on it to impinge on a totally enclosed striker. This latter form is shown on the drawings.

Also shown is a clever safety arrangement in which a small flat spring raises the rear of the striker clear of the tumbler, so that the lock will only fire the gun if the rear of the striker is depressed. This is done by the grip safety working a rocking lever set under the top strap. Thus when the gun is gripped, as in the act of firing, the rear of the rocking lever is raised and hence the front and rear of the firing pins are lowered. The gun we have studied has plugged holes on the trigger guard strap which could have been the site of this mechanism.

The final feature of the patent which is present on the gun we have seen is a cam barrel bolting system worked by a side lever. On the front face of the rear barrel lump is cut a semi-circular recess. Running transversely through the action bar is a spindle, one side of which is filed flat to permit the lump to pass as the gun is opened and closed, but which when rotated will, if the lump is in position, fill the semi-circular recess in the barrel lump with the whole part of the spindle and so hold down the barrels.

I. Hammond gun possibly originally built to the patent of 1859

From the evidence at our disposal it is the authors' view that, in the period covered by this chapter, while the seeds of breech loading were well sown there was nothing like the rush to acquire breech loading guns after the Great Exhibition that some would have us believe. The Great Exhibition itself was a great stimulus to the adoption of breech loading sporting guns in Great Britain but the movement had begun earlier with a few private importations by a few very progressive sportsmen. It is our belief that the general adoption of this style of gun can be really dated from the events which form the subject of our next chapter.

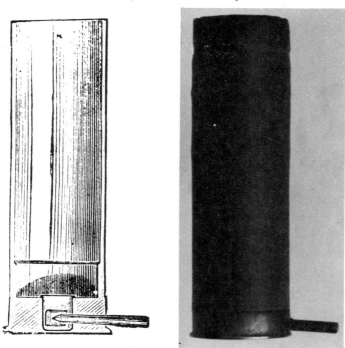

The pinfire cartridge: left: *sectional drawing* right: *early Gevelot cartridge showing pinched ring to hold top wad* below: *tools for extracting fired pinfire cartridge cases or parts of cases stuck in chamber*

Chapter Three

JOHN HENRY WALSH, THE FIELD AND THE FIELD TRIALS OF 1858 AND 1859

For the next portion of our story we must look to the first two of what were to become a whole series of Field Trials. But to understand these we have first to consider the man who organised them.

John Henry Walsh ('Stonehenge') was one of those men of whom it could truly be said that he was a legend in his own life-time. He was a man of many talents, great energy and a prolific author who wrote, either on his own or in conjunction with others, some 12 books, most of which referred in some way to sporting matters in the widest sense of that term. He was originally educated for the medical profession, and indeed practised for a while in Worcester, and came to journalism by way of his profession. However, his love of field sports led him to write about these too and, after contributing to *The Field,* he accepted the post of editor in 1857. From this position he was able to exert considerable influence on the development of the sporting gun and rifle, and it is from this that his reputation now stems.

When Walsh became editor *The Field* was but five years old, being first published on 1 January 1853. Its aim, then as now, was to be a weekly newspaper for the country gentleman, but at its inception it covered an even greater range of activities.

It is important to realise that Walsh had lost the forefinger and thumb of his left hand when a muzzle loading gun he was using had burst, and this accident had naturally left him with a great concern for the safety of sporting firearms. On this score alone he was convinced of the superiority of the breech loader.

One of the things that he inherited when he assumed his new position was a very lively correspondence column on the subject of the merits, or otherwise, of the breech loader as compared with the muzzle loader. This had originated in a letter published in *The Field* of 20 December 1856:

> Sir,
> If any of your numerous correspondents have used the Breech Loading shotguns, would they be so good as to say what they think the advantages or disadvantages of them may be.
>
> CURIOUS

It is ironic that this letter, so courteous and mild in tone, should have set off

John Henry Walsh

so bitter an argument as that which was to follow. But we must remember that the scene had, to some degree at least, been set about a year previously by another acrimonious discussion in the columns of *The Field*. This was on the effective range of a sporting shotgun, and several of the contestants in this first skirmish were to reappear in the second.

The first letters to be printed, and what was to become a flood started as a trickle in the very next issue, were mild in tone and in favour of the breech loader. One which bears particularly on our general theme was a letter from 'G.M.' who claimed that both he and his friends used French made breech loaders and, having tested them found them superior to British breech loaders, either London or country made. Then in the issue of 10 January appeared a letter which was to alter the whole character of the discussion. Part of this letter ran:

> Sir,
> With respect to shotguns loading at the breech, what I have seen would not make a dint in a pound of butter at 40 yards, setting aside the principle being 200% more dangerous. I should like nothing better than to match for £50 one of my favourite size guns for general shooting, 11 bore, 2ft 8in long, $2\frac{1}{2}$–3 drachms of powder and $1\frac{1}{4}$oz of shot against any breech loader....
> A LINCOLNSHIRE GUNMAKER

Then in the issue of the following week there came a letter in reply of which the following is an excerpt:

> Sir,
> In reply to your correspondent signing himself A Lincolnshire Gunmaker, I beg to say I have used the Breech Loading shotgun made by Lang of Cockspur Street for two years and have not only tried some thousands of shots with them at game but have tried them by the severest tests possible, namely with quires of thick brown paper and powder canisters (no better trials) also against a gun of Joseph Manton's which I believed for many years to be unequalled as well as several other guns by the first London makers. My Breech Loaders beat them all in strength and closeness of shooting: and I am prepared to accept the bet he offers that for £50 I can beat his in strength at 40 yards at sheets of paper and that I can put more shot into a target say 3 feet square at 40 yards, being £25 each match, that is provided he shoots with a fair sporting gun (but not a young cannon).
> THOMAS CHARRITIE (MAJOR-GENERAL)
> 32, Bryanston Square

General Charritie was a distinguished veteran of the wars against the French, having served with the Second Life Guards in the Peninsula from 1812–14 and taken part in the Battles of Vittoria, Pampeluna and

Toulouse. He was therefore a contemporary of Colonel Hawker and, it would seem from the letter reproduced opposite, cast in a similar mould.

In a further letter from General Charritie at the end of January he refers to buying ready loaded cartridges from Lang's. These must have been French made cases, as it was not until January 1858 that Eley's advertisements mentioned cases, and probably Gevelot made because they were the only brand mentioned in the correspondence of the time.

All through 1857 the battle went on back and forth, most of the writers hiding behind pseudonyms. Of those who can now be identified we find *An Old Shekarry* – H. A. Levenson, the famous big game hunter who was strongly pro breech loaders. *The Inventor of the Minie and Enfield Rifle*, who was undoubtedly W. Greener, was a staunch champion of the old system. He set down his opposition in no uncertain manner, at one point describing the muzzle loader as 'the only legitimate sort of gun'. Very interestingly, in view of subsequent events, a letter published on 5 December 1857 from *A Glasgow Gunmaker*, who turned out to be none other than James Dalziel Dougall, was strongly anti breech loaders. Dougall, it should be noted, was one of those involved in the earlier affray over the range of guns. Amid this dour contest a note of light relief is struck by a writer complaining that another correspondent had stolen his pseudonym.

Then, in *The Field* of 2 January 1858 there appeared a very long statement announcing the first Field Trial scheduled to take place on 25 January. But in the next issue the date was altered to 26 January as the Princess Royal was to be married on 25th. In the following weeks the letters were in general concerned with getting the trial postponed on the grounds that insufficient time was available to prepare entries. This plea was, it seems, in part accepted by Walsh, who, in the issue of 23 January wrote:

> Both parties to the controversy seem content to write forever, but when a trial is offered they hang back fearful of the result . . .

The trial was then scheduled for April.

As might be expected the controversy continued at such a pitch that Walsh was moved to write:

> Until the trial is over, columns will be closed to the numerous correspondents.

On 13 March he staked the credit of *The Field* upon the proper management of the trial and pledged that the trials should be beyond suspicion of collusion. Finally, on 20 March, came the announcement that the trial was to be held on Friday 9 April 1858 at 11am, under the superintendence of the editor of *The Field*. The aims of the trial were to compare:

1. The driving power at 40, 50 and 60yd as tested by sheets of brown paper.

2. Regularity of delivery of shot at each distance within a circle of 30in diameter.
3. Amount of recoil when clean and after 30 discharges measured by a recording spring attached to the fixed rest.

There then followed a list of 12 rules, details of which can be found in the appropriate appendix.

So, at last, on 9 and 10 April 1858 the long heralded trial was held 'in a large tent' at Ashburnham Park, which stood adjacent to the Cremorne Pleasure Gardens off the Kings Road, Chelsea, about half a mile west of Battersea Bridge.

The official results of the trial were published in *The Field* of 17 April and can also be found in the appendix.

Since no mention is made of the problems that must have attended firing so great a quantity of black powder in an enclosed space, we must assume that the 'tent' was in fact little more than an awning and that at least quite a stiff breeze blew during that trial. Otherwise, as any user of black powder will confirm, conditions inside the tent would have very rapidly deteriorated to a degree which would have stopped the trial.

As might have been expected the results of the trial provided more material for the letter writers. In the issue of 1 May appeared a letter signed 'C.F.W.' crowing at the success of the muzzle loaders and repeating what was by then a well worn theme of his, that is the extra cost of ammunition incurred by the breech loader user. To this the redoubtable General Charritie replied in the next issue:

> Two gentlemen in my Square are minus fingers and thumbs and the trifling extra expense, so much dwelt on by C.F.W. is unworthy of the notice of gentlemen.

But C.F.W. was not to be squashed. He came back with a letter challenging the General to shoot his breech loader against his (C.F:W.'s) muzzle loader. Furthermore he chided General Charritie for not entering the Field Trial and suggested that he would not shoot for a lesser stake than £25.

Inevitable too were the requests for a further trial. To these Walsh replied that the considerable trouble and expense made this impractical. But despite claims to the contrary the trial had not been an unqualified success, owing to the recoil of the guns tested being greater than anticipated and outside the capacity of the machines available for measuring it. So this important aspect had gone untested.

But even the die hard muzzle loaders sensed defeat. Evidence of this can be gleaned from the fact that they were starting to change their ground and were now attacking the breech loader as unsporting. Remarks like, 'But confound it sir, you don't want to exterminate the partridge do you?' are to be found in print. Yet further evidence is to be seen in an advertisement put out by J. D. Dougall, who not a year previously had been one of the anti breech loading brigade.

By the end of 1858 he was advertising as follows:

> Breech loaders. J. D. Dougall, Gunsmith, Glasgow, (Author of Shooting Simplified, London, Arthur Hall, Virtue and Co.) having of late paid great attention to breech loading guns, has given complete satisfaction in those he has manufactured. These guns are now much improved in principle and better understood and any Gentleman wishing to have a carefully made and genuine article, may confidently entrust his orders to the advertiser.

Against this background came the decision to hold another Field Trial. The reasons for this change of heart after the earlier refusal to do so are not recorded, but it is the authors' belief that it had been realised at *The Field* that the trouble and expense which had been complained of after the first trial were in fact more than repaid by the kudos and increased circulation.

So a second trial was arranged originally for 28 and 29 June at Hornsey Wood House, then a venue for live pigeon trap shooting on the outskirts of London, but now covered by the north west corner of Finsbury Park and the adjacent roads. But this had to be postponed until 4 and 5 July owing to a clash of dates with Newcastle Races and Dog Show. The Newcastle Dog Show of 28 and 29 June 1859 is of more than passing interest in that it is claimed as being the first event of its kind to be held in Great Britain. There were but two classes, one for pointers, the other for setters. The whole organisation was the work of no less a person than W. R. Pape, who gave two of his own guns as first prizes. This, and Pape's obvious general interest in the sporting dog, may well be the basis of the jibe of William Wellington Greener about 'gunmakers who know more about dogs than guns'.

The rules of the gun trial were substantially the same as the previous year and great hopes were held for the recoil measuring machine. In the event this was smashed by a gun which fired both barrels at once, leaving the guns of Egan, Prince and Green and one each of the entries of Pape and Reilly untested for recoil.

The results showed the degree of improvement which had been made in breech loaders in the short space of a year. The breech loader emerged as the equal of the average muzzle loader, indeed the greatest penetration was recorded by a 16 bore breech loader by Elliot of Wigan. These improvements were the first fruits of a better understanding of the requirements of loading cartridges and chambering the guns to receive them, which was to grow during the next two or three years. While this progression was perhaps not as spectacular as that of the gun mechanisms we shall shortly consider, it was vital to the story of the success and hence the general adoption of the breech loading shotgun.

The only contemporary description and illustration of the loading of cartridges for the new breech loaders which we have been able to find is in the first edition of *The Shotgun and Sporting Rifle* written by J. H. Walsh, using his nom-de-plume of 'Stonehenge'. In this both the over-powder and over-shot wads appear to be of the same thickness. Furthermore the turnover of the cartridge is inadequate. It was contrived either by a hand-held stamp with a shallow circular groove which, when rotated over the end of the loaded case, partially rolled over the edges, or by crimping a ring round the case just above the top wad.

This form of loading was far from ideal for achieving the best results in regard to either velocity or pattern, and was, we would assume, a significant reason why the shooting was in general less powerful than with muzzle loaders of the time, even with increased powder charges.

Firstly the heavy over-shot wads would have tended to obstruct the true flight of the shot leaving the muzzle. Also a wad of the same thickness placed over the powder would have been too thin for efficient obduration. This latter problem was compounded by the cartridge chamber having a sharp shoulder or only a slight bevel where the barrel and chamber met. If the edges of the wad were damaged on entering the barrel from the chamber, gases from the burning powder charge would escape into the column of shot, both reducing the impetus given to the shot and causing the pellets to fuse together, to the detriment of the final pattern.

As if this were not enough, the two methods of retaining the charge in the case, referred to above, offered little resistance either to the shaking the cartridge would receive when carried in the field, or to the shock of the discharge when the first barrel of a double gun was fired. The recoil tended to loosen the charge in the cartridge case in the other barrel, so releasing the complete shot charge in some instances! Nor would these closures produce the fractional retention of shot in the cartridge case itself which is vital to ensure that the powder charge fully ignites and so develops its full power by burning only in the length of the barrel and not carrying on in a futile manner after leaving the muzzle.

The earliest reference to a turnover we have discovered is a French patent, No. 12945 granted to Chaudun in 1855 and this is followed by French patent No. 20108 of 1857 granted to Houllier, which claims to 'retain the charge in the case'. Both these patents were probably protecting the simple 'stamp' as described above.

The first British patent was that granted to Charles Lancaster in 1858, No. 1361, for 'an Instrument or Apparatus for charging cartridges for Breech Loading guns'. This consists of a tube in which a plunger may be wound up and down by means of a crank handle. The purpose of this was to ram the wads, after which a metal plate with a shallow groove the diameter of the cartridge case was inserted, and, while pressure was applied to the crank, the plate was rotated back and forth to effect a simple turnover.

The next attempt at improved turnover may well have been a wooden tool similar to the original stamp, which was made to rotate by means of a handle, while the case was urged forward by a short lever. But, if the one we have examined and tried is anything to go by, the groove was still too shallow to effect a satisfactory turnover.

44

In 1860 George Jeffries of Norwich, who will reappear later in our account, took out patent No. 1900 for a combined filling and turnover tool. In this the capped case is placed under an open tube, which fits inside the case. The powder was poured through the built-in funnel on the top of the tube, the over-powder wad was then placed in the case and rammed by pressing down this same tube, which then returned upwards by the action of a coil spring to receive the shot charge. A similar operation was repeated for the top wad. The loaded cartridge was removed and placed in the turnover machine, made horizontally on the upper part of the complete tool. The cartridge was placed in a brass tube and a brass shutter closed behind it. At the other end was the turnover chuck, containing a shallow annular groove, which moved forward on a slow coarse thread when the handle was turned to roll over the edges of the loaded case. Although this turnover had an adjusting screw to stop the top of the cartridge being turned in too far, it would have been very easy to have over-compressed the loaded cartridge, and, from experiments we have made, the turnover has proved to be not fully efficient.

Jeffries turnover tool

What we regard as the first machine to produce a really effective turnover was that invented by another famous man, who will reappear later in this story, James Purdey. His invention was included in Patent No. 302 of 1861, in which the following process was described. The previously loaded cartridge was first placed in a die and rammed by means of a lever under the machine, raising the die which was just long enough to receive the cartridge

45

and containing a plug in the bottom which performed the ramming. The cartridge was then reversed and a spindle with a deep circular groove in its end containing a small steel pin was rotated at high speed by means of a crank handle and bevelled gears. At the same time the lever pressed the cartridge up to this spindle so giving a full turnover, 'by a kind of burnishing action'.

Although a heavy over-shot wad is shown in the specification drawing, 'pasteboard or other like stiff material' as over-shot wadding is mentioned in the text of the patent.

Once this improvement had been perfected, together with the provision of the cone or tapered lead of some half to one inch length from the chamber to the barrel (which G. H. Daw claimed to have discovered in 1848!) the way was open for the full potential of the breech loading cartridge to be realised.

To return to the Field Trial of 1859, whence we started, the actual lists of guns, their makers and owners, as recorded in the appendices, make interesting reading. Firstly, it should be noted how few of those who wrote to *The Field* actually put their claims to the test. Secondly, we remark the absence of guns entered by the London names, who had a reputation to lose and nothing to gain. We, with the benefit of hindsight, can see this as the beginning of a picture which was to reappear at subsequent trials.

For a contemporary view perhaps we should let Walsh have the last word, in a reply to a questioner who called himself *Kill grouse:*

> The discussion of the respective merits of breech loaders and muzzle loaders has been worn out in our columns. Even the staunchest advocates of the old gun now admit the superiority of the new.

Chapter Four

THE INERT ACTIONS

As a direct result of the Field Trials and Walsh's advocacy of the system week by week in *The Field,* breech loading shotguns were now becoming even more common. It is the authors' view, based on the study of such gunmakers' records as they have seen that, prior to the 1858 trial there were no more than a couple of hundred British made breech loading shotguns in the whole of the British Isles. But by the very early 1860s the total must have been several thousand. Among them was a pair of base fire Lancaster shotguns made for His Royal Highness, the Prince Consort, in November 1859. Nowhere is this upsurge of interest better illustrated than in the records of the Patent Office as gunmakers and lay inventors alike sought to protect their ideas, doubtless in the hope of making their fortunes thereby. From this deluge of invention, which was to continue for the rest of the century, one can see the various phases of the evolution of the shotgun we know today. Of necessity they are arranged and numbered in the patent records in order of the date on which the patent was obtained, and this chronological sequence is frankly a confused jumble. In the hope of making more sense of this tangled mass it is the authors' intention to sort the inventions, as far as possible, into their various classes and so consider like with like.

The most urgent problem that the gunmakers were presented with, as breech loading gained acceptance, was the need to design better breech actions. For with wider use the design that had been copied from Lefaucheux was found to be only barely adequate for the job in hand. The basic weakness of this action lay in the fact that the single bite was too near the pivot pin, which resulted in any wear being much more apparent at the action face. As this loose condition developed in a gun it would gape as it was fired and there would be a tendency, since the cartridge head was therefore not properly supported, for the rim of the cartridge to burst. This problem was made worse by the fact that, due to their inexperience with the requirements of a breech loader, the makers made the action bars and standing breeches of their guns unduly light and flimsy. So that even if the bolt was tight there was still a possibility, particularly with a heavy charge, that the action might spring open on firing.

This problem was to occupy not a few ingenious minds over a long period and the results were many and various. These we have attempted to classify, the first group being those which bear the closest resemblance to

Joseph Lang forward lever action

the Lefaucheux pattern, in that they are simple drop down actions which are held shut by a bite or bites into which the bolt or bolts are driven by a hand lever, not assisted by any spring. These we call inert actions.

Before we enter the realms of the patented actions we should perhaps first look at the type of gun as made in 1859 by the British gun trade. We have it on Walsh's authority that all the breech loaders at the 1859 trial were of the forward facing underlever type of which the Lang gun illustrated is a superbly preserved specimen. One point of interest is the small stud standing proud of the action flats. This is free to slide up and down and is so positioned that, when it is depressed by the closing barrels, its lower end bears on the locking cam and assists in the closing of the lever. But very soon it was realised that, if the lever were reversed and its length maintained, by fitting it round the trigger guard, a much more convenient gun was produced. However the basic weakness of the Lefaucheux style, that is the bite being too near the hinge, remained. If we discount the Lancaster with its special cartridge, the first attempt to improve on the French action was the design Westley Richards patented on 24 September 1858, No. 2149. The most striking point about this gun was that the inventor had appreciated the fault in the siting of the locking surfaces and had moved the bite as far as possible from the hinge pin, right up to the top of the standing breech. It is greatly to the credit of this justly famous and practical house of gunmaking that, with what was among the first attempts to improve the 'French crutch gun' as the breech loader was then popularly called, they should have produced a system which, with subsequent modification, was to remain their standard action for the rest of the century and on into the next. However this first essay was a simple extension of the top rib which fitted into a slot in the top of the standing breech. From the illustration will be seen the long top lever which made a very tight binding grip possible. Note too the early use of the *'bar in the wood'* style of action in which the action bar is sheathed in wood on the lines of a muzzle loader. This again was to remain part of the Westley Richards style right through the hammer gun period.

At this point we must raise another of the unresolved and perhaps now unresolvable questions in the story of the British breech loading shotgun. Back in 1857 there was correspondence in the columns of *The Field* on the strength or rather the lack of it in the then current breech loaders. In the issue of 26 December a correspondent who called himself *'Armourer'* wrote: 'Has he seen Tathams – advertised in your columns – C.F.W. (being such an advocate of great strength) would surely feel content with the double bolting into the solid bed of the frame of that gun. . .' We are frankly ignorant on the point of which gun this comment refers to. It could be the design provisionally patented nearly a year later by Smith, Townsend and Williams, No. 2778 of 4 December 1858, which would seem to fit the description. As shown in the illustration, this gun has a lump on each barrel

Westley Richards patent no. 2149 of 1858

Smith, Townsend and Williams double lump gun

49

which drops into a separate slot in the action bar. Each barrel lump has a slot cut in it into which a rotating bolt actuated by an underlever bites. Or the Tatham could be the double bite Lefaucheux referred to in Chapter one of which we have found two French specimens, one by Chaudun dated 1853, the other unnamed dated 1856.

By coincidence the next inert action patent in chronological order, No. 2040 of 7 September 1859, bears at least some resemblance to the Smith, Townsend and Williams provisional patent. But while the latter is all but unknown, the invention we now come to consider is one of the best known of all time, for it is none other than the double screw grip underlever. This action is to be found on guns of our period and beyond, of all qualities from the vile to the very best, and on guns ranging from light game guns to the biggest wildfowling pieces and the most mighty of rifles. The inventor of this action was Henry Jones, a Birmingham gunmaker, who reaped neither the financial reward nor the fame which so successful an invention should have brought him.

Henry Jones portrait

Henry Jones stamp

His failure to make money from his invention is easily explained in that he let his patent lapse on 19 September 1862, for the want of payment of the £50 stamp duty necessary to keep it in force for a further four years. Why he let his patent lapse is a less easily answered question, but the fact that he went bankrupt four years later, and that the contents of his home at Key Hill House, Hockley, were sold, is probably not without significance. It seems highly probable that his finances were in so parlous a state in 1862 that £50 was simply beyond his means. This, in turn, raises the point of why he didn't sell the patent. We must remember that at least part of the success of the invention inevitably stems from the fact that it was a sound action, cheap to make, which, when the bulk of the guns that used it were produced, was public property. So that what we now think of as its great potential may not have been so apparent then. That in modern times his

50

memory has not been preserved is due, in very large measure, to the shabby treatment he received from the pen of W. W. Greener. The latter must have known the facts of the case. They must have been part of the gossip and folklore of the Birmingham gun trade. Yet in all Greener's books Jones's name is not even mentioned and we find phrases like: 'This important improvement was effected by a Birmingham gunmaker, who omitted to patent this modification' in the fifth edition of *The Gun and its Development* and right on to the ninth edition of this book we read: 'This gun – the invention of a Birmingham gunmaker. . . .' In 1910, when this last edition of Greener's magnum opus was published, the author was a rich successful man of property, and Jones was nearly a hundred years old, living in simple state. Under such circumstances whatever enmity may have once existed between them, could surely have been forgotten and Jones given his due.

That we know so much about Henry Jones is because he achieved, or rather claimed to have achieved, his century. When some friends applied to Buckingham Palace for the congratulatory telegram they were informed that this could not be sent without proof of his age and since, in 1811, the putative year of Jones's birth, the registration of births was not compulsory and no record of this event could be found, the telegram was not forthcoming. But he was not forgotten by the Birmingham gunmakers, among them W. W. Greener, who subscribed to a 'purse of gold', which in fact contained a total of 21 sovereigns. The local press did not let such an occasion pass unnoticed, but it is to be regretted that at least some of the remarks they published were pure penny-a-line rubbish. For instance, Jones had been sent to a most unsatisfactory school, very much on the lines of the fictitious Dotheboys Hall in Dickens' *'Nicholas Nickleby'*, and one journalist in his enthusiasm went as far as to say that Jones had been a pupil of Dotheboys Hall. But at least an account published in *The Ironmonger* was more factual.

So much for the man. What of the action that is his main claim to fame. The gun described in the patent is more complex than the specimens usually encountered. These have a T-shaped slot cut in the barrel lump with two inclines cut on the undersides of the cross piece. These are engaged by what is, in effect, a very coarse pitched screw thread turned by the underlever, so that, as the latter is brought back to its closed position over the trigger guard, the barrels are drawn tight to the action face. In a variant of this design, we believe peculiar to Purdey's, the underlever is combined with a movable trigger guard and extended even further to the rear of the gun to give greater leverage. In addition to this the patent describes a means of 'cutting of communication between the barrels of double barrel breech loading firearms'. This was to be done by a rib that extended back from the breech to enter a corresponding slot in the action face, or a rib on the face entering a slot between the barrels. This is exactly the same system as that used by Pauly and Robert. Its inclusion in this patent would suggest that the pinfire cartridge of this date was very prone to rupture on firing, and this precaution against a double discharge was therefore deemed necessary.

In addition, on the top of the turret, in which is cut the locking screw, is a further piece of steel which acts like a cam on the top of the front of the rear barrel lump to force the barrels back on the face of the action. This cam is said to be adjustable but exactly how is not shown, or it can be replaced when worn as it is a separate piece.

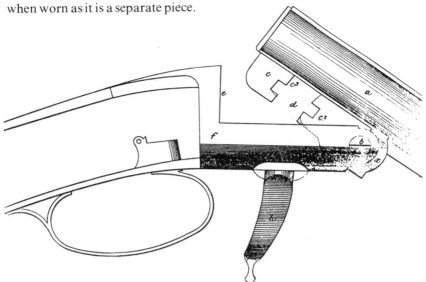

Screw grip and underlever, Henry Jones patent no. 2040 of 1859

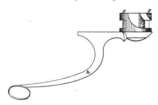

The final claim of this specification is for a spring loaded forend iron which, either by a strong coil spring or a leaf and roller arrangement, is to be held back onto the joint pin of the action. Presumably this would compensate for wear at this point.

So much for what is actually claimed; as always the drawings show additional points of contemporary gunmaking practice. On this specification are two recesses cut in the forward part of the action bar, presumably for lightening. Also shown is a very long top strap which contributes to the strength of the stock at its thinnest point at the hand.

There is another Henry Jones patent which was taken out two years later on 18 April 1861, No. 950, and, while it breaks the chronological sequence, we feel that complete understanding of this action demands its inclusion at this point. This second specification, while it does not claim to be an

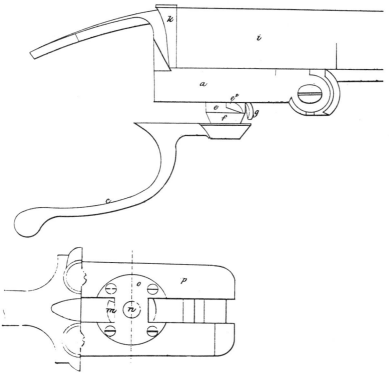

Henry Jones patent no. 950 of 1861

improvement of the earlier one, is obviously a modernisation of it and in theory an improved version as well. It is interesting that now the protrusion between the two barrels has been abandoned along with the spring forend iron and the facing cam. The claims of the second patent are firstly, that the body of the action should be so machined and the parts of the locking bolt so arranged that the latter can be fitted from the top of the action, thereby enhancing the strength of the gun, secondly that a projection should be formed on the bottom of the rear of the front lump to provide a bearing for an inclined piece of steel fitted to the turning turret bolt. The purpose of this cam arrangement was that, as the lever was turned beyond the protrusion, the bolts were released and the barrels partially raised, and, as the barrels were brought back on closing the gun, the process was reversed and the underlever started on its travel.

As we remarked at the beginning of this section, the double screw grip action was made by the Birmingham trade in particular in vast quantities. Naturally these differed with the various makers and with the quality of the gun in question. In general the gun of moderate or better quality followed the pattern of the first patent with the exception of the projection into or from the action face, the separate cam to force the barrels back as the gun closes and the spring loaded forend iron. It was found that, with careful sloping of turret and lumps, the functions of both the separate cam, and indeed the assisted opening and closing cam of the second patent, could be incorporated more simply, but the necessary inclines are subtle and needed careful fitting and so are found only on better guns. The mode of construction was also simplified to a certain extent. The turret was inserted from the bottom of the action and the spindle for it left solid from the substance of the action. Into this central pillar a large headed pin was screwed from the bottom. On a proportion of guns, which would seem to be in general relatively early models, the retaining screw for the opening lever is fitted from above, thus conforming more closely to the 1859 patent.

Further evidence of the popular adoption of the breech loading shotgun was the appearance, towards the end of 1859, of a patent, No. 2583, which had as its object the conversion of muzzle loading shotguns into breech loaders. The patentee was Henry John Daniell, who in the specification claims: 'By this Invention, which applies to both rifled and other percussion guns, and whether made with single or double barrels, it will be understood, that I am enabled to utilize those weapons, or parts of weapons in course of construction, which by reason of the advance of improvement in the manufacture of firearms, have been cast aside as comparatively inefficient or useless, and thereby to produce a weapon well adapted to civil or

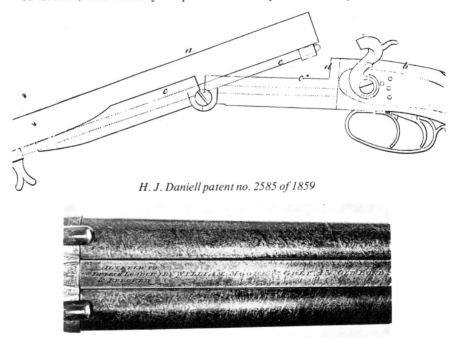

H. J. Daniell patent no. 2585 of 1859

Detail of top rib from Moore and Grey gun converted to breech loader from muzzle loader

Photograph of gamekeeper in Windsor Great Park taken about 1860. This is the earliest known photograph of a breech loading shotgun in Great Britain

military uses.' The conversion of muzzle loaders to breech loaders was an undertaking that was to go on right through our period. Indeed some makers, for instance Sylven in The Strand, Murcott in The Haymarket and Fletcher of Gloucester were to establish something of a name for this work. It was not the easiest of operations and rather mixed results were obtained, with the inevitable consequence of lively correspondence back and forth in the columns of the sporting press.

Henry Daniell, with evident pride, noted on his specification that he was 'late Colonel in the Coldstream Guards' and gave his address as Donnington Park in the county of Leicester. He had retired from the army some three years previously having served nearly 27 years with the Coldstream Guards, and had commanded the first battalion of that famous regiment during the final assault on the Redan at Sebastopol on 8 September 1855. For this, and his part in the siege of the city, he was awarded the Sebastopol clasp to his Crimea medal.

His invention was adopted by the gunmaker Orlando Smith of Derby who was probably the Colonel's local gunmaker. In any event, in *The Field* of 26 November 1859 there appeared the following advertisement:

> Orlando Smith, Practical Gunmaker, London Road Derby, calls the attention of the sporting world to the Proteus Gun invented by Colonel Daniell. Manufactured solely by Orlando Smith possessor of the patent to whom all applications regarding it are to be addressed.

We have not encountered a specimen of this design and so must look to the patent drawing, which, it must be admitted, is rather sparse on the question of practical details. The basic idea was to replace the ram-rod of a muzzle loader with a short sliding steel bolt which would engage under the standing breech. No details are given as to how this bolt was to be controlled beyond the wing nut like handle shown on the drawing.

In contrast to Henry Daniell, whose contribution to the story of arms is limited to the one invention noted above, as far as we are aware, Robert Adams was very much part of the establishment of mid-19th century firearms, being particularly concerned with revolvers. In 1860, when he obtained his patent No. 285 for an inert shotgun action, he had recently resigned his position as manager of The London Armoury Company and previous to this had held a similar post with Deane, Adams and Deane. Having left the London Armoury Company he turned his attention once more to his business at 76 King William Street, which he quoted as his address on his patent.

His improvement to the tilting barrel breech loading sporting gun, which at this date was still widely called 'Lefaucheux', was to form on the rear lump two projections so that, in transverse section, the lump was an inverted T. The portions which formed the horizontal part of the T were, in longitudinal section, slightly arched so that, when picked up by the top of the underlever, which was hung on a transverse pivot and formed to a

56

Robert Adams patent action gun by Burtinshaw of Leeds patent no. 285 of 1860

Prince Christian of Schleswig Holstein, early 1870

double claw shaped hook, drawing the underlever up to the trigger guard would bring the barrels on to the face of the action. The underlever was held shut by a spring catch on its bottom end which latched into a slot in the trigger guard. This is the pattern that is usually encountered, however the specification also shows a gun in which the lever is formed to lie forwards. This arrangement could not have made for a convenient gun, which probably explains why this variant is not seen. In fact the Adams action saw wider use than most; nothing like the ubiquitous Henry Jones but still it is found in modest quantities. No doubt it was built on a semi industrial scale by Adams and his contacts and sold to the trade in some degree of finish.

Another gun, also the product of a maker not usually associated with shotgun development, was that patented by Frederic Waller Prince of 15 Wellington Street, London Bridge, in the County of Surrey. This time the claim to fame of its inventor lies with rifles and in particular a type of capping breech loading weapon which at one time looked as if it might be adopted by the British Army. While details of this arm are beyond the scope of our present theme the fact that 12 London gunmakers signed a testimonial urging official use of this rifle can have done nothing but good to the reputation of its inventor. 'We, the undersigned, being actuated by no other motive than a desire to see the most effective weapon in the hands of our soldiers. . . .'

Given that he had previously invented so practical an arm as his rifle, it is not surprising that his shotgun, patent No. 1291 of 24 May 1860, while of novel design, should, on paper at least, seem to be a very convenient gun. The basis of the idea was very simple, to link the barrels of a drop down breech loader to an opening lever which curved round the trigger guard, by a vertical spindle. The outside of this spindle was shaped as a quick thread with a corresponding thread in the action bar, so that a quarter turn of the lever raised the breech ends of the barrels sufficiently for cartridges to be inserted or removed. The advantage of such a system would be that, instead of it being necessary to close the gun and then apply the bolt, all the user would have to do was to turn the opening lever back over the trigger guard and the gun would be shut. What is surprising is that we have discovered no contemporary reference to this gun, except of course for the patent. Perhaps the inevitably slightly ungainly appearance brought about by the necessary protrusion of the opening jack when the gun was closed told against it. Or we feel it more likely that its inventor was so engrossed in his rifle that he was just not able to promote his shotgun to the extent it deserved. We have therefore no knowledge of a specimen of this gun.

In sharp contrast to the relative fame of Prince and the probable convenience of his gun is the contraption patented No. 1808 of 25 July 1860 by William Rose of Hales Owen (sic) in the county of Worcester. Of the inventor nothing, beyond the fact that he was a barrel maker, seems to have been recorded and his gun, as drawn in the patent specification, would have been most awkward to use. The drawing shows a shotgun with a rigid forend with the barrels hinged at the extreme forward end. About 1½in (3·7cm) back from the barrel pivot a laterally moving lever extending towards the user was pivoted on a vertical axis. The head of this bearing carried a double screw grip while the rear of the lever had yet another bolt which locked a projection from under the barrels with a slot in it, into a corresponding recess in the action bar. If well made there can be no doubt that such an arrangement would have produced a very sound system of bolting, but its cost in terms of inconvenience in the field, occasioned by the long awkwardly placed and moving lever, must have weighed impossibly heavily against it.

Without doubt the most famous inventor in the chapter of inert actions was Stephen Grant, who obtained patent No. 1538 on 15 June 1861. At this date he had been the managing partner of Thomas Boss & Co for five years and gave their address, 73 St James's Street, Westminster, on his patent. Previously he had worked for Boss; coming to them from Lancaster's, which firm he had joined on completion of his apprenticeship, which he served with Kavanagh of Dublin. Five years later he was to establish his own business at 67a St James's and from there he made for himself the reputation of one of the top rank of London gunmakers. In his earlier years in business his reputation depended to a considerable degree on his pigeon guns but, having so established his name, he, like many other makers, concentrated less on competition guns and more on sporting guns. His success can be gauged by the fact that he obtained Warrants of appointment from the Royal Houses of France, Spain, Germany, Austria, Hungary, Russia, Persia and Turkey, as well as from a number of Indian Princelings.

The chief characteristic of the gun he patented in 1861 was that the barrels pivoted at the extreme end of a rigid forend, but no mention is made in the specification as to why this was an improvement. The gun also

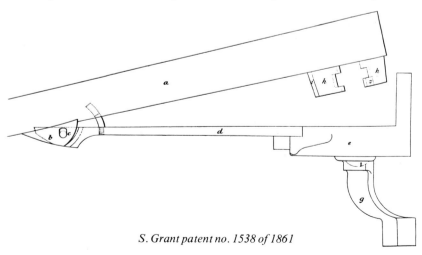

S. Grant patent no. 1538 of 1861

featured an adjustable face on the front of the forward lump of a Henry Jones type double grip action, by which means the gun was to be kept on face. There is also mention of spring assisted opening but with no indication of how this was to be applied. A search of Boss's records unfortunately reveals nothing helpful in this matter.

A name familiar to many arms enthusiasts was that of the Birmingham company of Tipping and Lawden. Partners in this enterprise were Thomas Tipping Lawden and Caleb Lawden and they enjoyed the reputation of making a sound product, not for the titled heads of Europe and beyond but of producing honest guns for yeomen and small gentlemen farmers. The gun they protected with patent No. 1648 on 31 May 1862 is interesting in that, while an inert action, it was of a type that was used in a variety of guises as a snap action. Indeed, with the addition of a suitable spring and a bevel to the front of the bolt, this action would become a perfectly satisfactory snap, and it would therefore come as no surprise to find this action either converted or built as such. But as patented it is certainly an inert action.

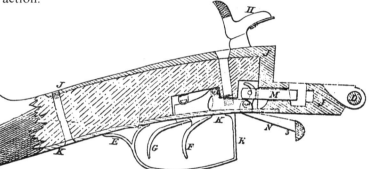

Tipping and Lawden patent no. 1648 of 1862

The drawing shows a horizontally sliding bolt drawn as cylindrical but the specification mentions a flat form. This was so positioned that it would slide through a hole bored through the barrel lump in the axis of the barrels. The back and forth motion of the bolt was governed by a lever which, when the bolt was in the forward or shut position, was nearly vertical in front of the trigger guard. Pushing this lever forwards until it lay under the action bar caused a hook-like cam, formed on the top part of the lever, to act in a slot in the bolt and draw it back and so permit the barrels to pivot open. Until the date of the Grant patent in mid 1861 there was a steady flow of designs for inert action guns, as we have shown. After it, as popular demand became ever stronger for shotguns that snapped shut with a spring bolt and as inventors of all sorts naturally sought to satisfy this demand, fewer inert designs appeared.

Nearly a year elapsed before Frank Emsdorff Walker was granted patent No. 411 on 14 February 1863. In this the influence of the snap gun can be

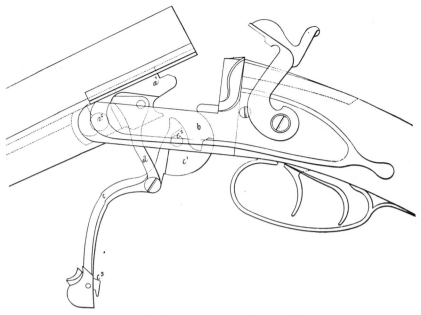

F. E. Walker patent no. 411 of 1863

seen in that, like the Prince gun, the act of unlocking the gun also opened it. The Walker design, as shown on the patent, has an underlever which is thrust forwards and down, somewhat like the Adams gun. Once again a sample has not come to light. Pivoted on the main lever is a secondary lever, or link connecting it to the barrel lump. So that, as the main lever turns about its axis in the action of the gun, the breech ends of the barrels are raised or lowered. The actual bolting of the barrels in the closed position is effected by two bites staggered one above the other on the rear lump, to which the head of the main lever corresponds.

A major point stressed in the patent specification is that this design claimed the use of bar action locks and a bar in the wood action. Both features would aid the production of a handsome sporting gun.

One of the features of the patent specifications of our period is that under a single date and number can be found not merely a variety of applications of the same idea, but two or more guns totally dissimilar. Such is the case with the patent granted to Samuel Mathews on 6 October 1863, No 2441. The bulk of this specification concerns a snap action gun, which will be considered in detail with others of that ilk, but tucked away at the end of the specification is an inert action. What is shown is a relatively unusual arrangement in that the barrel lump carried the locking bolt, which was made to slide back out of the lump to lock the action. The bolt is worked by a crank from a spindle set transversely across the action. On the right hand side of the action is a rearwards facing lever which is pressed down to

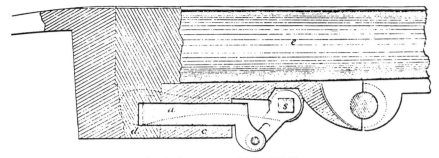

S. Mathews patent 2441 of 1863

withdraw the locking bolt. A gun so fitted would seem to have been a rather curious tool to use for, as the barrels opened carrying the bolt with them, the side lever would flick up. Then, as the barrels were returned to the closed position, the lever would rotate through nearly 180 degrees to an almost vertically down position, whence it had to be rotated back to a horizontal position to lock the gun. All this sounds rather disconcerting but perhaps it proves not quite so alarming with practice. We regret not finding an example of so interesting an action but suspect that it was little used, being overshadowed by snap actions in general and its co-patented gun in particular.

A complex, and so necessarily expensive to produce, design was patented by Edmond Pope of Clonmel in Ireland in 1864, No. 1465 on 14 June. This was another double bite action with a cam mounted transversely in the body of the action worked by a side lever and locking with a cut-out in the barrel lump. Also linked to the spindle of the cam was a sliding bolt under the standing breech and it was so arranged that it worked in conjunction with the cam.

In addition to these actual bolting devices further solidity was to be

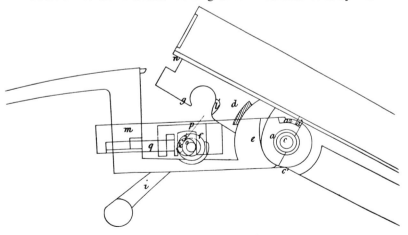

E. Pope patent no. 1465 of 1864

62

obtained by circle jointing the gun. This means that, in this case, the front of the rear lump is formed as an arc that has as its centre the centre of the hinge pin. The slot in which the lump fits in the action has a similar arc cut in it. By careful fitting the two arcs are a rubbing fit giving extra bearing. On this Pope gun the closeness of the fit was to be maintained by making provision for an insert which could be removed and replaced with a larger one to take up wear. Most unusually the forend was also circle jointed on to the gun with a similar insert on the rear of the forend lug to take up wear at this point. Indeed it was proposed to fit the forend so tightly that it was necessary to have a built-in cam and lever on the tip to help prize off the forend when it was desired to take the gun apart. A further feature of this design was to make the barrel hook and the rear of the forend to enclose the hinge pin totally, and to so shape the action bar that there was no possibility of the opening gun nipping a user's hand.

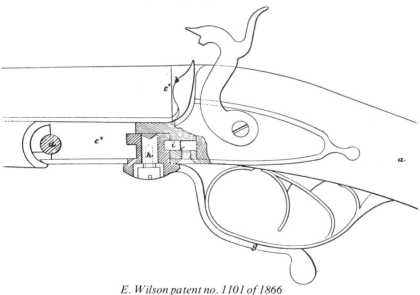

E. Wilson patent no. 1101 of 1866

It is one of the features of our story that, while the bulk of any particular group of inventions appeared fairly close together, there are always some before their time and others, stragglers who come in long after the rest. One such late comer to the inert action patentees was Edwin Wilson, the Horncastle gunmaker, who patented his idea in 1866. This was incredibly a single bite action worked by a lever which curved round the trigger guard, and therefore indentical to the first modification of the Lefaucheux action. Wilson's improvement took the form of a projection from the action which also engaged with the turning bolt to steady it and, it was claimed, to take the strain off the pivot and 'render a single grip as effective as a double grip'!

In all fairness we should note that this patent, No. 1101 of 19 April, also included yet another means of putting a worn gun back on face. This time what was protected was a conical joint pin which could be screwed in further as required.

The inert actions are therefore a curious mixture. Without the Henry Jones double grip they would be no more than a side turning. But the Jones system, being by far the most common action applied to guns of our period, lifts the importance of the group. Furthermore the double grip was still being made, used and praised when later inventions, intended no doubt to supersede it, were but faint memories.

Belgian-made 14-bore pinfire retailed by Horsley of York

Chapter Five

THE SLIDE AND DROP ACTIONS

While the better inert actions among those previously described were, if well made, capable of excellent service – indeed examples of the Henry Jones double grip are still in use after well over a century of use and occasional abuse – there were inventors then and later who believed that the simple pivoted action based on the Lefaucheux was basically at fault, and that a more radical answer than better bolting was needed if a really sound gun was to be made. From this readiness to re-think the whole concept of the breech loading gun was to spring a variety of novel actions; not all of them sound or practical, but, for the student of arms, fascinating. One of the ideas that was tried by a number of inventors was to have the barrels move forwards, perhaps a quarter of an inch, before they were free to pivot down. Why this line of development, which was to prove a blind alley, was chosen, can now only be guessed at, but, as Dougall mentioned, the Lefaucheux action could not stand the continuous vibration. So a more rigid method of bolting the barrels firmly at their extreme rear end was sought, and a connection between the standing breech and the barrel breech was thought to be worthy of investigation. As we remarked in the description of the Lancaster gun, the system was not new even when Lancasters initially employed it. But the soundness of the Lancaster gun

Later Lancaster built as centre fire

65

cannot possibly have escaped notice and must surely claim a major part of the credit for the inspiration of later inventors. After the introduction of the true centre fire, the Lancaster gun continued to be made to accept the new cartridge, and existing guns were modified to the same end. Indeed it is certain that more were built as centre fires in the 1860s than as the original base fire system a decade previously. It is a tribute to the design that it was able to hold its own well into the 1860s, admittedly as the exclusive and expensive example it had always been, in competition with guns of much more recent invention.

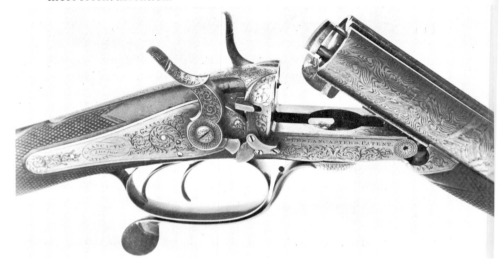

One of a pair of Charles Lancaster centre fire guns no. 3273/4 made for H.R.H. The Prince Consort, 9th November 1859

There were in fact fifteen separate British patents, including the Bellford/Gastinne/Lancaster, taken out during the period covered by this work. We believe that they can be better understood if they are broken down into two basic categories. Firstly there are those designs in which the forend is permanently and rigidly fixed to the stock proper, in fact just like a muzzle loader. The barrels are, in all cases in this subgroup, pivoted at the extreme front of the forend, the pivot being where the ramrod enters the forend on the usual type of muzzle loader. The second of our groups comprises those more numerous designs, which more closely follow the pattern of the simple drop down Lefaucheux gun. These have the pivot for the barrels perhaps $2\frac{1}{2}$ or 3 inches from the breech face and have the advantage that, in a gun of conventional form at least, a wider and therefore more stable hinge is possible.

This last point is of some considerable importance in the authors' eyes, in that all slide and drop guns give the impression of being variously shaky when open, no matter how securely they lock shut. Indeed the solidity of the muzzle loader was one of the major points claimed by the diminishing number of staunch adherents to the old style of gun, so any feature of the design which reduced the apparent rigidity of a breech loader can have done nothing to recommend it to prospective purchasers.

This, we feel, explains why the first group is the smaller and why actual examples are met with less frequently. It is perhaps not unworthy of mention that of the five patents which compose this group, three are the designs of foreigners.

They are a very varied assortment and, beyond the general classification, little parallel can be drawn among them. This being the case, we will consider them in order of their patent dates.

In fact it was an English invention which was the first to be patented. It forms part of Joseph Needham's specification dated 22 May 1862, No. 1544. This contains details of three basically different guns besides some secondary mechanisms, all of which we will consider with their fellows. The slide and tilt gun is of advanced concept and deserves to be better known. Not least since the drawing shows what appears to be a centre fire cartridge. It is noteworthy that, in date, the specification is after the original Schneider patent but just prior to the Daw modification of the Schneider, which is usually taken as the beginning of the popularisation of the centre

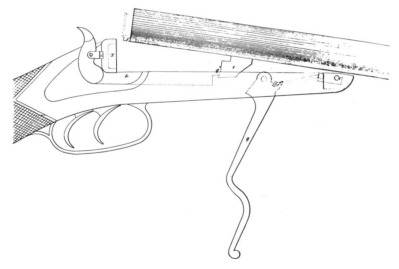

J. Needham patent no. 1544 of 1862

fire cartridge in Great Britian. The specification is infuriatingly vague and, while it refers to a needle cartridge, such a description was applied at first to the centre fire as well as to the cartridge we now know by this term. It is a pity that, as far as we are aware, no additional contemporary information has survived and we must conjecture on the sparse but incontravertible evidence of the patent.

The drawing that prompted the above remarks shows a gun with an underlever which curves round the trigger guard and pivots well forward in the rigid forend. Thrusting this down both released the barrels and, via a link between the forward lump and the front of the underlever, unlocked them and pushed them forward, when they would pivot open by their own weight. The extent to which they could pivot was limited by a projection on the rear of the rear lump, which caught on the action bar. To shut the gun it was necessary first to bring the barrels back onto the action and then to draw up the underlever. This final movement, via the link, would first draw back the barrels and then lock them, as the rear of the underlever fitted up behind the front of the rearward lump. In addition, this gun is also drawn with an automatic half cock mechanism and a firing pin linked to the breast of the cock. These features will be considered in Chapter 12.

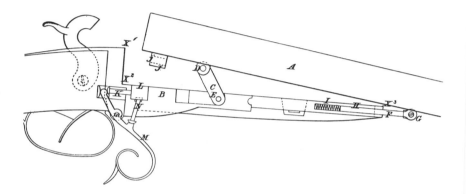

Cassegrain patent no. 2079 of 1862

The second slide and drop forward pivoted gun to be protected was the invention of Paul François Cassegrain, a Parisian gentleman, and from his patent specification this would seem to have been a curious and not over practical design. It was patent No. 2079 of 22 July 1862. This French invention had the distinction that it featured spring assisted opening. Twenty or more years later this was to reappear as a refinement applied to a proportion of guns built by the very best makers. But in 1862 it certainly was a novelty. The patent drawing shows a pinfire sporting gun with a lever of continental style in front of the trigger guard. Pushing this lever forward withdrew a cylindrical bolt into the body of the gun and so freed the barrels. These had then to be lifted up, presumably by depressing them forward of the forend, and, once the two lumps were clear of the slots in the action the spring in the forend would tend to force the barrel assembly forwards. The extent to which the barrels were permitted to gape and travel was governed by a toggle link, as shown, which would have helped to steady the barrels when open. To close the gun the barrels would have to be forced back, compressing the spring in the forend, and the underlever would have to be pushed forwards to with-draw the bolt from the recess in the action slot, to permit the lump to drop home.

A further feature of this patent, which was to reappear in many guises over the years, was an adjustment to take up wear in the action and so, in gunmakers' parlance, keep the barrels on the face. In the Cassegrain gun this was to be achieved by a sliding false front to the rear action slot, which could be screwed back to take up the play resulting from wear in the moving parts. But in view of the design of the rest of the gun, we are not convinced of the efficacy of this provision.

The next member of our present group was patented nearly three years later, on 14 February 1865, No. 425, and this gap, we feel, points yet again to the low regard in which the forward pivoted slide and drop gun was held. Again it is a foreign design, this time the brainchild of a New Englander, Charles Edward Sneider, of Baltimore (US patent No. 47755 of 1865). However the patent was obtained in Britain by Benjamin Thompson, who simply and unhelpfully describes himself as a merchant of Birmingham.

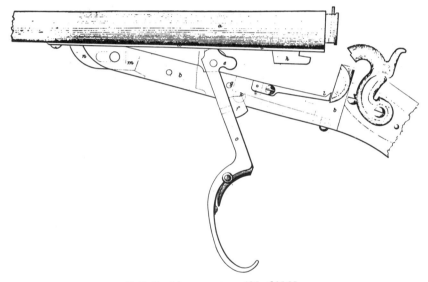

C. E. Sneider patent no. 425 of 1865

As we have come to expect of Yankee designs, this gun had the virtues of a simpler and sounder mechanism but would have nevertheless suffered from the basic problems inherent in this layout. It will be seen from the illustration, which is of the provisional specification, that the design uses a long underlever, the rear part of which is also the trigger guard. The forward end of this lever is pivoted on a lump projecting from the underside of the barrels. The head of this lever has formed on it a rather complex double cam which works against the slot in the action bar so that, as the lever is depressed, the barrels are moved forwards until the locking lugs, one at the breech and one at the far end of the forend, are free. The latter lug works in a slot which is S shaped to form a stop to limit the gape of the barrels. Two other features of the drawing should be mentioned. First is the upward projection on the underlever for additional bolting. Second is the extractor so designed that, as the cartridge was forced into the chamber as the gun was closed, the rim rode over the sloping front of the hook, but as the barrels slid forward again, the vertical rear face of the extractor would retain and so extract the cartridge. Beyond the patent drawing we have no knowledge of this gun and have never seen or heard of an example.

These remarks also apply, but with even greater force, to a provisional patent granted later the same year, on 24 April to be exact, No. 1136. The patentee and the inventor were, we presume, both Frenchmen and the most remarkable feature of this specification are their magnificently extravagant names. The inventor was Monsieur Marie Joseph Eugène du Liège de Puychaumeix and the patentee, Peter Armand le Comte de Fontaine Moreau. As to the actual invention, beyond it being for a gun that slid forward and then pivoted down, we are at a loss. There is no drawing and we believe that an original vague French specification has been made completely unintelligible by translation.

The final member of this sub-group is that patented by James MacNaughton, the Edinburgh gunmaker, on 5 July 1867, No. 1971. We believe that, of this group of forward pivoted slide and drop guns, it was the one that was produced in greatest numbers in the British Isles. It is most unfortunate that although MacNaughton's records survive they were so poorly kept as to be now near useless for study. We are, however, led to our conclusion by the fact that we have encountered, and been told of, several specimens of this gun during our collecting careers. The only one which we

MacNaughton patent no. 1971 of 1867

were able to photograph was a specimen which had evidently given long service and will be seen to bear the marks of it.

The action is worked by a forward and downward swinging underlever pivoted in the body of the action. To open the gun this lever is thrust down, when a cam on the front edge of the head pushes forward the barrels. As they move forward, a conventional extractor is operated by a lever pivoted at the bottom of the front of the third barrel lump. The top of this lever is pushed back by the forward motion of the barrels and so extracts the cartridges. When the action lever has been pushed through some 90 degrees the bites on the second and rear lumps are freed from the action and the barrels are thus free to pivot down. Their travel is limited by a stop formed on the underside of the front or first lump. To lock the gun the barrels first have to be shut and then the underlever raised, this latter motion causes a cam on the rear of the lever head to act on the front of the rear barrel lump and so move the barrels back to lock.

The gun we examined was capable of being taken down by removing the pivot pin, when the barrels could be lifted off the stock. As we mentioned earlier, the gun photographed had seen a lot of use and was very shaky on its hinge pin when open, and far from tight when shut, but that was after nearly a century of shooting.

As far as the British arena was concerned, the archetype of our second group of slide and drop sporting guns, that is those with the hinge in approximately the same position as a simple drop down gun, was the Gastinne/Bellford/Lancaster as previously described. We do not find it particularly surprising that so sound, simple and well known an action should have inspired imitators. The first of these was also the next patent obtained for a slide and drop gun after the Bellford – patent No. 1703 of 20 July 1859. The patentee was James Erskine of Newton Stewart, Wigtownshire, who died on 20 November 1891 and whose personality was outlined for posterity in *The Field* of the same year in a letter from An Old Shikari:

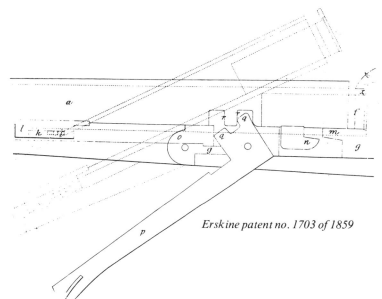

Erskine patent no. 1703 of 1859

71

Sir – It occurs to me that some of your readers may like to hear a few more particulars about Mr James Erskine, whose recent death at Newton Stewart was noticed in your columns. His excellent machine for loading cartridges with all its recent improvements sufficient to ensure economy, safety and rapidity, is too well known to need any further notice. James Erskine may be said to have completed the revolution in sport and gunnery which breech loading began, just about 30 years ago.

Erskine followed the profession of his father, and in his youth gained much professional knowledge in a house in Liverpool. As an inhabitant of Newton Stewart for the last 50 years he was well known to all sportsmen, fishermen, gamekeepers and farmers in the south of Scotland, and his shop used to be littered with letters of correspondents from all parts of the United Kingdom. His constructive talents, his inventive powers, his rare skill in the adaptation of means to ends, which he had carefully calculated and foreseen, were combined with a remarkable simplicity of character, which prevented his deriving the solid and substantial benefit from his discoveries which he really deserved. With a little more of hard headedness he might have made a fortune for himself; but the absence of hard, practical self seeking views of life only served to make his character more attractive to those who like simplicity and originality. He was full of anecdotes and reminiscences of old days, when trout were less shy, salmon more plentiful (as they always are in such cases) and when the horrible grouse disease was almost unknown. He generally has aviaries and stews in his back yard, tenanted by hawks pheasants of the rarer kinds and ravens, all of which were endowed, he said, with some remarkable attributes not to be found in similar specimens anywhere else. His remarks on men and measures were always quaint, suggestive and amusing and never sarcastic or ill-natured. He was a skilful fisherman and, in his younger days a reliable shot. He used to maintain – though not given to boasting – that he was one of the few persons who could kill a hare going straight away artistically and properly. It was remarked, by one who knew him well, that he would have been made immortal had he been only known to George Eliot or to Walter Scott. I may add that in height, figure and face he bore a decided resemblance to Dr Bradley, the present Dean of Westminster.

The respect in which Mr Erskine was held amongst a large circle of friends and acquaintances was shown by the number of townsmen and others who recently followed him to his grave, in spite of a thick sea fog and most inclement weather.

An Old Shikari

But it is another of Walsh's curious errors that, in his book, *The Shotgun and Sporting Rifle* of 1862, 2nd edition, he writes, in his best pompous style: '. . . . a Mr Erskine of Scotland who is not connected with the gun trade. . . .' In fact the Erskine patent describes two mechanisms, and, beyond the fact that both guns are of the type we are now considering, there is no real resemblance between them. Yet again we must rely on the patent drawings as we have been unable to trace a specimen.

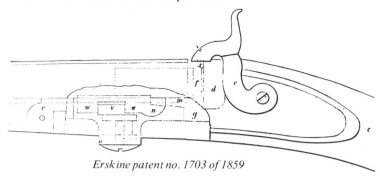

Erskine patent no. 1703 of 1859

The drawings show a handsome gun with a forward facing Lefaucheux style lever and this has to be rotated horizontally back towards the user to open the gun. This motion of the lever rotates a stud and turret arrangement in the action bar, just like the Lancaster, and so moves the barrel assembly forwards. The locking is by a bolt just forward of the standing breech which slides under the action bar. The gun is drawn as a pinfire with a vertical breech face and shows no other bolting mechanism.

The second gun which was protected as No. 1904 of 29 June 1867 by the prolific patentees, S. R. & W. Trulock of Dublin, so closely resembles the more common Lancaster as to give rise to some confusion. Not only is the mechanism virtually identical but the style of the gun encountered is so strongly Lancastrian as to suggest that both were the work of the same hands. The important difference between them is that in the Trulock gun the forend is fixed to the action and the barrels slide on the forend. Thus it does not share with its more illustrious forebearer the vice of nipping unwary users' hands.

The Trulock gun belongs almost to the end of our period, but very much earlier appeared the design of J. D. Dougall, No. 1128 of 7 May 1860, which was to become famous as *The Lockfast*. This action must be regarded as one of the great designs of the period and one by which others were judged, and it doubtless served as an inspiration for some that followed.

The writings of J. D. Dougall form another important legacy. Due to the considerable quantity of autobiographical material which they contain we can learn something of at least one facet of our man from them. His books were, *Scottish Field Sports*, *The Rifle Simplified*, *Shooting Simplified* and *Shooting, its Appliances, Practice and Purpose* and it will be noted that they are all sporting rather than gun-making books. If he had attempted to write one of the latter he would have been in competition with William Greener and if we regard his authorship as a means of furthering his main business then he was wise to direct his remarks to the sportsman rather than the

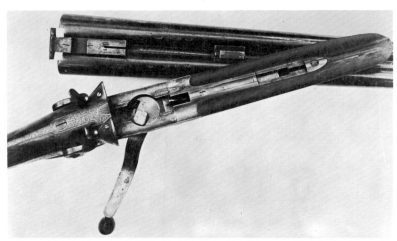

S.R.&W. Trulock patent no. 1904 of 1867

student of arms. From the comments included in his works it would appear that he had extensive shooting experience, he remarks on renting various sporting rights, mainly in the south of Scotland. There is a passage in *Shooting Simplified* where he tells of how a roe escaped his gun, due to the fact that he had left a spent case in one barrel by mistake, while on a shooting holiday of five weeks. In both *Shooting Simplifed* and *Shooting, its Appliances, Practice and Purpose* there is the story of how he shot his first widgeon on the Clyde when he was a mere lad and was taken out by one Malcolm Macrae, a noted wildfowler and boatman. This story incidently suggests parental approval, if not actual encouragement. He was thus able to present himself to his readers as an experienced sportsman on the one hand while, at the same time, not letting it be forgotten that he was a gunmaker: the obvious inference being that his readers could safely entrust their commissions to him, as a gunmaker who fully understood their needs.

Among his remarks on the preservation of game there is one which was probably rather novel to some of his readers – that the falcons should not be exterminated, as their preying on smaller more destructive vermin more than repaid for the odd grouse they took. On the other hand we see him very much as a product of his time when he insists, in a section on ferreting rabbits, that it is quite infra dig for a sportsman to assist in the digging out of a laid up ferret. This should be left to the keeper while the sportsman takes himself off in search of more sport.

If, as we suspect, it was his intention that sporting books should reach a wider public than would a simple gunmaking book he probably laid the right course, for certainly *Shooting Simplified* is widely seen even now. The autobiographical material is of the greatest interest to us seeking to know something of the man because, strange as it may seem, we have been unable to discover an extensive obituary. There was a note of his death on 28 February 1891 at his home at 51 Bedford Gardens, London, but nothing else beyond being told of a letter, which could not be refound for actual study, of his writing, to the Master of the Gunmakers' Company to beg his fare back to Scotland, that he might die in his native land. If this, indeed, was the fact we wonder what disaster or vice brought a man so successful in his younger days to so parlous an end.

First pattern Dougall Lockfast patent no. 1128 of 1860

In part the fame of his action and of himself derives from the fact that James Dalziell Dougall had not only the ability to design a sound mechanism, but also the skill and drive necessary to exploit it. To this end he advertised regularly in *The Field* and *Land & Water*. Not only did he pay for inserted advertisements but he also wrote many extremely long letters to both papers, not merely puffing his product, Walsh would certainly not have permitted that, but commenting on a whole host of gunmaking and sporting topics. By this process he made his name a household word among shooting men. His earlier letters he wrote under the pseudonymn of *'A Glasgow Gunmaker',* but later he ceased this practice and wrote under his own name. We cannot help but feel that Walsh was conscious of the debt he owed to Dougall for this regular letter writing, for what every magazine needs, and never more so than when it is new and establishing itself, are contributions of stature. Though Walsh, by the time he published his seventh edition of *British Rural Sports* in 1867, had become convinced of the need for a top connection between the barrels and the action and had some hard things to say about the Lockfast: '. . . It is a pretty toy and no more. . . .' Yet he points out that when sound it was paradoxically an excellent rifle action. But when the second edition of *The Shotgun and*

Early pattern Dougall Lockfast

Sporting Rifle was published in 1862, Walsh, though he admitted to not having used it, praised the Lockfast, actually going a long way to answering his own later question by saying that the cam could be easily and cheaply replaced. Certainly in the early 1860s *The Field* gave Dougall and his gun good and friendly coverage, to the undoubted benefit of the latter. For instance Dougall's trip to Belgium in 1861, when he licensed some of the Liège makers to use his system, got prominent cover in *The Field*. Dougall also exhibited his gun at the London International Exhibition of 1862 where it gained one of the two medals awarded for principle, the other being awarded to Samuel Colt for his revolver.

If the spread of serial numbers seen on Lockfast guns and the style of them is accepted as a reasonable guide, then we must assume that they were made for a period of perhaps 25 years, from the date of the patent. In this time there were inevitably detail changes made in the design. It would therefore seem logical first to consider the model as patented, which we must accept as the original, and then to describe such variants as are known to exist.

The patent drawings show two distinct guns, one a double barrel smooth bore for a pin fire cartridge, the other a species of capping breech loader drawn loaded with a bulleted cartridge. The text describes this latter as a military rifle and explains how a combustible cartridge with an expansive wad at its base is used in the piece – the wad being either removed after each shot or pushed up the bore by the next shot fired. This potential military rifle aspect of the design was doubtless included as, at the date in question, it looked as if the British army might well adopt a capping breech loader, and numerous inventors sought the rich reward that the official use of their gun might reap.

The basic idea of the Lockfast was to make the hinge pin, upon which the barrels pivoted, capable of partial rotation and to effect this by a lever which lay down the side of the gun. This pivot was also a cam, so arranged that a quarter turn of the lever gave the barrels the slight fore and aft motion necessary to the slide and drop concept. An unknown variation on the theme shown in the patent, which would seem to have been included in the specification almost as an afterthought, was to achieve the motion of the barrels by making gear teeth on the pivot and a short corresponding rack on the lump.

Also shown are two different forms of lever, one pointing forwards from the hinge, the other to the rear, and four styles of mating the back of the rear lump to the action. In three cases these are different shapes to slide under the standing breech and in the fourth a cylindrical stud projects from the standing breech to engage with a circular hole bored in the rear of the lump. Other variants illustrated in the specification are the use of the bosses on the action face to engage with the breeches, and one drawing shows the reverse, that is the barrels sliding back into a recess in the standing breech.

Very few examples of these different varieties have come to our notice,

Late Pattern Dougall Lockfast

indeed as we remarked previously, it is very doubtful whether any were ever made. The earliest Lockfast we have ever seen, a pin fire 12 bore shotgun, differs from the patent in that, to open the gun, the side lever which projects backwards from the hinge has to be lifted rather than depressed. In order that this lever can clear the barrels it is hinged at its forward end and so has to be moved out and up. This gun also has a form of barrel bolting different from that described above. In addition to the two bosses on the face of the action and the stud in the slot under the standing breech, there is a spring loaded bolt which works across the action and engages with a hole on the right hand side of the rear lump.

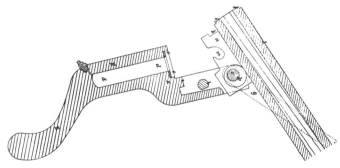

J. Dougall patent no. 2468 of 1863

In contrast, Lockfast No. 2750, a 12 bore centre fire with rebounding locks, is a very late specimen and was probably built in the early 1870s. It bears a very much closer resemblance to the patent specification, quite the reverse of the usual pattern of events. The opening lever is depressed to open the gun and the bolting is by the bosses on the action face and a lug on the rear of the lump. This particular specimen, which was one of its maker's very best guns, has been restored from a quite appalling state of disrepair, but even when first found was tight in the action. Surely an effective answer to Walsh's criticism.

Further evidence of the energy with which Dougall exploited his invention lies in the fact that he adapted the design for use as a punt gun or a light military cannon. This was the subject of a separate patent, No. 2468 of 8 October 1863. In this modification a chamber was formed in the stock and the barrel cammed back into it. This use as a weapon of war, while of passing interest in itself, brings us back to our theme of advertising, as this development was reported in *The Field* along with glowing accounts of the value of the weapon to the troops so armed. We are unaware whether the Lockfast cannon, which was manufactured by the Blakely Ordnance Company Limited of 7 Pall Mall, ever saw active service, but we may be sure that its production was rewarding to its inventor, both in terms of cash and publicity.

The soundness of the Lockfast action and the publicity it received resulted in a flood of orders which Dougall was hard pressed to handle. First he increased the size of his works but he was still unable to satisfy the demand. He therefore advertised that he was prepared to license other makers to use his design for 'a moderate royalty'. The exact amount per gun we have been unable to discover. Of those who entered such an agreement we have found record of B. Cogswell, W. & J. Rigby, Reilly of London and Lyell of Aberdeen. It is said that it was a customer of the last mentioned, one Colonel Knight Erskine, who suggested the modification to the Lockfast by which the rotation of the operating lever was reversed. That is, it had to be pushed down instead of being lifted. This alteration was adopted by Dougall and is indeed the commonest pattern of Lockfast encountered. Evidence both of the length of popularity of the Lockfast and the keenness with which the inventor looked to his rights can be seen from the following advertisement:

Infringement of Dougall's patent:- We hereby regret having infringed Mr J. D. Dougall's Patent Rights by converting a Purdey gun to the Lockfast system without Mr Dougall's permission or authority. We now consent, to prevent legal proceedings, to pay the usual royalty on the said gun and to insert this advertisement at our expense three times in The Field and Land & Water newspapers.

Nixon & Lawton, Gunmakers, Newark

December 24 1872

Parallels to both the Dougall and Lancaster guns can be seen in a gun which produced one of the minor puzzles of the research for this work. We first discovered the gun which we illustrate with the inscription 'R. Jeffery Guildford patent'. The specification to which we assume this refers is provisional patent No. 296 of 5 February 1861. This however is meaningless and has given rise to the suggestion that, either the inventor was far more at home with a file than a pen, or that the gun we have found may be a later product, and the reference on it to 'The Patent' is little more than a status symbol.

R. Jeffery patent no. 296 of 1861

This gun is one of those which could so easily be missed as when closed it looks exactly like a Henry Jones screw grip. The opening lever however carries in the body of the gun not a grip but a cam which bears on the rear of the front barrel lump, and forces the barrels forwards. This movement frees them from the bolting lugs which are two bosses on the action face which mate with the rear ends of the chambers and a projection from the rear lump which slides in a slot cut under the standing breech.

A gun which sounds identical to the above is that described in William Horton of Glasgow's specification No. 1847 of 23 July 1863, but, lacking an actual example, our knowledge rests solely with this specification.

After consideration of the Lockfast, mention must be made of two actions that were obviously inspired by it. These are the guns patented firstly by Harris John Holland, the Bond Street gunmaker and Walter Payton of Johnson Place, Harrow Road, watch and clock maker, No. 1904 of 13 July 1861, and secondly by John Gibson and Samuel, Richard and

H. J. Holland and W. Payton patent no. 1904 of 31 July 1861 by H. J. Holland

William Trulock, No. 1696 of 8 July 1863. Since the Dougall Lockfast patent was still in force at the date of both of these two, could either of them have been produced commercially without at least the risk of litigation? These two guns are so similar that one general description will, in large measure, cover them both. The drawings show, in both instances, double barrelled pin fire guns with back action locks. In the action bars, at a point about midway between the action face and the hinge pin, there is a transverse spindle which carries, on the right hand side, a rearwards facing side lever which is depressed to move the barrels forwards. This motion is

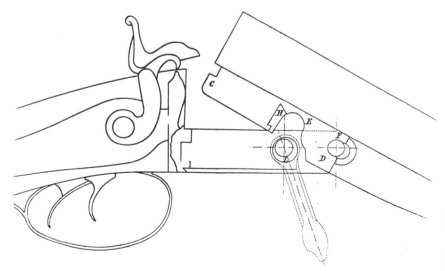

Drawing of Gibson, Trulock, Trulock and Trulock gun patent no. 1696 of 1863

given to the barrels by a cam carried on the transverse spindle acting on the lumps. In both cases the actual bolting is achieved by a projection of the rear lump which slides under the standing breech.

Of the two the Holland and Payton design is the more interesting and would seem to have had considerable potential in that the side lever, drawn slightly longer in this case, would raise the barrels and then draw them back to bolt all in one movement. Such a gun must have been quicker and more convenient to use than the general run of slide and drops, in which the barrels had to be raised and the bolts applied as two separate motions. This desirable feature of the Holland and Payton design is achieved by having the bottom of the cam slot enclosed. In order that the gun could be taken down in the ordinary way, this bottom was to be formed by a rearward projection of the forend, which keyed onto the front of the back lump. It was this portion of the forend that the segment shaped cam was to work against to close the gun and then rotate further to bear on the rear lump to force the barrels back to lock.

On the Gibson, Trulock, Trulock and Trulock gun the barrels had to be raised onto the stock as a separate motion as the cam slot in the lump had an open bottom. A more minor difference between this gun and the Holland and Payton is the shape of the cam, it being circular in the former as will be seen from the patent drawing.

There remain three other guns of this type introduced during the span covered by this book. First we should consider the other Erskine design which appeared on the same patent as the one considered earlier in this chapter, No. 1703 of 1859. This too uses a forward facing underlever but this time it swings back and down. The pivot is formed in the action bar and above this fulcrum are two projections which go up between the barrels which are shown set wider apart than usual to accommodate this mechanism. Fitted between the two projections on the underlever is a single tooth or stud. On this stud and on the front and back of the recess which contains it, the underlever, as it is pulled down, works to force the barrels forwards when the single bite is freed and the barrels are able to drop.

Another invention which owed nothing to its contemporaries was a further product of the fertile imagination of Henry Jones of double grip fame. This time the patent is No. 2395 and it was obtained on 29 August 1862. The basis of this is a complex compound cam set in the action bar and worked by an underlever shown curving round the trigger guard. One of the authors (IMC) has seen a gun of this type, but was unable to obtain a photograph. Therefore once again we have to use the patent drawing to illustrate, and we believe this action is in fact best so explained. Reference to the drawing will be essential to understand how, as the underlever is thrust forwards, the front part of the cam moves the barrels forwards and then, as the lever is raised to the trigger guard, how the rear of the cam draws the barrels back. This ingenious action, with its two bites, would certainly have been a strong one, but the complex and therefore necessarily

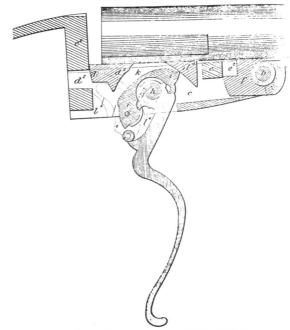

Henry Jones patent no. 2395 of 1862

expensive mechanism would have told against it.

It is, we feel, very significant that the last slide and drop gun that was patented within the period of this work represents a valiant attempt to make a slide and drop snap gun, doubtless to compete with the snap action guns that were, at the date of the two patents on this basic design (1869), becoming ever more common and beside which the inert slide and drop was at a disadvantage for speed of manipulation. It is noteworthy that the patentee of this action was James Mackie, who gave his address as that of J. D. Dougall's London shop at 59 St James's Street, Westminster, and that the specification states that it is an improvement on the Dougall Lockfast action. This latter claim we feel to be somewhat fanciful, for, while the two guns were both slide and drop actions, there is only one point in common between the mechanisms. We know Mackie was an employee of Dougall's but in what capacity is not certain. His two patents are No. 1342 of 1 May and No. 3003 of 15 October both of 1869.

That it was not easy to devise a slide and drop snap gun is evident from the specimen of this type of gun which it has been our good fortune to examine. Admittedly now over a century old but, when compared with most Lockfasts of a similar vintage, it is a very shaky affair. Incidentally it has on its action flats the curved two line stamp, *Patent Lockfast*. It differs fundamentally from the Lockfast in that the fore and aft motion of the barrels is not produced via the hinge pin. Indeed the Mackie lacks a hinge pin in the normal sense of the term. Instead the forend is hinged to the bar

J. Mackie patent no. 1342 (provisional) of 1869

of the action and the barrels are fixed to the forend by the usual loop and cross bolt. However the slot in the loop is wider than the bolt so that the barrels can slide back and forth. In use this motion is produced by an underlever that curves round the trigger guard and to open the gun it has to be pushed forwards and down. This lever is pivoted on a transverse axis midway in the action bar, and both the front and the back of the head of this lever act as a cam. When the lever is thrust forwards the front cam pushes forwards a small bolt, which bears on the rear of the front lump and pushes the barrels forwards until the locking lugs are disengaged and the barrels can tilt open.

On closing the gun, the front of the rear barrel lump bears on the back of the head of the opening lever, which stays down when the gun is opened and trips it from its over centre state, so that the snap spring now causes the underlever to return to its closed position. In so doing the rear cam of the underlever forces the barrels back to the locked position. The locking bolts are in fact two bosses on the action face and a lug on the rear lump, the only real resemblance to a true Lockfast.

The gun which we have studied is No. 3008 and number one of a pair, and, in that it seems much more like the provisional specification of May than the full patent of October, we would suggest that it was made between the dates of the two specifications. As we remarked earlier it is now in a very shaky state but was in active use until a couple of years ago, far longer service than its makers could have possibly envisaged for it when they advertised in *The Field* in 1872:

'The Underlever Lockfast.' It is a marvel of ingenuity, it has the solidarity of the Lockfast with the rapidity of a spring gun while its shooting powers are of the very highest quality.

There remains a further small group of designs which, though their connection with the mechanisms previously considered here is but tenuous, have more in common with the slide and drop actions than with any other design. These are the actions in which the barrels do not drop down at all but merely slide forward away from the standing breech along some form of track or guide to a distance sufficient to permit the removal of the spent case and its replacement by a live round. They are most usually seen as pin fires but there is a patent for an extractor system to enable a centre fire cartridge to be used. This is Purdey's patent No. 424 of 14 February 1865 and will be considered in the Gadgetry chapter, as the slide system is not claimed as part of the specification.

In theory, with a pin cartridge, if the cocks have a recess in the striking part of the head this will grip the top of the pin after the cartridge has been fired, so that the cartridge will be held stationary as the barrels are drawn forward. By this method it was claimed that the spent case would be fully extracted and fall free as the barrels reached their fully open position. This is not borne out in the authors' experience. We have found that frequently instead of drawing out the spent case the cock merely levers off the cartridge head, leaving the cardboard tube in the chamber which needs to be winkled out with whatever tools are to hand. In addition these guns are among the most awkward of breech loaders to handle, so much so that at times a third hand could be well employed, and they would be the most infuriating of guns to find oneself with in any warm corner. All of which we are quite sure explains why so few patents were obtained or guns made and why specimens are often encountered in such excellent condition.

Yet again the idea appears to be of French origin, arms of this type, including pistols, being made by Lepage. But commonest of the continental designs, certainly in the authors' experience of shotguns in Great Britain, are those built on the Bastin action as patented by Bastin Frères, but never protected in Great Britain.

The Bastin gun is essentially a very simple mechanism. A lever lies under the forend and is pivoted at its rear end on a lump projecting down from the barrels. Hinged on this underlever about a third of its length forward from the point where it joins the barrels, is a second short lever, the other end of which is pivoted in the action. These two levers are so arranged that, when the main lever is freed at the far end of the forend and pulled down towards the user, the barrels slide forwards. It would seem that the patentees produced actions which they sold, presumably in the white, to other makers, both British and Continental, who stocked and finished them. There is, in the collection of one of the authors (DJB), a gun of this type bearing the name G. Masu, Wigmore Street, on the rib but the action has

Bastin Frères No. 1069 stamped on it, while the gun has the serial number of 3783.

It is a gun of superb quality and when new must have been a most strikingly handsome piece. The stock is very dark tiger striped walnut, the lock plates are nickle plated and the furniture a very bright lustrous blue.

There are six British patents for guns with forward sliding barrels specifically intended for self contained cartridges, those of Harvey, Palfrey, Needham, Brooks, Wilson and Gedge. But there are several capping breech loaders of this general type and it is not impossible that specimens may be found, of one or other of these, adapted to take a pin fire or even a centre fire self contained cartridge.

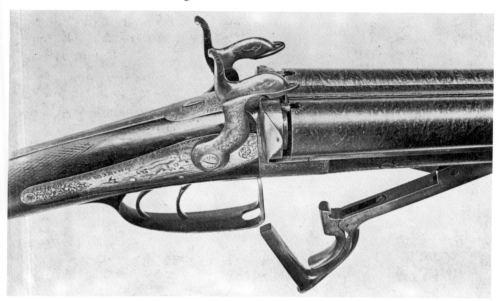

Harvey patent no. 1056 of 1860

The Harvey patent, No. 1056 of 26 April 1860, describes two guns. Firstly, there is an exact copy of the Bastin previously described. (Since a gun with a Bastin action by Francotte of Liège had been shot in the 1859 Field Trial and the action was therefore well known in this country, the value of a patent obtained the next year would have been nil.) Secondly there was a design in which the lever work was reversed. In this second system to open the gun the underlever is disengaged from its hook catch just in front of the trigger guard and pushed forwards and down. It is pivoted at the forward end of the forend and connected to the barrels by a short linking lever. The barrels, which are then free to slide on the action bed, move forwards. When in the open position the extra bolting arrangements of this action are revealed. The operating lever terminates in a portion which, in the closed position, stands vertically in the gun, this engages with a slot in the slide. The effectiveness of this is questionable but it represents an attempt at least to strengthen the action.

There were five more patents in our period for guns with sliding barrels using self contained cartridges. We have no first hand knowledge of these and would venture what we hope to be an educated guess, that only one or two of them may have been made in even small numbers and that the rest existed only as prototypes.

On 29 March 1862, Patent No. 873 was granted to Youngs Palfrey, who quotes his address as Upper Belgrave Place, Pimlico, London and his profession as engineer. His specification describes two variants on the idea of a gun which slides its barrels forwards. The main emphasis of the patent is placed on a design which achieves this motion by a rack fitted under the barrels which is engaged by a pinion about 1in in diameter set some 4in from the breech face. This pinion is rotated by a lever which swings nearly 180 degrees from the closed position, when it lies forwards under the barrels, to the open position, when it points to the rear. The bulbous swelling, resulting from a cover for the pinion, would have done nothing for the lines of the gun. Indeed the whole gun, as drawn, is particularly graceless. This point alone would have marked it down in the eyes of many sportsmen at a time when the elegance of a gun was a point of some importance, and guns were advertised as, and praised for, having the lines of a muzzle loader.

The second gun on the Palfrey patent dispenses with this rack and pinion set up and uses a simple lever catch at the front end of the slide which merely frees the barrels and permits them to be pushed back and forth by hand. Added to these, almost it seems as an afterthought, is an idea which has been used on literally millions of guns. It is a long bolt running from the centre of the stock, under the heelplate up to the action. As Palfrey claimed, this strengthens any gun on which it is used. We feel it to be one of the

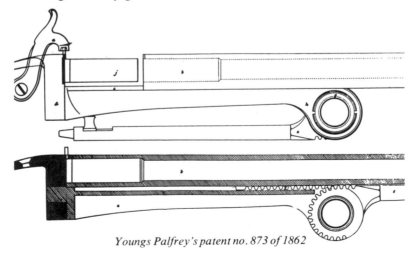

Youngs Palfrey's patent no. 873 of 1862

ironies of our story that this device, added as a codicil to the patent, should have been used in such numbers by shooters and makers alike, who have never even heard of Youngs Palfrey of Pimlico and his patent.

A very ingenious gun of this general type appears as part of Needham's patent, which we mentioned earlier, No. 1544 of 1862. There is no indication in the drawing as to the type of cartridge to be used beyond mention of an adaptation to a capping breech loader, so we assume that it was the pin cartridge that was intended. In the closed position a lever lies forward down the right hand side of the barrels, and to open the gun this has to be lifted and rotated back towards the user and on down through almost three-quarters of a revolution. This motion turns a spindle set across the gun, through the action, behind the standing breech. To this spindle is fitted firstly a cam which lifts up a spring catch, which bites down into a notch on the top rib between the barrels. Also to the spindle is fitted one end of a curved lever pivoted at its other end to a rod running under the barrels. This has an upward projection fitting into the bottom of the lump, which has a slot cut in each side for the slide. So that the barrels are moved in both directions by the side lever.

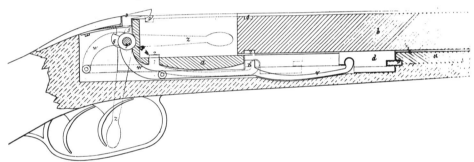

J. Needham patent no. 1544 of 1862

Next in this group of patents is that of Edgar Brooks, manufacturer of Birmingham. The patent is No. 1585 of 23 June 1863. In our opinion this is the most interesting and, given the overall limitations of the design, the most practical of the group. It would have lent itself to the production of a very good looking gun. The heart of this Brooks gun lies in a rotary bolting system worked by a lever which, when closed, follows the trigger guard and, when open, faces forwards. This lever turns a boss on a vertical pivot in the body of the action with its axis under the standing breech. Formed in this boss are two curved slots, one in the flat top and the other in the side. The latter slot carries one end of a rocking piece, the pivot of which and the slot are so arranged that, as the main lever reaches the closed position, the rocking piece is brought up and, if the barrels are at the rear, engages with the lump to hold the barrels shut. The other slot on the top of the boss performs a similar but subtly different function. This slot is formed as an eccentric which picks up, when the barrels are almost closed, a projection

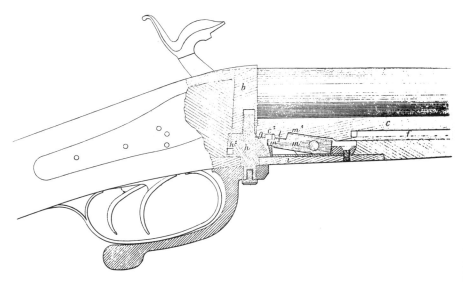

Brooks patent no. 1585 of 1863

from the rear lump so that, as this underlever is brought right home, the barrels are drawn back into recesses on the action face and, as they are, the main bolt is being lifted as previously described. There is no provision on the gun, as drawn, for moving the barrels the rest of their travel but rather vague references are made in the specification to levers and/or gears.

We have no knowledge of this gun beyond the patent drawing and specification, but we would be very surprised if specimens do not exist – it being, in the authors' eyes at least, a practical mechanism.

Amid all the patents which we have considered in this work, one stands out as a researcher's nightmare. It is a long, rambling provisional specification devoid of drawings, and it describes its many parts in a most vague fashion. This problem document is the provisional specification, No. 3001 of 1 December 1864, taken out by Thomas Wilson of Birmingham who describes himself as a mechanical engineer. His patent claims attention at this point, since described in it are two slide forward opening guns. In one a projection from the breech carries a bolt which locks between the barrels, in the other the reverse happens and a tongue from between the barrels enters the standing breech where it is engaged by a spring catch. We have been told of such a gun but unfortunately missed the chance to see it and cannot therefore be sure if it really was made under this patent. Perhaps it was the sole prototype which has managed to survive. Such are the frustrations of a study such as this.

The last member of this group is, we feel, a rather sad ill-favoured creation born after its time. It brings to mind W. Greener's remarks in his book *Gunnery in 1858,* when he counsels inventors:

Before spending your money, make acquaintance (and an intimate one is necessary) with all that has been done before, and if in your own production you find principles which have been untouched by any previous invention, and untainted by any of the previous causes of failure, then patent your invention and make your fortune – if you can.

At the date of this patent, 14 January 1868, as we hope to demonstrate in succeeding chapters, the drop down shotgun had reached a high state of development. Almost a decade previously the Bastin and Harvey guns had been tried, found awkward to use and rejected. How true Greener's remarks ring.

However the patent, No. 121, was obtained in the name of William Edward Gedge, a patent agent for Benoit-Dulin, 39 Faubourg St Martin, Paris. The drawing, and we have no illusions about ever seeing an actual example of this gun, shows a gun of continental style. The barrels are to be moved most of their travel simply by grasping them and pushing them forwards. They were to be held shut by a lever pivoted under the standing breech which had a claw-like cam on the upper part of its head which both forced the barrels back to the standing breech as the lever was raised and moved them the first part of their travel forwards as it was lowered.

Gedge patent no. 121 of 1868

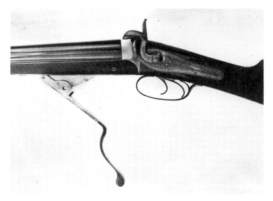

Egg's Improvement. Henry Egg no. 3607 c.1860

Charles Egg, when Master of the Gunmaker's Company

The specification also describes an extractor which would hold the bottom of the cartridge heads as the gun was opened and which would thus avoid the problem of levering off the heads experienced with the Bastin gun. The point is also made in the specification that the gun was easily adaptable for use as a muzzle loader. While it seems there was some demand from the colonies for such a facility, it was easily satisfied with 'everlasting' steel cartridges or breech inserts for a centre fire gun and this feature would have in no way made up for the general unhandiness of the slide forward gun adapted for a pin fire cartridge. The avidity with which the sporting public turned to the centre fire can be gauged from the fact that by 1867 Reilly's were advertising pin fires at reduced prices as they were liquidating their stock.

Many of the foregoing remarks also apply to the final gun of this type produced in our period. This time it was not the subject of a patent and has come down to us known by the inscription engraved on it – Egg's Improvement. What it was an improvement on is not stated, but it would be reasonable to suggest that it was the Bastin/Harvey gun since the mechanism is, for all practical purposes, identical. As to the exact date of this gun, the only information we have is that it was advertised in *The Field* in 1866, and the firm of Henry Egg ceased to exist by 1869.

The failure of sporting guns with barrels that open fully or in part by sliding forward to make any lasting impression on the development of the British shotgun has not deterred inventors in other countries over the last century. So with this type of gun we see not a true blind alley but a once promising avenue of development which has petered out to a bridle track, but one which some believe may, in the future, perhaps through economic necessity, regain its importance.

Chapter Six

THE SIDE OPENING ACTIONS

In contrast to the jostling crowd of inventors whose guns we considered in the preceding chapter, we now turn to a small select group who sought yet another radical solution to the problems posed by the breech loading shotgun. Their idea was to have the barrels turn on a vertical pivot, so that the breeches moved to the right, as would have been convenient for a right-handed man to use. These guns form a distinct group but are remarkable for the variety of ways in which the problems peculiar to this idea are tackled.

It is self evident that, if a simple vertical pivot is placed between the barrels of a side by side double barrelled shotgun, for these to swing on this axis and, when closed, to abut closely to a standing breech, then the face of this breech and the rear end of the barrels must be in the form of an arc. In this condition the flat head of a standard cartridge would not be fully supported. However, this simple arrangement was the design of Rigby and Norman, patented on 10 April 1860, No. 899. This patent covers a variety of ideas but the only one relevant both to the theme of this work and the present chapter is a side opening double gun as described above, which was locked shut by a rising bolt on a quick thread turned by an underlever

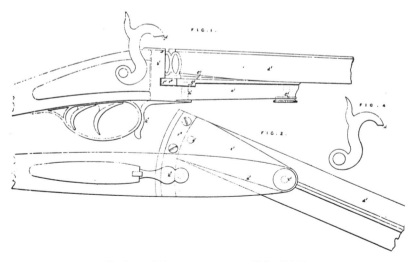

Rigby and Norman patent no. 899 of 1860

91

which, in the closed position, was made to fit in front of the trigger guard.

From the patent drawing it seems as if this gun was intended to fire a rimless pin fire cartridge with a very short pin which was to be driven right into the case by a cock which terminated in a sharp point like a punch. The idea was that the case would then be driven up the barrel by the next charge fired, to the almost certain detriment of the shot pattern thrown. It is therefore not surprising that no example of this gun appears to exist.

The next patent in the chronological sequence of guns of this general design was No. 368 of 13 February 1861. The patentees were Thomas Tipping Lawden and Caleb Lawden, who were partners trading as Tipping and Lawden, and a machinist employed by them by the name of Thomas Jones. Described in this specification are two quite different guns, despite an implication to the contrary in their introduction. In the simplest of these it is the breech that pivots while the barrel is fixed. From the illustration the details of the very simple design will be apparent, with the sturdy pivot pin on the centre of the top strap and the operating lever which, in the closed position, lies along the left hand side of the barrel. This layout still has the problem of the curved joint between breech and barrel. But, on the other gun described in the same patent, a novel solution to this difficulty has been found. Now it is the barrels that pivot, hence the inclusion of this patent in the current section. The seemingly impossible combination of barrels swinging horizontally on a central pivot with straight breech ends mating to a straight breech face is achieved by the ingenious expedient of arranging the central pivot far enough forwards to permit the barrels to swing and then, when they are in the closed position, of having a sliding piece to fill the inevitable gap. As with all the guns of this basic design, the breeches move

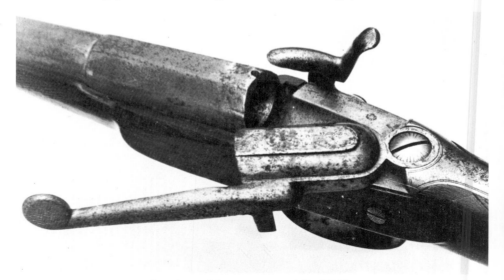

Lawden and Jones patent no. 368 of 1861

to the right. Therefore, in order that the chambers are accessible for loading, the sliding piece has to move to the left. The barrels and the slide are held in place by a bolt which moves back and forth under the sliding breech and which is withdrawn by a handle, shaped rather like a trigger, situated ahead of the trigger guard proper. It will be noted that to operate this gun it was first necessary to withdraw the bolt, then pull out the slide, and finally to swing the barrels.

We now come to consider two patents taken out by George Jeffries of Norwich, whose name has come down to us as being almost synonomous with the side opening shotgun. The Golden Ball Street, Norwich address on George Jeffries patent was only a part of the Jeffries' organisation. The advertisements are usually in the name of Lincoln Jeffries, who is perhaps better known than George and who, we believe, was an older brother, and give the 31 Whittall Street Birmingham address. This evidently was where the guns were actually made. Of George little is known, but late in life he attempted to make a machine which was capable of perpetual motion. To do this he had a six foot diameter wooden fly wheel with an iron rim under which were lead weights to finely balance the whole. This attempt to achieve the physically impossible may seem to bear no importance to our

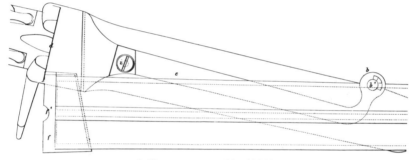

Jeffries patent no. 22 of 1862

story except that the inspiration for this may have come from the barrel grinders in Birmingham who then used massive grinding stones, which were cranked up to high speed during the working day and found still turning the next morning.

George Jeffries' two patents are Nos. 22 and 3300, both of 1862 and, while there is inevitably some common ground between them, they both being the brain children of a single inventor, they are, in execution, quite distinct.

It is the second design which became so well known and of which we have encountered several specimens. But to preserve our sequence we will first consider patent No. 22 taken out on 2 January 1862. This solved the problem of the curved breech and barrel ends by the seemingly obvious notion of placing the pivot to the left of the barrels. Then a condition exists which can be thought of as a conventional drop down gun turned on its side. But, by using a long forend and by positioning the pivot almost at the far end of this, some eight inches from the breech face, the angular deviation needed to expose the chambers is greatly reduced. As will be seen from the drawing, there is no great depth to the pivot and it is therefore necessary to support the breech ends of the barrels as they open. This is achieved by the use of a flat, wedge shaped, piece attached to the underside of the barrels which projects backwards under the standing breech. The forward face of this wedge has a bevelled edge so that, when the barrels are closed and this slope dovetails with the corresponding shape in the action, the barrels are held very firmly in place. The actual bolting is the work of a cam bolt set vertically in the standing breech which engages with an arc cut out of the rear of the flat wedge under the barrels. The bolt is turned by an underlever which, when closed, lies round the trigger guard. To limit the travel of the barrels a curved slot is formed on the underside of the barrel wedge into which a spring loaded stud projects. When it is required to take the gun apart this stud is pushed out of engagement by a button on the top of the forend iron. Then the barrels can rotate until they are at right angles to the stock, in which position the lugs in the hinge can be disengaged and the barrels lifted off the stock.

It will be noted that the operation of this first Jeffries design, while simpler than the Lawden, Lawden and Jones gun, still requires that the barrels be opened and shut and the locking bolt applied as separate movements. This would compare unfavourably even with the simple Lefaucheux and especially with the Horsley, Needham and Daw snap guns patented in the succeeding months of 1862.

Sandwiched between the two Jeffries patents, the next design in our chronological series simplified the manipulation of a side opening gun. To this end the hinge was made an eccentric and the opening lever formed as part of it, rather like the Dougall Lockfast, so that the barrels were first moved forwards from the standing breech and then turned aside, all by the action of the underlever. The idea was only provisionally protected by John Rigby, the Dublin gunmaker, patent No. 1966 of 8 July 1862. As there is no drawing in the specification, nor has an example come to light, we know no more about this gun.

The second Jeffries design would seem to have taken note of this provisional specification and the potential that it offered to speed the working of a side opening gun. All that remains of his first model is the flat wedge under the breech ends of the barrels and the method of assembling the gun, again by the placing of the barrels nearly at right angles to the stock, when the lugs on the head of the pivot pin can enter the bearing in the tip of the forend. This bearing has now become a centrally placed curved slot for reasons which will soon be apparent.

The operating lever is still an underlever which follows the trigger guard but now it is pivoted some two inches from the action face. When this lever is turned it carries with it a curved forked arm which rotates laterally on the

94

G. Jeffries (Norwich) patent no. 3300 of 1862

top of the action bar. Into the slot on this forked arm a stud from the barrels projects so that the movement of the underlever causes the barrels to move forwards (hence the slotted bearing as previously described) and at the same time sideways. The extent to which the barrels are permitted to open is governed by a movable stop in the action which limits the travel of the underlever. To remove the barrels from the stock this stop is pulled down. Thus the lever can rotate even further when the barrel stud ceases to be governed by the forked arm and the barrels can be rotated until the pivot stud can be lifted out of its curved slot.

All of which adds up to a much more convenient sporting gun that opens

G. Jeffries second patent no. 3300 of 1862

and closes simply by working the underlever. Indeed contemporary opinion was that, for speed, it was not much inferior to a drop down snap action. Jeffries advertised it widely, his usual advertisement being:

> JEFFRIES NEW CENTRE FIRE SIDE MOTION BREECH - LOADER is now complete. Five times the resisting surface of any double grip drop guns. Two hard pieces of tempered steel working together in the vital parts never before attained. Quick as any snap gun. The only sporting breech loader invented in Great Britain. It can be made to use either pin or central fire combined. See "Field" August 15th 1868. To be had through all first class makers; or of Jeffries and Sons, Norwich and Potter's Lane, Aston New Town, Birmingham. Also Jeffries New Patent Central Fire Cartridge Machine now ready; to be had of all gunmakers.

Certainly this was the most successful of all the side opening designs and was made and sold by its inventor over a period of perhaps ten years. One was exhibited at The Workmen's Exhibition of 1870, where it won a gold medal for 'excellency of workmanship and construction'. This success had probably only a limited impact, as the Exhibition was somewhat over-shadowed by the Franco-Prussian war, which was raging just across the Channel.

In this story we have previously noted inventions that appeared after their time. Another that recalls Greener's warning is the design of a Birmingham barrel maker by the name of Patrick O'Hagan, which he provisionally patented on 10 May 1865, No. 1293. This is almost three years after the Jeffries, but, for practical purposes, it is all but identical with the Rigby and Norman design which appeared a decade before. Not only are side openers proposed, but also drop down guns with curved breech faces, with no indication of any practical details.

A class of fowling piece which answers the general description of a side opener, but which is totally distinct from the preceding guns, are those in which a pivot for the barrels is formed in the axis of the bore and permits the barrels to roll aside to expose their breeches. This idea was felt worthy of exploration, to what degree is, as always, difficult to assess accurately. Certainly there are a number of patents on the idea. W.W. Greener felt them worthy of mention in his magnum opus, *The Gun and its Development*, and a sprinkling of specimens have been preserved to this day. How accurate an indication of the numbers built are these survivors is a moot point. The authors feel that any unusual gun, especially an awkward unusual gun, is liable to see less use anyway and there is a natural inclination to preserve anything that is a curiosity.

As to the actual patents, there are six British specifications, whole or partial, dealing with this type of gun which have come to our notice and which we regard as dealing with breech loaders using self contained cartridges, that is with capping breech loaders excepted. The earliest is the provisional specification of Joseph Rock Cooper, a gun manufacturer of Birmingham, No. 300 of 2 February 1859. In this he gives a description which could equally apply to most of the rest of this group; of a spindle projecting forwards from the action under the barrels upon which the latter turned, and with a spring catch to hold them shut. He further mentions that the pivot can be formed as a screw which would have the effect of forcing the breeches back on face as the gun was closed.

Although he only bothered to take out a provisional specification this roll-over idea seems to have been put to the greatest use by the gunmaker, Edgar Brooks, to judge from the evidence of surviving specimens already discussed. He quotes his address on his patent, No. 2196 of 25 August 1866, simply as Birmingham. The only guns which have been brought to our notice have Brooks & Co. Patentees engraved on them. These we believe to be the same concern as the Brooks, Son & Co. listed at 34 and 35 Whittall Street, Birmingham in 1860. Edgar Brooks went bankrupt in March 1869 but was rescued in April of the same year when his bankruptcy was annulled. Two variants of this gun also have turned up, one with a turning top lever to work the spring catch, the other with a pull back top lever to the same end.

Very similar to the Brooks gun is a rather puzzling gun that our researches have revealed. It is clearly engraved CHAS. OSBORNE makers

Brooks turn-over gun with turning top lever opening

for Greaves & Smith Patentee, but since we have discovered no patent in this name, our knowledge rests solely on this one gun. It is of the same general type but with the difference that the spring catch to hold the barrels in the shut position is formed from the front of the trigger guard, which is made vertical with a catch sliding horizontally in a small protrusion on the bottom of the action.

Another turnover gun which has been reported to us carries the name Jeffries, Norwich, which we feel to be a Brooks gun, very interestingly retailed by Jeffries.

With the Brooks we have the highwater mark of the use of the roll over barrel sporting gun. While there were four more patents deposited, in every case they are our sole knowledge of the guns concerned. In the next two, part of the Harlow 1866 specification, and that of William Payton, No. 2222 of 14 July 1868, the general description of the type applies. With the exception that both show evidence of the rise in the popularity of the centre fire cartridge and mention is made of an extractor and firing pins but with no practical details.

Greaves and Smith 'patent'

In contrast to this is the very detailed specification of Francis Boyd of Boston, Massachusetts, USA, American patent No. 88540 of 6 April 1869, and British patent No. 1017 of 3 April 1869. This, he records, was communicated to him by Francis Everitt Boyd and Philo Shelton Tyler, also of Boston. This roll over gun is a centre fire with a sliding thumb catch between the hammers. The barrels are to be maintained on face by an adjustable cam arrangement on the hinge pin. This last is threaded so that a 'facer' can be screwed back with a spanner when necessary. The other feature of this gun is the separate slide with a thumb catch on each barrel to work the individual extractors. The inconvenience of these extractors would seem to be the least practical feature of this gun and sufficient reason as to why it would have stood little chance of seriously competing with the drop down gun of this date.

These remarks are equally true of the roll over gun briefly included in the Henry Allen patent, No. 3097 of 25 November 1870. Indeed so brief and lacking in detail is this part of the specification that we feel it was included

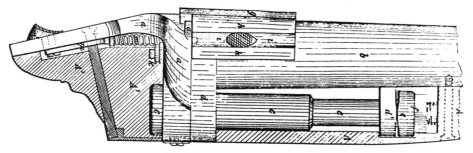

Boyd patent no. 1017 of 1869

very much as a make-weight rather than with any serious view to practical use.

The whole concept of laterally opening barrels, simple side openers and roll over guns alike, can now be looked back on as an idea which was unable to sustain the high hopes doubtless once entertained for it. For no matter what was hoped and argued for it, the awkwardness, its 'difference' and the ever increasing efficiency of the usual drop down gun ultimately told fatally against it.

Chapter Seven

DAW, SCHNEIDER & THE CENTRE FIRE

Inevitably, with the classification that we have adopted, having followed one line of development across our span, we must return to trace another, namely the developments of the principle of the original Pauly cartridge and the Lefaucheux breech loading gun, which culminate in the centre fire cartridge as we know it today and the gun which bolts automatically when closed. While the value of these two inventions was recognised on their introduction nothing really factual in the way of background information appears to have been published either at the time or when those who were able to recall the events were still in the land of the living. So we fear that certain details which we would regard as fascinating may well be totally lost.

The patentee of the form in which these two were introduced into Great Britain was a Parisian gunmaker, Francois Eugène Schneider of 13 Rue Gaillon, Paris. His invention must stand with the Lefaucheux as one of the most significant improvements in sporting gun design, and its introduction marks an important milestone in the story of the evolution of the modern gun.

The snap action of the gun is probably the most important feature of the whole, as the centre fire cartridge and the extractor necessary for it were known in a slightly different form at this date from the Gastinne/Bellford/Lancaster gun. The snap bolt on the Schneider gun is round in section

Schneider patent gun by Lepage

and slides in a hole bored for it under the standing breech. The bolt engages with another hole bored in the barrel lump so that, at a glance at the breech of an open gun, there would appear to be three barrels. Both the bottom of the rear of the barrel lump and the top of the front of the bolt are bevelled so that the act of closing the gun forces back the bolt until the barrels are shut. The bolt has a downward projection at its rear end and this is joined by a link to the head of the opening lever. This latter curves round the front of the trigger guard and is hung on a transverse pivot in the trigger plate just above the front of the trigger guard. Since the link from the bolt is hung above, and in front, of the main pivot, pushing the lever forwards forces back the link and bolt. The spring that causes the bolt to return to the shut position, the snap spring, is a leaf fixed behind the trigger work, and projects forwards with a slot cut in it to take the trigger blades. The free forward end of the spring is hooked under a pin also in the head of the underlever but behind the main pivot so that the snap spring is bent down by opening the gun and, when the pressure is taken off the underlever, the spring will return it to its position around the trigger guard and hence the bolt to its forward shut position.

Compared with the contemporary pin fire guns the action body of the Daw-Schneider was much stronger owing to a much more substantial standing breech with a well designed U section of the action bar. The method of fitting the barrels to the joint pin deserves mention. The hole into which the locking bolt fits is repeated at the other end of the barrel lump to fit upon a screw stud extension of the forend iron which is pivoted on the joint pin. This screw stud may be undone to allow a thin steel shim or shims to be fitted as an effective method of bringing the breech ends of the barrels back onto the face of the standing breech; and thus it needs little refitting and blacking down compared with the work entailed when a complete new joint pin is fitted.

A variant on the patent, significant in view of subsequent events, was so to arrange the bearing of the snap spring in the head of the lever that the locking bolt was not completely driven home by the spring, and it required a final squeeze by the shooter on the underlever to force the bolt home.

Also shown is the distinctive extractor with two legs which slide on either side of the barrel lump and are joined by a head which arches round the hole for the locking bolt. This extractor is worked by the forward ends of the two legs bearing on backward inclined faces at the hinge pin which force the extractor back as the gun is opened. The final feature of this gun is a stop to limit the opening travel of the barrels. This is shown as two projections from the knuckle which enter slots on the forend iron.

The obvious merits of this invention were recognised by the London gunmaker, George Henry Daw of 57 Threadneedle Street, who very soon after the date when the patent was taken out in Great Britain, 11 June 1861, bought the rights to it, and subsequently took out a further patent to cover improvements to the original. These improvements are on essentially

George Daw, trade label

G. H. Daw patent no. 1594 of 1862. Improvement on F. E. Schneider patent no. 1487 of 1861

minor points of the Schneider design. They consist of a catch on the underlever to engage with the bow of the trigger guard to hold the lever shut. An unnecessary complication it would seem as the snap spring should already do this, or could be made to do so more firmly if needed by altering the bearings of the spring.

Daw also added a transverse bar at the bottom of the slot for the barrel lump midway between the hinge pin and the action face. To accommodate this a slot, which is a semi-circle in section, is cut from the bottom of the barrel lump. It is claimed that this arrangement 'takes the strain from the hinge pin as the gun is fired', and thus forms the germ of the idea of circle jointing.

Another addition is a stop to prevent the extractor being inadvertently drawn right out. A projection from each leg fits into a slot in the barrel lump and if the extractor is to be removed for cleaning the legs have to be sprung apart.

While they are not mentioned in the Schneider patent we learn from this Daw modification that spiral springs were incorporated with the firing pins to force them back. For greater 'durability and certainty of action' Daw replaced these with flat springs fixed vertically in the head of the action and having a forked top to bear on a projecting ring on the firing pins, or pistons as Daw originally called them.

A point sometimes unknown to owners of Daw guns is that it was usual to provide a spare set of firing pins and extractor with each gun. These are to be found set in recesses in the heel of the stock under the heel plate.

The final group of Daw modifications concerns the means by which the opening travel of the gun was to be limited. Firstly, this could be achieved by a reversal of the Schneider idea with the slots in the knuckle and projections on the forend, or secondly, by adding a sliding link between the action bar and the barrel lump. We feel that all of these changes add up to a patent for the sake of a patent, and that perhaps the real purpose of it all was to generate kudos for the 'inventor' rather than to promote genuine improvements.

An unexplained aspect of this story is the relationship between Daw and Schneider, for on the one hand we have the fact that Daw was the witness when Schneider obtained his British patent and yet three years later when Daw wrote his book *Gun Patents 1864* he did not once mention Schneider. Neither does Mr Daw's book contain anything in the way of autobiographical material beyond the remark: 'I am a practical gunmaker and have been all my life'.

In view of this, and the fact that our researches have not produced anything else, George Daw remains an enigma.

He first gained prominence as a result of his association with Colonel, later General, Jacob of the Scinde Irregular Horse, who, at his own considerable expense, experimented on a grand scale in the Scinde desert of North West India on improvements to rifles, concerning himself with both the form of the arm and the projectile that it fired. All of which, while of great intrinsic interest, is beyond our scope except for the fact that, as supplier of the bulk of the rifles and ancillary equipment, such as bullet moulds, Daw's name became known.

Officialdom in the shape of both the British Government and the Honourable East India Company, who followed the former's lead, declined to adopt the Jacob rifle. While this was the bitterest of blows to the inventor and Daw alike and was criticised by writers of the time, in retrospect it was probably a sound decision, for, at the date of the rejection towards the end of the 1850s, the Enfield rifle had only been adopted for a few years, and the increasing use of the breech loader for sporting purposes must have been noted, so that we feel that any alteration of the rifling system of the barrels would be best incorporated in a new arm which would embody some form of breech loading. While we have no evidence on this point it seems very reasonable to suggest that as much may have been intimated to Jacob and hence to Daw, and that the latter therefore set out to find a suitable system of breech loading and in this search found the Schneider. If this is so, again it would be of great interest to know the details of the events. In this context the fact that the Daw patent of 1862 also has details of a rifle sight may be significant.

We return to much surer ground with the launching of the Schneider/-Daw gun in this country at the end of 1861. This date it will be noted precedes that of the Daw patent so it may well be that the earliest guns made by Daw were of the design we would regard as pure Schneider. When we consider that many other gun inventions were being introduced, the degree of editorial space given to the Daw gun is surprising. We feel it would be naive to assume that this was achieved solely on the merits of the gun, indisputable as we now regard them. This line of thought is prompted by the publication in *Bell's Life in London* of a long notice by an anonymous author on the virtues of the new gun. It would seem from this that the writer had seen and handled one of the new guns but had not quite understood the mechanism. Since Bell's concerned itself with life in London and the only shooting material it regularly carried were accounts of Live Pigeon Trap shooting, this lengthy insertion on a new sporting gun is even more noticeable. We feel it very likely that 'influence' in some form or another was brought to bear by Mr Daw, who appears to have been a first class public relations man when it came to his own products.

There was a second patent taken out by F. E. Schneider in 1861, No. 2203, which was not duplicated by George Daw but was simply bought and worked by him, and in the context of later events was the most important of the three patents. The subject of this specification was a centre fire cartridge and the machinery to make it. What was to prove the crucial part was the description of the so-called anvil, a small piece of brass that was placed inside the percussion cap and against which the cap was fired by a blow from the firing pin. This anvil was formed from a brass rod or drawn wire of such a diameter that it was a snug fit inside the cap, had four grooves formed in it and was then cut to suitable lengths. The number of grooves was not claimed as significant, but the fact that the anvil should more or less fill the cap was.

The patent also included a cartridge which can best be described as a small rim fire set in the head of a larger case.

The events of the next four years in the story of the Daw gun and centre fire cartridge are, for the most part, another tantalising blank which we doubt can now be filled. One fragment of information is the fact that George Daw presented to the Italian leader, General Garibaldi, an example not only of one of his shotguns but also a revolver that he had invented and was promoting at the same time. This was a shrewd piece of publicity, Garibaldi being popular in this country, and the reports in the press provided valuable advertising for Daw. Undoubtedly it was a period of growing popularity for the new gun and cartridge, and satisfied users wrote letters to the sporting press remarking on what to us are the obvious virtues of the centre fire as compared with the pin fire, namely the speed and ease of

Caps and anvils from Eley & Daw cases

loading and the ease with which the new cartridge could be reloaded. All of which must have been very gratifying to Mr Daw who, we can imagine, looked with satisfaction on his purchase of the Schneider patent in the confidence that it would amply repay his outlay. While nothing we have discovered published at this time hints at any problems for Mr Daw, later events suggest that, at this period, other makers of guns or cartridges were attracted by the obvious advantages of the centre fire system but were successfully dissuaded from entering the field by Daw or his lawyers with threats of legal action. But soon the bait became too big and the fish it attracted were equally large and not to be tackled in the same way. When the Eley Bros cartridge and ammunition makers started to manufacture and sell a centre fire shotgun cartridge, Daw was forced to implement his threat of legal action. The resulting trial and subsequent appeal were long and therefore inevitably expensive, and at the end of it all Mr Daw had precisely what he had originally bought, that is to say the Schneider patent, and not, as he had claimed, the master patent of the centre fire. While this must have been a crushing blow for George Daw, and the hopes that he must have had for making his fortune from a monopoly on this were thus totally destroyed, it had the effect of throwing open the development of the centre fire gun and its cartridge to the considerable talents of the British gun trade.

Daw advertisement

The cartridge that Messrs Eley had manufactured which had produced this upheaval, contained in the cap an anvil which in section was triangular. This was in fact held to be an infringement of the Schneider patent. Eleys then reverted to the original Pottet design of a flat anvil stamped from sheet brass but of a greater thickness than Pottet had used, as the thinness of the metal was realised in retrospect to have been the fault of the system. Daw then took refuge in the claim that his cartridge was essential for guns with sloping strikers. To this claim Eleys responded by providing Walsh of *The Field* with a supply of their flat anvil cartridges which he proceeded to test in an actual Daw gun. These tests were apparently entirely satisfactory and put the Eley product squarely on a par with the Daw. Thereafter it was a question of preference on the part of sportsmen, and what gunmakers were supplied with. We also have the spectacle of the weekly side-by-side

Eley advertisement

106

advertisements of the rival cartridge makers, which continued for a number of years. These appeared in *The Field* while the two sides in the law suit continued their squabble.

This is all but the end of the story, as Eleys put it in a long letter published in *The Field* of 9 December 1865 part of which ran:

> Although we have for the present failed, we are not altogether losers. We have been enabled to frustrate a daring attempt at a monopoly. An exclusive claim was made to the manufacture of central fire cartridges. We have now compelled Mr Daw and the embryo company to come forward and prove in what their patent really consists, and so set the matter definitely at rest. The patent has come through the ordeal in a very tattered condition – in fact, only hanging together by a single shred, and nothing but the extreme tenderness of the Vice-Chancellor prevented its falling to pieces altogether. They will be fortunate if it escapes through any future trial; a flat anvil to a central fire cartridge is public property, and is every bit as good, if not better, than the cartridge known as the 'Daw cartridge'.
>
> We will back our non-patent cartridges to be shot against the patent for £500 or any other sum, either in Mr Daw's or any other guns, so as to test more which cartridge is the surer of ignition, the stronger in construction, and more capable of being recapped the greatest number of times.
>
> Eley Bros

The results of the judgement were soon to be seen in that sensitive barometer of the trends of the time, the records of the Patent Office. Whereas before the ruling on the Daw/Eley case there had been but a spattering of patents for guns using centre fire cartridges, most it will be seen in the latter end of 1865, after the ruling there was a perfect avalanche of extractors, firing pins, as well as guns, all protected by patent. These we consider in subsequent chapters.

Before we leave the consideration of the Schneider/Daw gun and the events in which it played so vital a part yet one more gun should be included. This is a gun with obvious parallels to the other two but is patented in the name of Georges Schneider, gunsmith, of 14 Rue Ste. Anne Paris, who was Francois Eugène's brother. Georges Schneider's gun differs from the other two purely in the fact that the snap bolt is worked by an upward projection of the underlever which directly enters it, and the leaf snap spring now bears on a step on the opening lever below the pivot.

Also included in this patent are improvements to a laterally rolling block rifle action, again a link with François Eugène Schneider who, in 1862 along with Jacob Snider of Sullivan County, Pennsylvania, patented a similar action in Great Britain, No. 1828. Subsequently this was the subject of another patent taken out on 22 November 1864 No. 2912 solely in the name of Jacob Snider, which became the standard rifle of the British Army

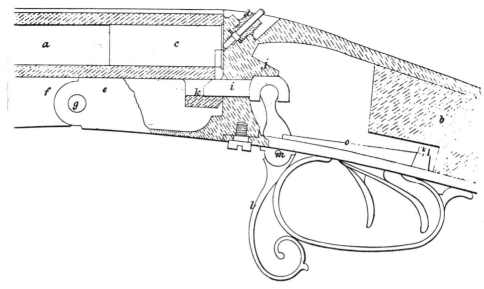

G. Schneider gun

in 1867 and was known simply as 'The Snider', and may occasionally be found as the breech action for a shotgun.

Largely as a result of our ignorance of George Daw we are left with mixed feelings towards him. For, on the one hand he deserves the credit for publicising the Schneider gun and cartridge in this country, while on the other we cannot admire him for his attempt to impede further progress by seeking to monpolise the central fire gun and cartridge.

John Rigby & Co. muzzle loading 8-bore converted to centre fire breechloader using J. Snider action

Chapter Eight

SLIDING BOLT SINGLE BITE SNAP ACTIONS

By the very early 1860s the gunmakers had solved the early and basic problems of the breech loader and, with the various inert actions, the still quite new gun was a perfectly practical tool. While some gunmakers and their customers were possibly content to build and shoot respectively the new guns, there remained a leavening of inventors and sportsmen who were not prepared to let things rest so easily. Indeed 1860 was the beginning of a spate of invention which was to continue for the rest of the century.

One of the great points that the breech loader scored over the muzzle loader was the rapidity with which it could be loaded and fired, and it came to be realised, particularly after the publicity generated by George Daw, that, if the gun would automatically lock shut on closing this margin of speed could be further increased. Numerous inventors were to apply a spring of some sort to the locking bolt so that the latter would snap home, like the spring catch of a door, as the gun was closed. Walsh in a rather patronising passage in *British Rural Sports*, seventh edition, which would appear to have been written in 1866 wrote:

> I have myself examined more than fifty patented principles, a great many of which are so similar to each other, that no law proceedings could separate them, nor, indeed, do I believe that there are more than four or five of them which could be safely defended from piracy.

While it is certain that the fifty patented principles is an understatement of the number of these actions, it is the authors' hope that these chapters dealing with them will not be too indigestible.

Now it would seem almost obligatory that, at every real improvement in gun design, an 'expert' should come forward to explain, sometimes at great length and with considerable rancour, why the new development was a mistake. So we find a gentleman, who hid behind the pseudonym of *Jäger*, writing this in *The Field:*

> BREECH LOADING GUNS – In answer to your correspondent 'A Sportsman', I must earnestly advise him to have nothing to do with the guns in which the locking powers depend on a spring. Most guns which are made on this principle are quick and neat in action but I myself consider that there cannot be a worse system than one in which a

spring bears all the strain. In a gun by Smith, of Loveday Street, Birmingham, I find the bolt is kept in its place solely by means of a spring; fancy the consequences if this spring were to break! I would certainly not like to have the gun in my hand at that moment, supposing the spring broke during the explosion of the cartridge. The fact is that simplicity is the chief point, and no spring whatever is a 'sine qua non' in my humble opinion. I therefore advise your correspondent not to trust to springs which, although neat and convenient, are certainly far from being safe.

Jäger

We have reproduced this fatuous letter in full in the hope of catching something more of the sentiments of the time, a very difficult thing to do, but we must not lose sight of the fact that the preserved comments are but a very small fraction of the comment and argument that surrounded every innovation.

While there was a body of opinion opposed to spring activated bolts, there was a corps of more progressive gunmakers and sportsmen, as noted above, who doubtless scoffed, as we do, at the sort of sentiments expressed by Jäger. One of these was a young man of 18 who, at this date, was probably still serving his apprenticeship to his father. That father and son were both Thomas Horsley adds to our problems, but it was stated on the patent No. 374 dated 12 February 1862 that it was Thomas junior who obtained the patent. That the patentee, as well as being a gunmaker, was a keen sportsman and had the reputation of being a fine shot cannot be without significance in that he was thus more keenly aware of the boon that a snap gun would be in the field.

Horsley patent no. 374 of 1862

Horsley patent no. 2410 of 1863

Despite his style, Walsh was undeniably correct in his remarks about the similarity between many of the snap action guns and the impossibility of legal defence of many of the patents. It is therefore the authors' intention to describe in some detail the Horsley gun, it being the first British one, and then to comment on some of the others only so far as they differ from it, in the hope that thereby the 40 odd patents can thus be covered in the least tedious fashion.

The most striking feature of this gun is the rather curiously shaped trigger guard with a vertical forward face. This was necessitated by having to accommodate the vertical lever pivoted on a transverse pivot. The longer, lower limb of this lever lay down the front of the trigger guard, and a backward projection from the bottom of the lever was carried through a slot in the front of the guard and terminated in a knurled button. Pushing forward on this would cause the upper short limb of the lever to move backwards and so draw back the bolt sliding in the body of the action. This in turn would release the barrels and at the same time compress a spiral spring placed round the rod which was the stem of the bolt. The actual bite was threaded on to the head of this and so shaped as to partially enclose the spiral spring. The bolt head has an inclined upper face which, as the barrels close, is acted on by a bevel on the rear lump so that the bolt is pushed to the rear, until the notch in the barrel lump is in such a position that the bolt can snap forward and lock the barrels down. A version of this gun, described very briefly in the patent specification which we have never encountered, has a horizontal lever pivoted on the bottom of the trigger guard. The head of this lever is a cam to force forwards a vertical lever as described above when the horizontal lever is turned.

Very much more common than this 1862 Horsley patent is the design protected the following year, No. 2410 of October 1863 by Thomas Horsley, Gunmaker of York. We have no means of knowing if this was father or son, but have always believed it to be the son. The second design is nothing more than the previous invention with the operating lever reversed and projecting through a slot in the top strap of the action. Here it is linked to a slide fixed in a channel in the top strap, the rearward end of the slide being formed as a thumb piece which opens the gun when pulled back. This seemingly simple modification lends itself to the production of a very much more handsome and convenient gun, which one of the authors (DJB) can confirm from personal experience. This action saw considerable use, usually on shotguns, but the odd light rifle and even pistols are sometimes seen. The serial numbers found would suggest that something of the order of 500 such guns were produced. Horsley breech loaders turned up quite frequently in the published results of Live Pigeon Trap shooting matches, and a correspondent to *The Field* in August 1866 who signed his letter *Hussar* claimed that: 'Most sportsmen in that county (Yorkshire) use his (Horsley's) gun'.

If we take the first Horsley patent as our basis, on it can be formed a group of guns in which a simple swinging lever hung on a horizontal pivot works a bolt sliding back and forth in the action and which have but a single bite on the barrel lumps. These, it is found, form a manageable sub-group and we thus continue with our aim of attempting to consider like with like.

The earliest of these is by Arthur Agnew of Welshpool, patent No. 2139 of 29 August 1863. It is but a subtle rearrangement of the earlier Horsley patent and indeed resembles it in having a vertical front to the trigger guard. Towards the top of this the opening lever is pivoted but the top end of the lever does not enter the body of the gun. The bolt has an extension which projects vertically down and is fixed to a slide on the outside of the

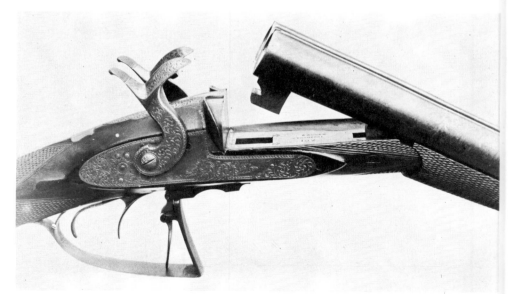

Agnew patent no. 2139 of 1863

112

bottom of the action. It is to this slide that the lever head is pivoted, and so the bolt is drawn back as the bottom of the lever is pushed forwards. The spring by which the bolt is made to snap is a flat spring set vertically behind the standing breech with its free end impinging on the rear of the bolt.

If the Agnew can be said to resemble the first Horsley patent then the provisional specification of Rowland Richards, gunmaker of Birmingham and Samuel Clement Willets, gun action filer of the same city, dated 7 December 1863, No. 3072, is the next thing to a carbon copy of the second. The differences, which can hardly be thought significant, are the use of a V spring instead of a spiral, and the thumb piece between the hammers being a projection of the operating lever instead of a slide jointed to it.

Another gun with a thumb piece between the hammers was the variant proposed in part of Thomas Wilson's provisional specification, No. 3159 of 14 December 1863. This time it was necessary to push forwards the lever to open the gun because the bite was in the front of the rear lump. The bolt plate, with an opening cut through it to let the lump pass, slid in guides cut in the sides of the action slot. Various positions for the snap spring are described, either in front of the bolt in the action bar or behind the lever in the head of the stock. Wilson had a second idea for using the motion of his thumb piece. This was to fix a spring loaded bolt which engaged in the top of the standing breech under the top rib, between the barrels. From this recess the bolt was to be expelled, when it was required to open the gun, by a 'pusher' connected to the push forward thumb piece.

Next in our present group we come to the Frazier patent of 19 May 1864, No. 1269. Here the opening lever is pivoted in the body of the gun just in front of the trigger guard. The top of the lever is jointed to the rear of the bolt, and the bottom of the lever curves round the front of the trigger guard. The only other feature of note is the use of a catch to hold the lever in the shut position – a very useful addition as in use such a lever is very apt to catch in a user's sleeve, usually at the most inopportune moment.

In the Patent Office in December 1863 it must have seemed as if it were snowing snap action guns, for, but two days after the Wilson patent, there appeared a specification from Joseph Smith, gunmaker of Loveday Street, Birmingham, in which two more snap action guns, both of which were in two versions, were described. It must have been one of this quartet of guns which prompted *Jäger's* remarks, but which one is a moot point.

Today the version of this gun that is occasionally found has a forward facing side lever pivoted on a transverse axis set through the lower half of the standing breech. To open the gun the forward end of this lever has to be pulled down when a single bite is withdrawn from the rear of the rear barrel lump. Externally this gun very closely resembles the much more famous Needham, which may be found in our section on single bite snap guns with rotating bolts. To transmit the motion of the lever to the bolt, Smith had two systems, one a short lever keyed to the spindle, on which the long opening lever turned which fitted into a slot cut in the rear of the bolt, the

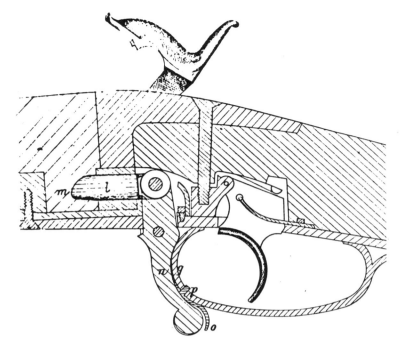

Frazier patent no. 1269 of 1864

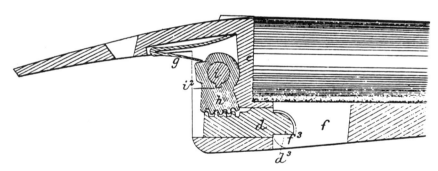

Smith patent no. 3171 of 1863

other, more novel, made the upper rear portion of the bolt a rack and moved it back with a pinion also keyed onto the spindle. In both the V snap spring is set up under the top strap with its free end bearing down on a step formed on the lever or pinion behind the pivot.

The other mechanism protected by this patent, No. 3171 of 16 December 1863, which is quite distinct from the one described above, has a lever lying transversely across the action bar, pivoted on a vertical axis on the left hand side and emerging on the right as a knob. One idea was to use the pulling back of this to work a J shaped sliding piece, moving back and forth in the action bar. The short limb of the J was the locking bolt which was held

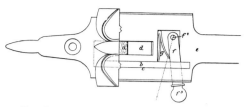

Smith patent no. 3171 of 1863

forwards by a V spring pushing the opening lever forwards.

Secondly the transverse lever was used as the actual bolt and it engaged, like a door latch, in the front of the rear lump. This time it would have to be pushed forwards to open the gun, the V spring now being set ahead of the lever holding it back. Perhaps it was one of these which so upset *Jäger*, but we shall probably never know for certain.

Yet another lever on a transverse pivot, this time so hung that its lower end projects in front of the trigger guard and has to be pulled back to withdraw the locking bolt, is described in a short, vague and unillustrated provisional specification in the name of William Ansell, Gun manufacturer. The number is 124 and the date 14 January 1865.

Also within the limits we have set for this section comes part of a design protected by Alexander Henry, the Edinburgh gun and rifle maker, No. 1071 of 17 April 1865. This patent yet again illustrates the impossibility of a rigid system of classification of gunmaking inventions. It claims protection for both a rifle and a shotgun, The latter is of a complex design and many of the features, we feel, are properly considered among others similar to them, in Chapter 12. However the action consists of a simple lever, with its lower limb curving round the trigger guard, pivoted in the action and actuating a single bolt. No exact details are shown on the surprisingly poor patent drawing which we have been unable to use, and, despite knowing of examples, we have been unable to obtain a photograph.

No better example of the fine variations on the theme we are considering exists than the design of Charles Golden of Bradford, protected by patent No. 1612 on 16 May 1868. Again there is a lever curving round the trigger guard, pivoted just in the body of the action, with a short upper limb of the lever working a sliding bolt. The novelty this time lies in a shoulder formed on the lever roughly level with, and in front of, the pivot. On this bears the free end of a leaf spring, the fixed end of which lies towards the front of the action bar.

Yet another use of this pivoted lever and bolt arrangement is contained in a provisional specification granted to one William Adams, gunmaker of Birmingham, on 27 December 1869, No. 3750. The main part of this idea was however, to dispense with the normal forend of a gun and, instead, to lengthen the action forwards and terminate this as a fork. Transversely through the two prongs of this was a 'knuckle' on the bottom of the barrels to fit a hinge pin, which would have resulted in a most distinctive gun.

Finally, perhaps as a warning that the patent records do not tell the whole story, is a pin fire shotgun in the collection of one of the authors (DJB) that conforms to the pattern we are considering. This gun by F. T. Baker of Fleet Street. is in good order but no claim to a patent can be found

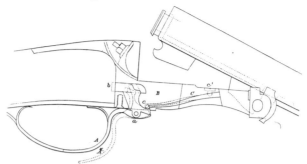

Golden's snap action patent no. 1612 of 1868

Golden's snap action – Field *engraving of above*

on it. From its style we believe it to belong to the early 1860s. The opening lever is short and curves part way round the trigger guard. The top of this lever works the bolt, and the spring is a flat leaf fixed vertically behind the standing breech. This gun therefore exhibits features of at least two patents in this section but in fact conforms to no particular specification. It is very similar to the action shown in Mr Baker's patent No. 403 of 9 February 1866, in which a lever brought round the side of the gun works the bolts, while the snap spring is shown as a leaf in the bottom of the action bar.

Single bite snap action gun by F. T. Baker

116

The idea of using a slide of some sort, as exhibited by the second Horsley action patent, to work a horizontally pivoted lever which, in turn, moved a single spring locking bolt was used on a number of designs, some of which were relatively successful. None of them were quite as successful as the Horsley but examples are encountered in a quantity which would suggest that, in the context of our study, they were more successful than most.

First in order of date is a provisional patent granted to Richard Brazier of Wolverhampton on 30 January 1864, numbered 259. This, perversely, is one of those ideas we know only from the records of the Patent Office. What he proposed was to have the whole trigger guard slide backwards, and with this movement to work a lever and bolt as previously described. He also claimed protection on a much patented idea, that of keeping a gun on face by means of an adjustable insert in the action.

It is tempting to speculate that a design patented by one maker should have inspired another to produce his own which evaded the first patent but embodied the same principle. This line of thought would probably lead to all sorts of false conclusions. We have, for instance, no proof that the action patented on 4 February 1864, No. 297 by Thomas Newton, gun and rifle maker of Manchester, was influenced by the second Horsley patent, but the difference between them is the position of a pivot. The Newton has a single sliding bolt which is moved by a lever hung at its centre on a transverse pivot above the bolt on the level of the action flats. The top of this lever, therefore, has to be pushed forwards to withdraw the bolt. This movement is effected by a thumb piece between the hammers which has to be pushed forwards and is connected to the top of the lever by a projection which slides under the top strap of the action. Newton advertised his gun in *The Field* and guaranteed it for two years in his advertisements. But he had the misfortune to have a customer who seemed to have used excessive charges in one of his (Newton's) guns with the result that the action, the bar of which is quite light, was strained. Walsh rather unfairly published the complaining letter, but refused Newton the space to reply on the curious grounds that he was the maker!

If the Newton and Horsley designs were very similar, a pair of inventions that were the next thing to identical were the Turner and Ebrall guns. Of

Newton push forward top lever patent no. 297 of 1864

these the Turner is the better known, being in its day extensively advertised, and sold in some numbers, so that survivors are seen today. Externally the most noticeable feature is a prong which projects behind the trigger guard. This is the opening lever which has to be pulled backwards to open the gun, the lever being pivoted in the stock. The action bolt is continued right back round the trigger work and is acted on directly by the lever. The patent on this gun is No. 2585 of 19 October 1864, and the patentees style themselves 'Gun Manufacturers and Government Contractors' of Fisher Street Birmingham. In fact they had a retail outlet in Reading which is normally mentioned in the advertisements. In conjunction with the latter they exhibited at the Reading Industrial Exhibition. The following notice is taken from the *Reading Chronicle*:

> Mr Turner, gunmaker of this town, exhibits some beautiful and costly breech loaders, with the latest improvements; also various materials showing the process of manufacture of Damascus gun barrels, from a bar of iron to the finished barrel. Also a handsome case of implements in use by sportsmen.

Turner patent no. 2585 of 1864

T. Turner Jnr. patent no. 2585 of 19 October 1864

The Ebrall gun which was only provisionally protected, No. 1382 of 9 May 1865, is unknown to us. The specification has no drawing but the description is of a gun which sounds a carbon copy of the Turner.

Another gun unknown to us 'in the metal', which bears at least some resemblance to the Turner gun, was that patented on 25 July 1867, No. 2168 by two Parisians, Guillaume Lorent Barens and Jean Fructueux Ladougne. Their design has three distinct features, the one which we believe warrants its inclusion at this point being its action. This was a sliding bolt under the break off which entered a recess in the rear of the barrel lump. Again a vertical inverted V spring was used, but the bolt was drawn back by a projection of singular form. It was no less than a third trigger, that is the front one of a trio in an enlarged trigger guard. This opening lever/trigger is not pivoted but slides back. While we wonder if such an arrangement might not be prone to bind, the idea of a third trigger must have been an awkward feature, certainly to a new user of the gun, it being all too easy to open the gun instead of firing it.

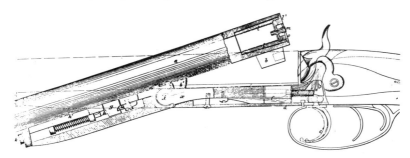

Barens and Ladougne patent no. 2168 of 1867

The patent also includes a metal chamber piece. This idea appears over and over again so that it would seem that a proportion of inventors were obsessed by the belief that, either sportsmen would run out of cartridges in wild places, or were unable to see the advantages of the Pottet type of cartridges.

The final claim made is perhaps, in retrospect, the most interesting. This is a forend fastening identical in design to that patented many years later by Westley Richards' foreman, William Anson, which is known as the Anson rod forend. The specification shows a snap forend which consists of a rod terminating at the tip of the forend as a knurled button. Coiled round the rod is a spiral spring so that, as the forend tip is pushed in, it compresses the spring, and at the same time pushes back the bite from the rear of the forend lug, the rod being bifurcated round the forend lump.

Very much capturing the spirit of the forces at work on its conception is the gun patented by John Hanson of Lincoln, No. 2657 of 26 August 1868. Again this has features which we will consider elsewhere, here we are concerned with its action. To open this gun the front portion of the trigger guard has to be pushed forwards. Made as one with the front of the guard is a horizontal portion which slides on two guides on the bottom of the action. This slide has linked to it a short lever hung on a horizontal pivot in the action so that, as the slide is pushed forwards, the top of this lever draws back the sliding bolt in the action. The snap spring is a leaf set vertically behind the standing breech.

Perhaps it is unfair to judge such a mechanism from the use of a single specimen over a hundred years old, but it is the experience of the present author (DJB) that, as this action wore, the slide cocked and began to bind and so the gun became very difficult to use.

This gun was widely advertised in *Land and Water* but curiously not in *The Field*. The reason for this can only be the subject for idle speculation. Another minor point about this gun is that, in our researches for this book, we found an advertisement for Charles Hamshaw of Oxford illustrated with a woodcut of this gun. Again we can only speculate that perhaps it was a convenient block used by the compilers of the directory concerned, or did Hamshaw retail the Hanson gun? In the absence of actual examples the question remains open.

J. Hanson patent no. 2657 of 1868

In a study such as this, concerning the perfection of the breech loader, it is perhaps all too easy to assume that the only quality being sought by the designers and makers of guns in this evolutionary and formative period was a strong action. As a general rule this is true, up to a point, but a parallel, more subtle search for elegance was going on simultaneously. These thoughts were prompted by the discovery of a patent granted to John William Parker Field for a gun action, the avowed intention of which was to reduce the width of the action to permit the use of what we now call a bar in the wood action and bar action locks. This combination results, in the authors view at least, in the most elegant and stylish of guns. Mr Field quoted his address as 233 High Holborn and gave his occupation as that of gunmaker. In fact Parker Field carried on a very much more varied trade than this implies. In addition to sporting guns they dealt in hand cuffs, leg irons, truncheons, cutlasses, military firearms of all sorts, in fact all the hardware necessary to equip a prison, a constabulary, or an expeditionary force.

Parker Field patent no. 3485 of 1862

To return to this sporting gun, the drawing shows an action bar reduced to quite alarmingly slim proportions. So slight in fact that it would be at considerable risk of bending or fracturing at Proof. A very fine example of this gun has been shown to us in our researches, but it was not possible to strip it down to see if this extra slim action bar was used in practice or if wiser counsel prevailed and a bar of more normal proportions used, which would still permit the use of bar locks and a bar in the wood style but with greater robustness.

The bolting action described in the patent, which is number 3485 of 31 December 1862, and found on the gun seen, consists of a sliding bolt worked by a lever which curves over the trigger guard. Turning the lever to the right causes the cam formed on its head to force back the locking bolt and to compress the spiral spring around the rear stem of the bolt.

A description of a gun with another distinctive means of working a sliding bolt is that contained in the patent records in the name of Charles Churchill, No. 3173 of 16 October 1868. As far as we are aware he was not connected with the gunmaking family of that name, which originated in the West Country. He quotes his profession as merchant and his address as

121

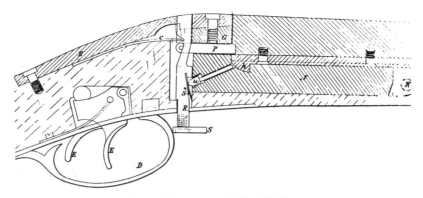

Churchill patent no. 3173 of 1868

Norwood, then in Surrey. In fact he was acting as agent for William H. Miller of West Meriden, Connecticut, USA, whose gun is also the subject of American patent No. 59723 taken out on 13 February 1866. To open this gun a stem that projects in front of the trigger guard has to be pushed up into the body of the gun. Cut into this stem, at the point where it slides through the bolt, are two inclines so that the upward motion of the stem draws back the single bolt which slides horizontally in the head of the stock and projects from the bottom of the action face. This arrangement is made to snap by a leaf spring under the top strap, fixed at its rear and bearing on a step cut in the top of the stem. Another feature is that the bolt is held back until the gun is almost completely shut. Another sliding bolt runs from the angle of the action face and bar, and is pushed back by a small lump on the barrels as they close. When the bolt is back it compresses yet another flat spring. This is fixed to the bolt stem and, when uncompressed, catches on a shoulder in the action. By this means the gun would be particularly pleasant to use as, when it was closed, it would not be necessary to compress the snap spring.

With the Field and Miller guns we embark upon yet another series of assorted single sliding bolt snaps, all variously very different from the Horsley. In the Mathews patent, No. 2441 of 6 October 1863, we have another of those bargain basement specifications which include several dissimilar guns. We have abstracted the inert action from this and put it

Mathews patent no. 2441 of 1863

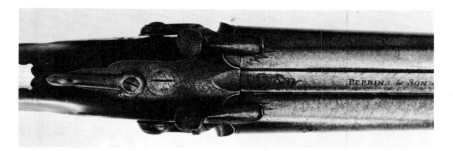

Top view of Mathews patent no. 2441 of 1863

with its fellows in Chapter 4, but there remain two more single bite snaps covered by the same specification.

The best known of these has a rotating top lever set well back on the top strap. Under the strap is a short forward projecting lever which has fixed to it a link, the front end of which is joined to the top of the barrel locking bolt. The bolt is made L shaped with the horizontal portion thicker, this is the actual bolt. The top lever is free to move to the right and, in doing so, draws back the bolt. The snap spring is a V lying horizontally under the top strap with its free end bearing on a rearward projection of the lever under the strap, so to oppose the motion of the opening lever as this is turned to the right.

Also shown is an action with a short rearward-facing thumb lever on the right side of the gun. The spindle that carries this has, on the inside of the gun, a slotted cam which works on a backward projection of the locking bolt, which has been brought up and along under the top strap. Depressing the thumb lever draws back the bolt and compresses the snap spring which is a V set upside down in the head of the stock, its free end bearing on the back of the bolt.

Two further features of this patent are worthy of note, the first is that the actions of the sporting guns are all drawn as if to be stocked bar in the wood style, the second that both snap actions are also shown holding down the breech ends of capping breech loaders, which are drawn in a military style. Presumably Samuel Mathews of 57 Loveday Street had ideas on a possible military market.

A firm of gunmakers very famous in the first two decades of the nineteenth century was Samuel and Charles Smith of Princes Street, Leicester Square. During this period they were noted as adhering longer than most of their contemporaries to the production of flintlock sporting guns, at a time when the detonator or percussion ignition gun was becoming all the rage.

Our present interest in this concern arises from the fact that on 11 April 1867 a patent, No. 1075 was taken out by 'Samuel Smith, Gun Manufacturer, of Princes Street, Leicester Square'. He was the son of the original Samuel and confusingly had a brother, Charles.

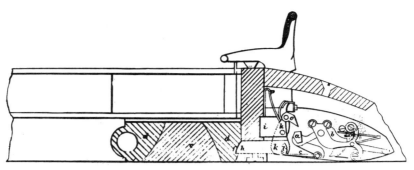

Samuel and Charles Smith patent no. 1075 of 1867

The gun patented by Samuel junior was a single bite sliding bolt snap of unusual construction which is why we come to it at this point. Its novelty lay in the fact that it used the motion of half cocking the right hand barrel to withdraw the barrel locking bolt. However it is an admitted failing of our system of classification that this gun, which was the last of such guns to be patented, should be considered first.

What was intended was that an extension on the tumbler of the right hand lock should withdraw the locking bolt but as the lock reached the half cock position the catch should trip out of engagement, and as the tumbler rotated on firing the piece, the catch should not interfere. However the drawing is incomplete, whether by design or accident we cannot now decide, but as drawn it is unworkable and in cases such as this we wished space permitted us to follow the precedent set by Paulin-Desormeaux in his work, 'Nouvel Manuel Complet de l'Armurier, du Fourbisseur et de l'Arquebusier' where he reproduced entire specifications for exceedingly complex guns, the drawings of which consisted of the gun stripped down to scores of component parts which were not always readily relateable one to another, with the terse remark which freely translated reads: 'We reproduce this specification in its entirety in the hope that those in the trade, more learned than ourselves, will understand it.'

Far more conventional to the eyes of a sportsman of the 1860s and even more so to us today is the top lever opening gun provisionally protected by William Wellington Greener, No. 1339 of 7 May 1867. This was his second patent and though the specification is not illustrated and the gun unknown, there is a very brief description and an engraving possibly of this gun in the inventor's book, 'Modern Breechloaders, Sporting and Military' published in 1871.

The gun has a near vertical spindle set to the right of the midline in the head of the stock. On the top of this is a lever which has to be turned to the right to open the gun, and on the bottom of the spindle is a cam or lever which transmits the motion to the bolt. The site or type of snap spring is not specified either in the specification or in the inventor's book.

124

W. W. Greener provisional patent no. 1339 of 1867

The patent further contains a vague description of a mode of fixing the barrels of a drop down gun which was to become almost a Greener trademark. This was the extension of the top rib that dropped into a slot in the top of the standing breech, where it was secured by a cross bolt sliding transversely. This was what was to become, with later modifications the Treble Wedge Fast, but here it is almost an afterthought in a provisional specification.

One of the minor anomalies that our research has turned up is the story of a gun designed, or at least provisionally patented, by Edward Paton of Perth, Scotland. No. 1433 of 25 May 1865. The curious fact is that this gun gets a long and very favourable write up by Walsh in *British Rural Sports*, where we learn that, by 1866, over 50 guns had been built on this principle, in addition to large numbers of muzzle loaders which had been converted to this system. At this work Mr Paton was something of a specialist, charging

E. Paton gun, possibly built on provisional patent no. 1433 of 1865

£15 per gun for his labours. Furthermore, one of the main points of the unillustrated specification was the ease with which muzzle loaders could be converted to this system. Why then was it not fully patented?

Now the tone of Walsh's writings on Paton, his gunmaking and fishing tackle business, suggests that he had probably visited the establishment and been impressed with what he had seen. The gun, as rather vaguely described in the provisional specification, seems a very ordinary single bite snap action with an underlever over the trigger guard, working a sliding bolt in the body of the action. It would therefore seem feasible to us to suggest that, in view of Walsh's remarks as quoted in the beginning of this chapter, he advised Mr Paton that a patent for this gun would be worth less than the paper it was written on, and the canny Scot saved his time and money and devoted both to more profitable ends.

One of the greatest difficulties that the authors have come up against in writing this account is to appraise the many and various gun mechanisms from the view point of a, perhaps not very dextrous, sportsman using them in the excitement of actually shooting live game in the field. There is all the difference in the world between sitting comfortably in a warm parlour giving full attention to some complex mechanism and attempting to use the same with cold, numb fingers, perhaps wet and slippery, and in indifferent light with the urgency to reload as the flight was in full progress, and simultaneously to direct a dog to a fallen duck.

Saville patent no. 1559 of 1864 (gun made in 1864)

Lang patent no. 1785 of 1867

126

While it has always been our practice to use such guns as form part of our collections, if they are in a fit condition, many of the examples are beyond their useful lives, and others that we have encountered have been impossible to use. It is therefore with some pleasure that we can record the use of any unusual shotgun, for it is perhaps too easy to forget that the subjects of our study were intended to be used and were not made for us, 100 years later, to collect and study.

The gun that prompted these remarks is a 20 bore pin fire marked 'Joseph Lang & Sons' but in fact the design is that of Thomas Prosper Saville, 'gunmaker of Birmingham' patent No. 1559 of 22 June 1864. Surviving evidence would indicate that this action was used exclusively by Langs. We believe that they may have bought the patent but have no direct proof of this. The point is further confused by the existence of a less than explicit provisional patent granted to Joseph Lang on 18 June 1867, No. 1785. This design employed a bolt which swung and therefore belongs in our next chapter.

Christopher Idle in the second edition of his book, *Hints on Shooting and Fishing,* which was published in 1868 and partly rewritten to take note of the changes wrought in the shooting world by the introduction of the breech loader, describes a gun as Lang's breech loader, and his description could apply to either the Lang or the Saville patent. The action of the latter is different from the majority of the snap actions in that the bolt moves transversely across the action. This movement is controlled by a knurled button which has to be squeezed against the action bar, so moving the bolt and compressing a V spring set in the action bar. Now, since the spring is compressed directly, with no assistance from a lever of any sort, it would be easy to imagine that the action would be inconveniently stiff. This is not borne out in practice, indeed quail shooting one glorious fall day in Virginia it proved a most convenient action to use.

Very similar to the Saville is the design patented little over six weeks later by two more Birmingham gun manufacturers, William Collins and William Pountney, No. 1967 of 8 August 1864. Again there is a laterally moving bolt, but this time a lever set on a vertical pivot is used. The push button is forward on the action bar by the hinge pin, the lever lies the length of the bar and has pivoted on its rear end the bolt proper. The bolt is held in the shut position and made to snap by a flat leaf spring set in the action, bearing on the forward end of the operating lever.

Both of these transverse bolted designs have the advantage of unobtrusive locking arrangements, and so lend themselves to the production of svelt guns.

The provisional patent specification of William James Hill No.191, dated 25 January 1867, describes another species of latch bolt. A stud had to be squeezed into the action of the gun, and the patentee attached great importance to the locking bolt going through a hole in the lump, instead of just catching on a bite.

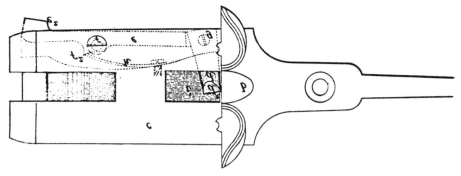

Collins and Pountney patent no. 1967 of 1864

Hill's patent latch bolt, conversion from fire pin. Patent no. 191 of 1864

The sliding single bite bolts so far described have shared one common feature, in that the locking bolt slid in the body of the action and engaged usually with the barrel lump. In the ferment of invention of this period it is perhaps inevitable that inventors should try this system backwards and put the bolt in the lump. We have previously written of the inert Mathews patent that used this system but in fact the first mention of this idea, which was also the first snap gun to be patented in Great Britain, was that registered in the name of the patent agent, William Edward Gedge, on behalf of two Frenchmen from Besançon in southern France, Joseph Humbertjean and Charles Matthey.

All we know of this is the provisional patent, No. 1153 of 10 May 1860, which, from its slightly quaint wording is obviously a translation. What is described is a bolt and spiral spring in the barrel lump, the spring pushing

Horsley gun using the firm's three latest patents,

Bastin actioned gun by Masu of London

Gibbs pin fire using Henry Jones double screw grip

Brooks patent turn over gun shown partly open

the bolt backwards into the action of the gun. To open the gun a lever which projected from the bottom of the gun had to be pulled, and since this lever was pivoted below the bolt, the top of the lever would move forwards. The lever was placed so that the top of it pushed the bolt forwards until it was clear of the action and the gun could be opened. To close the gun we must assume that the bolt was of such a length that the face of the action would bear on it and push it into the lump as the gun was closed, and when the barrels were finally shut the bolt would then snap home.

Its inventor being a frequent advertiser, the gun being made in some quantities and being mentioned in writings of the day, all mean that we know far more about the only other snap 'lump bolt' gun. This was what its inventors, Edward and John Tertius Harlow called their 'Wedge Bolt'. Though as Walsh pointed out this is a little misleading, there being 'no wedge concerned in the action and it is an ordinary snap gun merely'. The form of their advertisement changed several times over the years, but we feel the following to be the most interesting in content:

> Harlows Wedge Bolt Breech Loader: The mechanism of this gun differs entirely from that of any other breech loader and as numerous sportsmen can testify is as quick, pleasant and effective a weapon as can be desired, whilst that it is really preferred to other guns by those who have had an opportunity of judging is evinced by the fact that the patentees have had Lefaucheux, Dougall and Horsley breech loaders to convert to their principle. Testimonials and price lists on application Manufactory 132 Bradford Street, Birmingham.

Harlows were one of the specialists at gun conversion and used this snap action in undertaking this service, for which they charged £10 in 1866. In fact this is the lowest price that we have found advertised for the conversion of a muzzle loader to a breech loader. Harlows further claimed that, since it did not encroach on the head of the stock, their action was more suitable than some for conversion of muzzle loaders built with slim stock heads.

The bolt is in fact a sliding rod in the top of the rear lump. Connected to the front of this by a swivel link is a forward facing underlever pivoted on a transverse horizontal axis. The rear end of the lever turns upwards where the link joins it, so that pulling down on the forward end of the lever will draw back the barrel bolt and so permit the gun to be opened. The snap spring is a flat leaf fixed at its rear end and flush with the underside of the action. This bears on a short rearward projection of the underlever, and the operation is interesting in that, when the underlever is pulled right back, the snap spring goes over centre and holds the lever open. When the gun is closed the lever stays in the open position and has to be pushed a little forward to overcome the over centre condition, when the action will snap shut.

As a result of this it is perhaps more exact to look upon the Harlow as not a true snap action and regard it instead as a semi-snap. This mechanism

Harlow patent gun by Williamson no. 2380 of 1863

occupies a considerable portion of the Harlows' specification and from the evidence of this, surviving guns and the contemporary advertising, we assume it to have been the main emphasis of the patent. Obviously intent on value for money however, the patent further describes a variety of other ideas. In some detail is an extractor, which we will return to in the gadgetry chapter, but in far less detail are some other applications of the sliding bolt, connected to the opening lever by a link, and a falling block breech loader. The latter we believe to be a capping breech loader and so beyond our scope. There are two variants on the Bolt/Link/Lever idea shown. One has the opening lever reversed to the back towards the user, and the bolt sliding in the action and entering the front of the rear lump. The other has a rearwards-facing side lever working a bolt in the action, that goes backwards through the rear lump into the bottom of the standing breech. The text further states that each can use the bolt through the lump, or have a bite on the lump with which the bolt engages.

It is not clear from the specification or drawings if these last variants are, in fact, snap actions at all, and so they may perhaps rightly belong in Chapter 4, but we have included them here because they use the mechanism of the Harlow snap gun.

A totally different idea also protected by patent, No. 2380 of 28 September 1863, and claimed as a modification of the main idea, which it most certainly is not, is a means of opening the gun by half cocking one of the locks. This, like the Samuel Smith gun described earlier, uses a sliding bolt in the body of the action which engages with the rear of the rear lump. Pivoted on a step up from the back of this bolt is a pawl catch which is picked up by a hook on a tumbler carried on the hammer spindle. So that, as the lock is drawn towards half cock, the bolt is withdrawn. The bolt is fully withdrawn before the lock reaches half cock, and, just before the safety position is reached, the pawl catch trips out of engagement with the tumbler, and the locking bolt is propelled forwards by the snap spring which is a leaf on the head of the stock. The pawl catch and tumbler are so shaped that, as the lock is fired, the catch is knocked up and allows the cock to rotate, but the catch is spring loaded so that it returns to its correct position for the gun to be opened.

Again, like the Smith gun, this model is known only as a patent drawing, and this reinforces our views that the idea of so opening a gun was viewed with distrust by the Sporting Public. To date the only gun which we have seen of this design is of Belgian make.

Ironically, our layout has meant that among the last single sliding snap bolts we consider is the most famous of all. The Westley Richards design, usually known as the doll's head from its shape, is a feature of large numbers of guns made by this famous concern. In Chapter 4 we described the very early Westley Richards improvement of the Lefaucheux action, in which the inventor showed conclusive evidence of fully appreciating the fundamental problem of the French design, and took bold steps to rectify it, while retaining the virtues of the basic concept. The 1859 model was inert and, with its long lever, while strong, awkward. We feel it far from fanciful to suggest that the convenience of the Schneider and Daw guns, in particular, would have been noted and the fact that they pointed the way ahead perceived. The result was Patent No. 2506 of 11 September 1862.

With the possible exception of John Henry Walsh of *The Field* we know more about the patentee of this design than any other inventor whose work figures in our story. In great part this is the result of someone having the foresight to suggest that the story of the Westley Richards gunmaking company be recorded, while those who remembered the events were still this side of the grave.

This account was written by Leslie B. Taylor and published in 1913 to mark the centenary of the company of which he, Taylor, was then the Managing Director. It is dedicated to George Dawson Deeley who was the Chairman of the company and son of John Deeley, the previous Managing Director. From the pages of *A Brief History of the Westley Richards Firm 1812–1913*, Westley Richards emerged as the embodiment of much that was Victorian. A man who drove himself in the pursuit of his business and expected the highest of standards, both in work and personal conduct, from his employees. A hard man, with an almost Old Testament concept of justice, feared as well as admired by his workforce. But, for all this, he was a man of ability, as the quality of his inventions testifies. In fact he obtained twenty two patents, perhaps not every one of them as successful as Taylor would have us believe, but still of great importance. He worked with Joseph Whitworth on the development of the hexagonal bore rifle, which is usually regarded as the invention of the latter, but was in fact originally mooted by another great Victorian, I. K. Brunel. Westley Richards' leisure interests lay with horses and fox hunting, but equestrianism was to produce the great tragedy of his life, which had an effect on him that is now hard to calculate. In 1847, after only two years of marriage, his wife, Emma, who was the second daughter of Vere Fane and the niece of the then Earl of Westmorland, was killed in a riding accident, leaving him with an infant daughter. He never remarried.

The invention with which we are now concerned replaced the long top lever of the 1859 gun with a short pull back thumb lever between the hammers. The forward end of this thumb piece was the actual bolt. Through the tang project two studs from the slide, the one in the centre being a guide and the one illustrated and usually found on the left, being on a short lever. This lever is pivoted on the right side of the broad tang and is held forwards by a light V spring fitted to the underside of the tang. This spring and lever arrangement serves to maintain the bolt in its forward position where it enters a notch cut in the rear of the projection from the top rib. The shape of this is more complex than the previous design. In plan it is a stem from the top rib with an almost circular swelling at its end, hence the popular name of doll's head. When the gun is opened it can be seen that the swelling is curved in the arc of the closing barrels, to enter the slot in the top of the standing breech, and that the swelling tapers to the thickness of the stem. The bottom rear of this has a bevel to force back the locking bolt as the gun is closed.

Covered also by this patent is the method of so shaping the wood of the bar in the wood action and the forend that the hinge is always covered. This pattern has come to be called the 'crab joint' for obvious reasons.

Greener patent no. 2231 of 1863

At this point we feel that we should briefly leave the Westley Richards guns, and preserve our chronological sequence by the consideration of another very famous man in the story of nineteenth century gunmaking. William Wellington Greener obtained his patent No. 2231 on 10 September 1863.

The idea of this gun is essentially very simple: to have a round bolt sliding back and forth in the top of the head of the stock, and to work it by a vertical lever pivoted on the same level and just behind the action flats. The vertical lever is continued down and round the trigger guard, or, in some cases, is the actual trigger guard. Since this gun is naturally illustrated in Greener's book, it is well known, even if actual specimens are not often seen, despite it being advertised by Greener for many years. Not surprisingly Greener claims it as an excellent design, certainly it shares with the Westley Richards the most advantageous position for a locking bolt, but it must be regarded as inferior to the latter, in that there is no provision to lock barrels and action face together. Also covered in this patent are a means of half cocking the hammers and a novel extractor for pin fire cartridges, both of which will be considered in due course.

The method of bolting of the first Westley Richards snap action had the disadvantage that if the bolt were, for any reason, to bind on its bite, it depended entirely on the strength of the direct pull of the user's thumb to

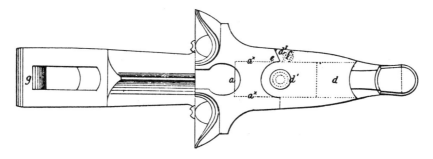

Westley Richards patent no. 2623 of 1864

free it. This was evidently not always sufficient, and the design was modified in two ways as part of the patent No. 2623 of 22 October 1864. Now, instead of a simple pull back top lever to work the bolt, there is a turning top lever pivoted on the bolt behind the doll's head. The forward end of the new lever is broad and, on its right hand side, projects behind a shoulder formed in the top strap. Pushing the lever to the right will cause the bolt to be drawn back as the projection on the lever works on the shoulder of the top strap. The locking bolt can be withdrawn by this motion alone, or by then pulling back the lever as in the previous model. Also included in the 1864 patent is a variant in which the top lever is only permitted to pivot on an axis set to the right of the centre line of the gun.

Westley Richards pin fire gun no. 10106 with pull back type top lever, made for H.R.H. Prince Albert Edward, Prince of Wales, for his 22nd birthday 1863

Just to the left of centre is a stud projecting down into the top bolt so that, as the top lever is pushed to the right, the bolt is withdrawn.

The identification, and therefore the dating, of Westley Richards guns is complicated by the fact that there is another patent for a turning top lever of the type just described. This is the design protected on 14 June 1871, No. 1572. While this strictly belongs to our next volume, completeness demands that it is at least briefly considered here. The top lever is very similar in form and linked to the bolt proper by a central pin. The lever, however, pivots to the right of centre, so that the bolt is drawn back as the lever is turned. Comparing the two patents, various other detail alterations are seen. The earlier one shows a much stouter hinge pin and a raised portion of the action flats that projects up between the barrels. The later patent has a smaller hinge and a second barrel lump that enters a slot in the bar of the action. A further difference in the drawings is that a spiral spring is shown in the 1871 patent as the snap spring, while the 1864 patent uses the small V, in common with the design of 1862. However, the accurate delineation is made infinitely more difficult by the fact that guns are found using a mixture of the features of both 1864 and 1871 patents. And, if a well-used specimen is found, such as the one in the authors' collection, on which inscriptions have been worn away to tantalisingly illegible marks, dating is by no means easy.

Walsh, in his *Modern Sportsman's Gun & Rifle,* of 1882, records that he used a Westley Richards breech loader of the 1864 patent type 'for some seasons without the slightest flaw', but goes on to claim that it was the 'first snap action brought out', which latter statement is another obvious error, the first model being preceded by the Daw/Schneider and the Horsley guns, of which Walsh must surely have known, and by the Humbertjean and Matthey, which he may well not have known.

H. R. H. The Prince of Wales in June 1864 with the Westley Richards gun which he was given the previous year for his 22nd birthday.

135

The success of the various Westley Richards designs can be gauged from a number of sources. Firstly there is the considerable number of surviving specimens. Secondly, it was a gun of the 1862 type that His Royal Highness, Prince Albert Edward, was given for his 22nd birthday in 1863, and with which he chose to be photographed the following year. This gun has survived, and we were fortunate to examine it in the course of the preparation of this work. It is now well worn but has evidently given excellent service. Thirdly, there is the statement in Idle's *Hints on Shooting and Fishing* of 1868 that he had been informed by Westley Richards London agent, Mr Bishop, that he had sold 700 guns of this description. Presumably both the 1862 and 1864 models are included in this total.

Westley Richards patent no. 1572 of 1871

Mention of Mr Bishop reminds us that no consideration of our period would be complete without some reference to this man who was, in all senses of the overworked term, a character. In addition to being London agent for Westley Richards, William Bishop was also a silversmith, or more correctly a dealer in silverware. His interests spread even further, to dogs and prize fighting, and his shop, at 170a New Bond Street, was a rendezvous for those interested in these various pastimes. Very likely it was via the boxing world that he had contacts with some of London's less desirable citizens, for he is credited with being able to procure the return of stolen property. What Westley Richards may privately have thought of his London agent we can only wonder. But such was the standing of 'The Bishop of Bond Street' and his contribution to the success of the firm, that it would have been the height of folly to dispense with his services.

A final indication of the success of the Westley Richards design is the fact that it was used, presumably under license, by Monsieur Renette of Paris, who, it was claimed by V. D. Majendie, RA in his account of the Paris Exhibition of 1867, had built 'large numbers' of guns of this type. This demonstrates that the cross channel traffic in ideas, which we have noted on several occasions, was not all in one direction.

Thus we come to the end of the sliding single bite snap actions. There are in fact 34 patents comprising these, but, since more than one mechanism is covered in some of the specifications and most of the patents include variants of the main idea, the total number is much higher and would be open to argument. Equally questionable is the number of patents that were ever worked commercially or those that only existed as prototypes and how big was the residue that never existed as actual guns. In general all we now have is the evidence of those specimens which have survived a long period of low regard when guns, which are fascinating to us, were scrapped without a second thought. What we can be sure of is that the single sliding bolt snap actioned gun was thought by many, in the decade of the 1860's, to be the complete answer to the needs of the sportsman.

"THE BISHOP OF BOND STREET."

137

Chapter Nine

ROTATING SINGLE BOLT SNAP ACTIONS

The second major group into which the single bite snap actions naturally divide are those in which the locking piece is pivoted and so swings on an arc instead of simply sliding. This collection of designs shows more individuality than did the sliding bolts, and, while odd pairs and trios that exhibit points of similarity can be picked out, an overall description such as we attempted in the sliding bolt section cannot be undertaken. Some of the rotating bolt snaps were of considerable importance in their day, and in one notable case, the Powell, well beyond the period under consideration.

The first patent of this type to be obtained was that of Joseph Needham, and was included in his patent, No. 1544 of 22 May 1862, parts of which we have considered earlier. The design, as usually seen, consists of having a spindle pivoted transversely in the standing breech, just under half way up from the action flats. This spindle is turned by a lever outside the gun which curves round the line of the right angle formed by the breech face and the action flats, the free end lying just behind the pivot of the barrels. Pulling the forward end of this lever down rotates the spindle, to which is keyed a segment shaped bolting piece swinging in a slot, which is an extension of that into which the barrel lumps drop. So that, as the side lever is pushed

J. Needham patent no. 1544 of 1862

138

down, the bolt is swung back out of engagement with the rear barrel lump, and the barrels are thus free to open. In addition to the action there is another important Needham feature included in the specification, that of automatic half cocking. This will be considered in the chapter on the gadgetry of the centre fire.

As is so often the case, we can only guess at the number of Needham action guns made, but it must have been considerable, as specimens are frequently seen. An even greater indication of the regard in which this design was held is the fact that guns using this action are found bearing the names of other famous makers, for instance H. Holland and, very interestingly in view of J. V. Needham's career, Westley Richards. This latter use is all the more interesting because Westley Richards had at this date their own highly successful snap action.

The gun was regularly advertised in *The Field* by J. V. Needham over a long period, the copy changing slightly at various times. In the earlier examples Needham remarked on his previous connection with Westley Richards, and later pointed out that his gun 'resembled in looks a fine muzzle loader', illustrating yet again the importance then given to appearance, which today is perhaps not as fully appreciated as it might be.

Having considerable basic similarity with the Needham is the famous Powell action which was to remain in use on some guns made by this renowned Birmingham firm right up to the present day. The demand for it has now almost vanished, but we were assured that this action could be incorporated in a new hammerless gun if a purchaser so desired. The patent is No. 1163 of 7 May 1864, the distinctive external feature being a lever between the hammers which has to be lifted to withdraw the barrel locking bolt. This, like the Needham, is hung on a transverse pivot which, in this

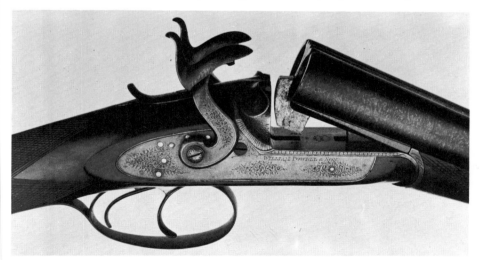

Powell patent no. 1163 of 1864

William Powell, Guardian of the Birmingham Proof House 1862–1901

case, is above the centre of the action face, and engages with the sloped rear face of the rear barrel lump. The locking bolt is in fact made out of the same piece of metal as the opening lever, the bolting surface being the forward end of the lever, which is angled down. The bolt is held in the shut position and made to snap by a flat spring fixed under the top strap with its free forward end bearing down on a projection of the lever/bolt behind the pivot. On closing the gun the rear lump has an incline on its lower rear surface which pushes back the bolt until the barrels are almost shut, when the locking surfaces come into alignment and the snap spring forces the barrels the last part of their travel. Yet a further similarity exists between the Powell and the Needham, in that versions of the Powell exist which incorporate ideas to make the centre fire safer. This time a loaded indicator was devised and a description of this can be found with the gadgetry.

The inventor of this gun was William Powell, who traded from 12 Carr's Lane Birmingham. He had joined his father also W. Powell as partner in 1843, when he was but twenty years old, in the business that his father had founded in 1802. For 40 years he was a Guardian of the Birmingham Gun Barrel Proof House.

While the Powell and Needham guns are both well known, an example of the ingenious mechanism which formed the subject of the patent granted to Stephen and Joseph Law, gunmakers of Wolverhampton, has not yet come to our notice. Like the Smith gun, noted in the section dealing with sliding

140

Gun Manufactory,
Carrs Lane, High Street,
Birmingham................186...

We beg to inform you that after much study and experiment we have succeeded in inventing a breech loading double gun which we believe will be found superior to any that has hitherto been presented to the public.

Our new gun is simple in construction & very neat in appearance. It is very safe & not liable to get out of order. Its action is immediately learned & the gun can be more rapidly fired than any of the ordinary breech loaders. We shall be glad if you will favor us with a call when we shall be pleased to show you the gun & point out its novelties.

We are,
Your Obed.t Serv.ts

William Powell & son

Circular letter from William Powell

snap bolts, the Law gun proposed to use the act of half cocking one of the locks to release the locking bolts, and so permit the gun to be opened. A swinging bolt pivoted up under the top strap was used hence the inclusion of this action at this point. The drawing on the patent, No. 2063 of 9 August 1865, shows a vertical V spring, the forward free end of which bears on the locking bolt, below the pivot and so holds it forward and the gun shut.

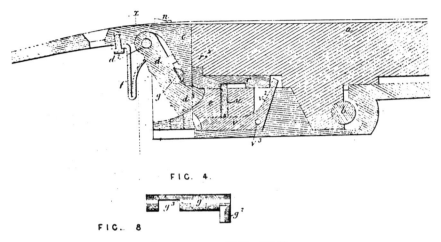

FIG. 4.

FIG. 8

Law patent no. 2063 of 1865

As with the Smith gun, provision has to be made for the fact that in using a hammer gun the hammer is brought to and passes the half cock position for other reasons besides opening the gun after it has been discharged. To make all the other legitimate motions possible, and to incorporate the desired improvement, the patentees chose to use a mechanism which, on paper at least, sounds less than sturdy, certainly when compared with the Powell and Needham for example, and this may be the clue as to why this gun appears to be unknown beyond its patent specification.

The drawing shows a rod through the standing breech parallel to, but in front of and below, the pivot of the bolt. This rod was able to move in two ways, either to rotate partially or to slide out of the action to a limited extent. The actual sliding motion was given to it by a spiral spring enclosed in the blind end of the hole bored for the rod. The outer end of the rod carried a short lever, called a tooth in the patent, which, as the hammer was brought from the fired to the half cock position, caught on a projection on the breast of the hammer, and thus the rod was rotated. Now the rod is so positioned in the standing breech, and part of the rod is cut away to permit the swinging bolt to move forwards to its full extent, that, as the rod is rotated, the remaining part of it acts as a cam and forces back the locking bolt. This happens as the lock reaches half cock. Drawing the hammer back further the tooth will trip out of the hammer notch, when the forward pressure of the action spring on the swinging bolt will rotate the opening

142

cam back and let the locking bolt swing forward to the shut position. If the barrels are opened at half cock and the locks, in the same motion, brought to full cock, the barrels can be shut as there is the familiar bevel on the back face of the bottom of the rear lump, which pushes back the bolt as the barrels close.

On firing, the opening tooth is forced sideways into the action of the gun, against the spiral spring, by an incline formed on the inner face of the hammer acting on the head of the opening lever which has a corresponding bevel formed on it. Thus, if it is desired to carry the gun closed but at half cock, a user would have to draw the opening hammer beyond half cock, to 'trip the tooth', and then lower the hammer back until the lock sear engaged in the half cock bent.

So it is an ingenious mechanism which has perhaps taken more than its fair share of space to describe, and one which it is easy to imagine a sportsman of the late 1860s, looking for a working gun, describing as 'a pretty toy' but 'not fit for hard work'.

In addition to the bolting mechanism, a firing pin and an extractor are protected by this patent, but these will be considered later.

A curious fact that a close study of the patents reveals is that the provisional specification, granted to S. & J. Law, No. 1276 of 9 May 1865, is identical to the first part of the provisional specification of their later patent.

Another variant on the idea of having a bolt which swung, rather than slid, was to employ a hook shaped bite which held the barrels by a slot

Elliot patent no. 1783 of 1863. Elliot patent action

formed just under the top rib. In fact there were but two such guns patented, one of which is found in some numbers, the other largely unknown. The widely distributed design was that of Henry Elliot, gunmaker of Birmingham, patent No. 1782 of 16 July 1863. We know of this gun not simply through surviving examples but from the fact that Mr Elliot entered three classes in The Field Trials of 1866. In view of his showing in the latter (his 12 bore was twentieth out of 32, his 16 bore second of two and his 8 bore the only one entered) it is perhaps fortunate that, as far as we have been able to discover, he was not taken up on the challenge that formed his regular advertisement, which ran: 'The shooting powers of these guns is now open to competition, the tests to be first penetration, second pattern and third lowest amount of recoil.'

Indeed it will be seen from study of the results of the 1866 trial that his 8 bore, costing £50 and shooting 1½oz shot, produced an inferior average pattern to the Pape 16 bore at £35 with 1oz. The remarks of the committee assembled by *The Field* to judge the guns in the trial are, as with most of their remarks, pleasantly bland but regrettably superficial.

In fact the concept of the Elliot gun is very simple. Pivoted on a transverse horizontal axis through the bottom of the action is a vertical lever. The top of this is curved over to form the actual locking bolt. The bottom of the lever projects down in front of the trigger guard as a thumb grip, and when this is thrust forwards the locking bolt is withdrawn. A V spring, set vertically in the body of the gun behind the lever, holds the top portion of the lever forwards, and makes the gun snap shut. The customary idea of a bevelled top to the bite, and an incline on the bottom of the barrels in this case, pushes back the locking bolt as the gun is closed, until the bolt can re-enter its recess.

The similarity between the Elliot gun and the patent obtained some three months later on 21 October 1863, No. 2580 by Joseph Hinton, gun action filer of Birmingham, is so great as to tempt speculation of inspiration, if no more. Having not a shred of evidence, we can but guess. But the fact remains that the site and shape of the locking mechanism are, for practical purposes, identical. The difference lies in the fact that the pivot of the Hinton gun is up behind the standing breech, and that the locking lug is keyed into the pivot which has to be turned to withdraw the bolt. The patent drawing shows two methods of doing this; either by a short thumb lever on the outer, right hand end of the lever, or by a double lever arrangement. In this latter, the bolt has formed on it a tail-like projection which is pushed forwards by one limb of an inverted V shaped lever pivoted at its angle up on the top strap. The other limb of this V lever is depressed by yet another lever, so shaped and hung that it is a thumb piece on the outside of the top strap, between the hammers, which has to be pushed down to unlock the gun. This time the snap spring is shown as a vertical single leaf spring bearing on the back of the bolt behind the head, so as to hold the gun shut and to permit it to snap.

144

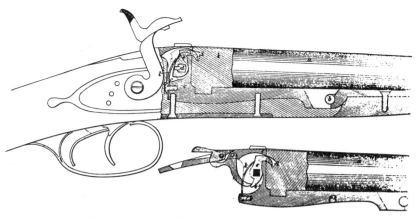

Hinton patent specification drawing no. 2580 of 1863

Fletcher patent 2554 of 1863

Only three days before the Hinton was patented, the first gun of our next pair of hook bite snap action guns was so protected. It was the invention of William Fletcher of Gloucester who was a younger brother of Thomas Fletcher, the latter being then in business in Westgate Street, Gloucester, near the Cathedral. Behind these premises was a workshop where about 10 men were employed, among them William Fletcher. A delightful story has come down in the family, which still owns gunmaking businesses in Gloucester, Cheltenham and Tewkesbury, that one day Thomas found William in the workshop doing some experiments. When asked what he was doing he explained that he was trying to design a breech loader, and, for his pains was told to leave it alone as there were plenty of muzzle loaders on order. Perhaps the ultimate result of William's disobedience was patent No. 2554 of 19 October 1863.

While it has no bearing, that we are aware of, on our story, it is of at least passing interest that Thomas Fletcher was married to a lady who was a direct descendent of William Shakespeare's sister Joan.

We feel that it is one of the quirks of collecting that one of these guns has only just come to our notice. One of the authors (IMC) has been, at the time of writing this, some 30 years in business as a gunmaker in Bath, which is but 40 miles from Gloucester. In general it is our experience that shotguns of a particular maker are more commonly found around the town where he was in business, having either stayed in the family who originally bought them or been handed down to more humble country folk who, until recent times at least, were not a very mobile section of the population. This being the case, the fact that a Fletcher gun has only recently turned up in Bath is quite remarkable. It may be that the writings of the 1860s give a false impression of the numbers produced, but, since these have proved to be an accurate gauge in other instances, we feel it unlikely.

In any event, two were entered in the 1866 Field Trial, where they did not distinguish themselves with any marvellous shooting, and it is a pity that the committee which considered the actions again failed to note anything that even remotely adds to our knowledge of the gun.

Fletcher's name is mentioned in the correspondence in *The Field*, regarding the conversion of muzzle loading shotguns to breech loaders. These letters inferred that it was this patent action that was used on the altered guns, and hence any guns found may well be converted muzzle loaders.

As described in the patent specification, and illustrated in its accompanying drawing, the action consists of a lever which curves part way round the trigger guard, and is hung on a transverse pivot set almost at the bottom of the action bar. The head of this underlever, which is of the type that has to be pushed forwards and down, is formed as a forward facing rounded hook. This engages with another hook on the rear lump, which is also made to push back the lever head as the gun closes.

The action spring was a single leaf under the bar of the action fixed at its forward end, and, at its rear bearing down on a projection from the underlever ahead of the pivot, so tending always to hold the lever in the shut position.

Also claimed in this patent is the idea of positioning the lockpin hole through the metal of the breech. By this means it was proposed to position the locks so that smaller hammers could be used, but those shown in the drawing do not seem significantly different in this respect.

Even more well known today, chiefly because it was illustrated in various contemporary books, and those illustrations have been reproduced in modern times, is the self half cocking pin fire of Edward Harrison. We include this at this juncture because it has a barrel locking mechanism very similar to the Fletcher. The patent is No. 271 of 1 February 1864. We will return to the self half cocking feature of this gun in a later chapter; here we

146

Harrison patent no. 271 of 1864

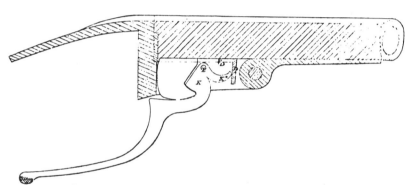

William Tranter patent no. 2113 of 1866, specification drawing

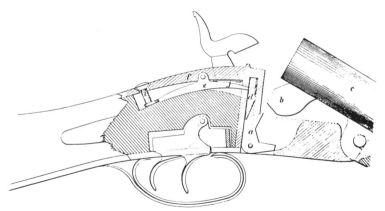

Purdey rocking bolt patent no. 424 of 1865

147

are concerned with the action which, for practical purposes, is so similar to the Fletcher as to render description superfluous. The difference exists in such subtle points as the shape of the locking bites, which are less hook shaped on the Harrison gun.

Employing a lever of a similar style and motion is the invention of another important figure in the field of British firearms of the nineteenth century. This time it was a Birmingham manufacturer, best known for his revolvers, William Tranter of 13 St Mary's Row. Indeed a large part of his patent, No. 2113 of 17 August 1866, is concerned with extractors specifically for such weapons. However tucked away in it is a snap action for a drop down breech loader, more usually seen on light 'rook and rabbit' rifles, but a shotgun use is known.

The front of the rear barrel lump has a broad< shaped recess cut in it and corresponding to this is the shape of the head of the lever. This lever is pivoted on a transverse horizontal bearing set well up in the action bar. The site of the axis is just in front of the top of the <. A spring bears down on the front part of the lever, and the shape of the barrel lump is such that it will displace the lever so that the gun will snap shut.

In February 1865 two gun actions were patented which bear a degree of resemblance to each other. The patentees however illustrate the variety of people who were interesting themselves in the search for a better shot gun action. On the one hand we have James Purdey, son of the founder of this famous firm, with his patent No. 424 of 14 February, and on the other a certain William Henry Aubin, 'Cabinet Locksmith' of Wolverhampton with his provisional patent, No. 506 obtained on 23 February. Both employed a rocking bolt which was wedged in place to hold the gun shut, and one version of the Purdey action, as drawn in the patent, employs a press-in stud between the cocks such as Aubin describes in his unillustrated specification. The similarity goes even further, in that in neither case does the snap spring bear on the locking bolt but on a lever connected to it.

Why such a mechanism was devised by Purdey's and money and time spent protecting it, is yet another of those puzzles to which the answer will probably never be known. For, at this date, the sliding double bite snap bolt known today simply as 'The Purdey Bolt' was already in use. Consideration of this latter action will be found in the next chapter. For whatever reason this second locking system was conceived, it must be regarded as one of the failures of this great concern, and none appear to have survived. It is therefore known solely from the patent specification. The fundamental idea was a catch rocking in a vertical plane on a horizontal pivot. This was situated in the bottom of the action. The catch is roughly C shaped with the internal curve made as three straight lines. The back face of the rear lump was made to fit this shape and the angles between the three inner faces of the C are such, and the pivot so positioned that, as the barrels come to the shut position, the catch tilts forwards, and the three flats on the inner surface of the C mate up with the three flats on the barrel

148

lump. As the catch pivoted forwards a wedge came into position behind its top and so the catch was locked. The wedge is the bottom portion of a vertical sliding bolt, the top end of which is connected to the front end of a horizontal lever pivoted under the top strap. The rear of this lever carries a button which projects through the top strap behind the hammers. So, depressing this button lifts out the wedge from behind the catch, and the barrels can then be opened. When the catch is in the open position the bottom of the wedge engages with the cut-out on the top of the locking catch to hold it in the open positon. Thus there would be no resistance to closing the gun but it would snap shut as the wedge tripped out of the catch. The spring necessary for this snap is a leaf under the top strap forcing down the front end of the rocking lever.

In addition to this form, a version of this action is shown worked by an underlever forward of the trigger guard which raises the wedge bolt as it is pushed forwards.

Yet more extractors and firing pins were covered by this patent and descriptions of these can be found in the gadgetry chapter.

The Aubin uses another C shaped bolt, this time pivoted in a slot cut in the standing breech. The pivot is behind the breech face and the C shaped 'tumbler bolt' is so proportioned and hung that, as the barrels shut, they depress the lower limb and so force the upper limb into a slot between the barrels, reminiscent of the Elliot and Hinton actions. Like the Purdey action there is a rocking lever under the top strap worked by a thumb piece but in this case it is the front end of this lever which holds the bolt in the closed position. Pushing down on the thumb piece enables the tumbler bolt to be forced back by an incline in the bottom of the locking recess as the barrels are opened. This action requires two springs, one to hold the tumbler bolt in the open position, and one above the rocking lever, as on the Purdey, to hold the gun locked.

Less ingenious than the previous pair, and probably, as a result, more practical, was the design patented on 11 April 1866 by John Crofts, gunmaker of Birmingham, No. 1033. With the benefit of hindsight we can look at this action as pointing the way forwards, in that it employed a rotating top lever to work the action, yet which conversely was a rotating single bite cam bolt calling to mind the earliest Lefaucheux guns, the bolt however being more advantageously placed in the action.

Shown in the patent drawing, which is again our sole source of information on this gun, is a sporting gun with a rather long top lever working a spindle set vertically in the action just behind the breech. The bottom of this spindle carries a cam or a rotating bolt which engages with a bite cut in the back of the rear barrel lump. The action spring is shown set vertically in the head of the stock and works on the back of the bolt.

A variant on the theme of having a bolt which rotated in some way was the design of Joseph Lang, No. 1785 of 18 June 1867, which we briefly noted in our previous chapter. This employs a vertical pivot in the left side

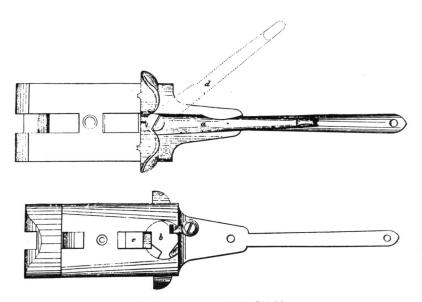

Croft's patent no. 1033 of 1866

of the bar of the action. On this is hung a transverse flat bolt that projects from the right of the action as a small catch. Pulling back on this releases the bolt from a slot in the barrel lump, just like a door latch. This patent of Lang's also yet again protects the idea of a chamber piece and a nipple that was to be screwed in in place of the firing pin to produce a gun able to use loose powder and shot if necessary.

Almost identical to the Crofts action is that shown in the drawings for another gun, designed by Charles Edward Sneider of Baltimore. This was the subject of two British patents, Nos. 1829 of 27 July and 3376 of 24 December, both taken out in 1870 and obtained by the patent agent William Robert Lake. This Sneider design is also the subject of American patent No. 85252 of 22 December 1868.

The main interest in the Sneider specification is that it contained the idea of a cartridge in which the forward portion containing the shot should be fired complete from the gun. The object was to obtain greater force in shooting and to have the barrel and chamber all of a single calibre, thus removing the source of weakness in the barrel caused by forming the chamber.

Very much better known is the distinctive single rotating bite action patented by William Rochester Pape, on whose career we have commented in Chapter 3. This design, No. 2488 of 3 September 1867, uses a vertical pivot in the right of the action just behind the plane of the action face. The pivot terminates in a small thumb lever on the outside of the gun which has to be pushed towards the centre of the gun to free the catch, which is a curved bolt carried on a vertical spindle, and which therefore rotates

Pape patent no. 2488 of 1867. Pape's retracting firing pins and extractor

horizontally. The locking is a bite at the rear of the rear lump and the snap spring is a leaf set forwards in the action bar and it bears on a projection on the vertical spindle.

Apparently well thought of in its day is our final single bite snap action. The patentee was John Thomas, a Birmingham gun and pistol maker, and, though a fair number of these guns have come to our notice, they have all carried the names of other makers. It is not possible to be certain if John Thomas made these guns or simply sold the actions in the white to the trade. For instance, a gun in the authors' collection carries the name 'Gye & Moncrieff, London', a firm who seem to have made extensive use of this action. On the action flats, in an oval, is stamped 'Patent No. 324, 1870' and '582' which is presumably the serial number of the action. While the total number of these action, can now only be estimated, one has turned up in Australia carrying a number of 1330, by no means a despicable total. One, which was made by Tipping & Lawden who may possibly have made all of these actions, was illustrated in *The Field* of 30 April 1870.

Engraved on the head of a turning top lever is the legend 'Solid Self Locking Vertical Grip'. This somewhat misleading title we imagine to have been the inventor's description of his creation. In fact the grip consists of a turret set on a vertical axis just behind the action face, and visible through a slot cut in the face. In the turret is cut a slightly curved slot, the top of which is just visible when the opening lever is in the closed position. On the rear of the rear barrel lump is a tongue like projection, the bottom of which is thinned slightly on one side to form a wedge. Then, as the gun is closed the tongue goes through the slot on the action face and enters the top of the slot on the turret. As the barrels are pressed down into the closed position, the tongue, passing down the curved slot, rotates the turret against a V spring

151

Thomas patent no. 324 of 1870

set under the top strap. Finally the tongue comes out of the bottom of the slot in the turret, which then rotates back, so that the top of the barrel tongue is held down by the bottom of the turret.

While all the actual guns of this patent that have appeared have been of the top lever type previously described, the patent drawing shows other positions for this lever – a forward facing underlever and a lever curving round the guard. It may be of significance that a drawing of this gun published in *The Field* shows a forward facing underlever, which suggests that this form may have existed, possibly the earlier examples were so constructed.

With the Thomas action we come at last to the end of our survey of the single bite snap actions. In fact we have considered over 40 separate designs, with over half of those being patented in the years 1863, 1864 and 1865. This is perhaps the best gauge we now have of the hectic flurry of invention that the ever more general adoption of the breech loader produced.

They range from the best, with examples like the Westley Richards and the Powell, which, when well made, as they were by these famous houses, were sound sportsman's guns, through the general run which were perfectly adequate for the job in hand but in no way outstanding, to others which were little more than talking points, and a cheap way of advertising by their inventors. This last group were probably never made in the true commercial sense and today it is doubtful if even the odd prototype that may have been made would have survived. This is even more to be expected in the case of those designs only provisionally protected, and many of these were never, we suspect, more than vague ideas set on paper.

But whatever the reason for their individual production, taken as a whole, they illustrate the wonderful vitality of the gun trade of this period. They represent such a series of, in general, beautifully made guns, that despite any abuse they may subsequently have suffered, that we marvel they have been so little prized.

152

Chapter Ten

MULTIPLE BITE SNAP ACTIONS

As part of the continuing search for a sound breech fastening, it was probably inevitable that the idea of more than one snapping bite should be explored. A feature of the pattern which was to emerge was that it followed very closely the one which developed concurrently with the inert actions. In both instances the most successful action appeared at the beginnning of the period and came to dwarf its later competitors.

If anything, the pattern was even more pronounced with the multi-bite snaps. The very first one of these became probably the best known action for the side by side double barrel, be it shotgun or rifle, besides being used on some single barrels, and under and over guns. It has become the standard by which all others are judged. We refer, of course, to the Purdey double bite action which was patented on 2 May 1863, No. 1104. Today this is normally found in conjunction with the top lever and spindle arrangement patented some $2\frac{1}{2}$ years later by William Middleditch Scott, No. 2752 of 25 October 1865. The two together are sometimes called 'The Purdey Action' or the top lever called 'The Purdey Lever', both of which are obvious errors.

Since the true Purdey part of this combination was in use for a number of years on its own, it must be considered first. Like so many other great inventions it is, in essence, very simple. The bolt is a flat rectangular piece of steel which slides in grooves cut on each side of the slots for the barrel lumps, in the bar of the action. The slot in which the bolt slides has to be carried through the portion of the action bar between the barrel lump slots,

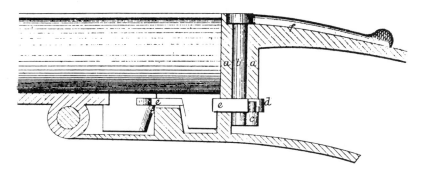

Scott patent no. 2752 of 1865

and two openings have to be made in the bolt piece to permit the barrel lumps to drop into the action. At the top rear of both barrel lumps recesses are cut, thus forming the two bites into which the bolt locks when it slides forwards, driven by the snap spring which is compressed as the barrels come shut. Now since it is the rear of the front lump, in close proximity to the barrel hinge pin, which forces back the locking bolt as the gun closes, the leverage thus exerted is far greater than if the rear of the rear lump were used. This is a very important point for it means that, for a given snap spring strength, a gun so built will be easier to close than one which uses the rear of the rear lump. Consequently, a stronger spring and hence a more positive snap can be obtained with no increase in effort required.

Before the adoption of the Scott spindle Purdeys used several other methods of working their sliding bolt. Probably the earliest is that shown on the patent drawing in which a lever is pivoted towards the front of the action bar and is carried to the rear to curve part way round the trigger guard. This latter is made unusually broad at the front to permit an opening to be made in it wide enough so that a user of the gun can insert his thumb to press down the opening lever. Hence the term 'thumb hole action' which has come to be applied to these guns. Above the pivot is an upward projection of the lever which enters a slot in the slide so that, as the lever is thrust down, the slide is pushed to the rear. An interesting point about the patent drawing is that it shows two separate springs in the action; a flat leaf in the head of the stock, fixed at its top under the underside of the top strap, and bearing with its free end on the back of the sliding bolt, and a V set in the action bar with its open end forwards, and the top limb working on a shoulder on the upward projection of the opening lever, so that the latter always tends to shut.

The second mode of operating the bolt, which is perhaps more widely seen, is also a thumb hole action. This time a shorter lever is used which is pivoted above the front of the trigger guard, and but a single spring which has two limbs, rather like a tuning fork, and lies backwards on either side of the trigger work. Having shot exclusively with a Purdey of this pattern for a number of years, one of the authors, (DJB) will, he hopes, be excused if he digresses to the extent of permitting his enthusiasm to show for a companion that has shared a wide variety of shooting, from sweltering days in midge-infested pigeon hides to bitterly cold nights flighting widgeon under the East Anglian moon, interspersed with a few more formal days of driven game shooting. Over this period his fondness for this particular period of British gunmaking was developed and this book owes its existence, in some measure, to the happy hours spent in the company of a prized thumb hole Purdey.

Then, as now, the proprietors of this action traded at the very top end of the bespoke gun trade, and it is more than probable that some of the variants on this action came about as a result of the foibles of customers. For instance, a gun of the second thumb hole pattern which, instead of the

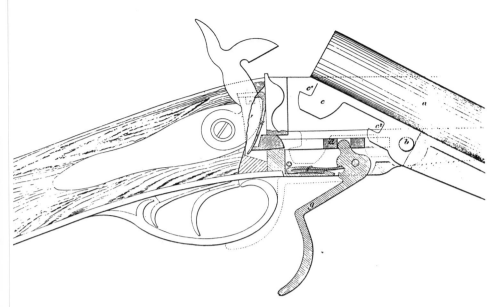

Purdey patent no. 1104 of 1863

James Purdey the elder

James Purdey the younger

155

bifurcated trigger guard, has 'ears' on the underlever, which project on either side of a guard of normal proportions. Or, another in which a long lever curves round the guard and has to be pushed down by its rear end, which curves away from the guard. The authors fully suspect that there are other variations on this theme that have not come to their notice.

The patentee of the Purdey action is recorded on the specification simply as James Purdey. In fact he was the son of the founder of this famous house of gunmaking. Our researches have traced a James Purdey, son of the late James Purdey, blacksmith, apprenticed to Thomas K. Hutchinson in 1793. We believe this entry refers to the founder of the firm, who later had worked for the great Joseph Manton before moving to Forsyth and Co which was the organisation that the Rev Forsyth had formed to exploit his invention of percussion ignition. From there, as a young man of 30, James Purdey had set up in a small way in Princes Street, Leicester Square, but his business prospered, so that by 1826 he was able to move to 314½ Oxford Street. In 1828, when he was 44, his son was born and christened James. In the writings of the last century the son was frequently referred to as 'the younger' which avoided any confusion. As a boy of 14 he started to work for his father and, in due course, building on the sound foundations he had inherited, he enhanced further the reputation of the firm. So much so that at the funeral of King Edward VII in 1910, when eight foreign monarchs assembled in London and were photographed together, they were all patrons of Purdeys.

Yet another potentially confusing father and son of the same name combination is to be found in the case of the Scotts. The firm was founded in 1834 at 79 Weaman Street, Birmingham, by a William Middleditch Scott who had two sons, William Middleditch and James C. Of the two, it would appear that it was William junior who was the most dynamic. Or perhaps it was that he did the things that made news in his day and history in ours, while his brother did the less glamorous job of the day to day running of the business. Be this as it may, the first public achievement of the Scotts that they were responsible for, the design of a triumphal arch to embellish the route taken by Queen Victoria, when she visited Birmingham on 15 June 1858 to open Aston Hall.

This was still the decade of the heady aftermath of the success of the Great Exhibition with the Queen happy with her beloved Albert still at her side. Though the triumphal arch has but little direct relevance to our general theme it is, we feel, of sufficient interest to warrant inclusion, and therefore we reproduce in part the description that appeared in the *Illustrated London News* of 3 July 1858, in the hope that something of the contemporary flavour can thereby be captured.

> At Gosta Green the Gunmakers of Birmingham upheld the honour and credit of the town by an artistic display of firearms. This singular and fanciful structure was designed by Messrs. William and James

Scott junior Gunmakers of Bath Street and as a work of art, was in the
highest degree creditable to them. The extreme height of the trophy,
from the ground to the top of the flagstaff, was 80ft, the span of the
arch 50ft, and the height of the keystone 42ft. The base of each pillar
was 8ft wide and the width of the pillars themselves 6ft. The depth of
the arch was 10ft.

Today such a structure might well be regarded as unnecessarily
flamboyant, but it gives some inkling of the temper of the time in general,
and Birmingham in particular. Coming nearer to the date of the invention
that prompted these remarks, 1865, we have the amazing boom that came
to Birmingham as the result of the American Civil War, when barrel
makers were earning £50 per week, and £20 was commonplace in the gun
trade. These times, as well as the comparable high spot caused by another
foreign conflict, this time the Franco-Prussian War, have come down to us
as part of the folklore of the gun trade, with tales of men lighting expensive
cigars in public houses with £5 notes, and of these men hiring two cabs to go
to work in – one for the man and one for his top hat!

To return to saner events of more importance to our story, it was also in
the period just prior to this patent that W. M. Scott established his practice
of making a yearly business trip to the USA. From this enterprise was to
grow a very fruitful connection with this, even then, important market for
sporting guns. Agents were appointed, principally Henry C. Squires of
New York, and Scott guns came to be well known and highly regarded.
This trade was to be virtually killed by the McKinley Tariff of 1890, when a
duty of 35 per cent ad valorem plus six dollars per gun was imposed. But in
1865 trade was relatively buoyant, in spite of some tariffs, as patent No.
2752 was obtained on 25 October. This specification protected two separate
ideas, one an indicator to show whether the gun was loaded, which we will
return to in the chapter on the gadgetry of the centre fire, and the action,
which we feel must be considered in juxtaposition with the Purdey bolt,
since the two are now used together.

A feature of this patent specification, which is now open to speculation, is
that it shows a locking bolt identical to the Purdey, when the latter was still
protected by patent. What is shown most clearly on the drawings of
peculiarly ungainly centre fire guns is a turning top lever working a spindle
set, in side view, vertically in and behind the standing breech. From the rear
the spindle is seen to be tilted so that its bottom end is to the right of its top.
At the bottom of the spindle is a short lever projecting horizontally towards
the centre of the gun. The inner end of this lever has a stud, which draws
back the locking bolt as the spindle revolves under the influence of the
rearward facing external top lever. The drawings show two methods by
which the spindle was to be supported; one, for almost its entire length in a
hole bored in the standing breech, the other with a bearing top and bottom.
This solidarity is one reason for the success of the design, and the essential

point it was to score over other, often superficially similar, lever work such as the Greener. Two forms of snap spring are shown, both leaves, one in the body of the action, bearing on the bottom of the lever, and the other set on the back of the standing breech, and working on the spindle at that point. Today the most common form is a V under the top strap with one limb fixed and the other entering a slot in the top lever boss so that the spring is compressed as the spindle turns.

Given the regard in which the Purdey double bite snap is now held, it is remarkable how little attention was paid, either to it or to the idea of a double snap bite, at the time of its inception. As far as we can now judge, it was looked upon as just another snap action and all but lost in the flood of single bites which composed the last chapters. For instance, Walsh, writing in 1866, dismisses the Purdey bolt with these words: 'It (the Purdey) is a neat piece of workmanship but somewhat deficient in durability.' And Christopher Idle, in 1868, wrote: 'In the slight difference which exists between Purdey's and Needham's snap gun, I think the advantage is on the side of the latter.'

Further evidence of this lack of interest comes from the records of the Patent Office in the shape of the remarkable fact that it was two years before the next double bite snap was protected, and this was a rather lame provisional specification. The patentee was William Hill, a gun finisher, of Birmingham. The rather impractical sounding idea which is embodied in his patent, No. 866 of 7 April 1864, was to have a bolt between the ribs and another sliding into the barrel lump. These two were joined by a bar in the head of the action being 'urged forwards by a spring', and withdrawn by a lever and rack and pinion device of which the details are not stated.

Showing signs of far more thought, and having been brought to a much higher level of development were the varieties of an idea provisionally protected later the same year, on 29 July, No. 1888, by Richard Redman, gun manufacturer and David Kirkwood, who called himself a gun filer, both of Birmingham. Their specification is unusual for a provisional gun specification in that it is accompanied by detailed drawings, and this fact leads us firstly to make our opening remarks, and to believe that guns of this type may once have existed. Their two bites were on the rear of the front and rear lumps. The bolts which engaged with these were, for the front bite, a swinging bolt in the bar of the action, and for the rear, the top of an underlever of the type that has to be pushed forwards. The two bolts were connected by a horizontal link hung below the pivot of the front bite and above the axis of the opening lever, so that pushing forward on the lower part of the underlever swung back the front bolt as the head of the lever also swung back. The snap spring is shown as a single leaf fixed at its forward end in the front of the action and bearing on the bottom rear of the front bolt, forcing it up and the bottom of the underlever back.

A modification, which is drawn but not explained, has both bolts engaging with one lump, one at the front and one at the rear. Also included

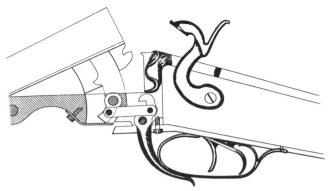

Redman and Kirkwood patent no. 1888 of 1864

is an inert action exactly like the Hammond as described in Chapter 2.

It would have been very strange indeed if, in the search for a sound snap action gun, the excellence of the Henry Jones double grip inert actioned gun had not been remembered and attempts made to make this action snap. This line of development led to five depositions with the Patent Office, two provisional and three full patent specifications.

The first of these was the provisional specification, dated 15 December 1866, No. 3302, taken out in the name of David Kirkwood, presumably the co-patentee of the previous patent. Now he is described as a gun action filer, which is a recognised trade, and this leads us to believe that his previous calling was a result of a clerk's error.

The mechanisms that were covered in this specification well illustrate the problem that it was not a simple matter to persuade the double screw grip to snap. Indeed, it will be seen that the majority of these adaptations of the Henry Jones grip were semi snap rather than true snaps, and, since they were in direct competition with the more convenient true snaps, the reason for their limited use becomes apparent. In the Kirkwood patent there are no less than five variations on the theme of making the familiar underlever spring loaded. They all involve making this lever go over centre of the spring arrangement, which is compressed as the gun is opened so that, to close the gun, the lever has to be moved the first part of its travel by hand. Then, as the spring takes over, it will snap. It is not clear if this was to be the only means of shutting the gun, or if it was necessary to complete the motion of the screw grip by a further pressure of the user's hand. A specimen of this gun has not been available for examination, so we are unable to be sure on this point.

In the first action described in the patent, the top of the turret of a Henry Jones gun has a slightly elongated C shaped recess cut into the curved face above the action lever. Into this recess projects the long limb of a short lever which is pivoted so that it can swing from side to side in the action. On the shorter rearward end of this lever is shown a leaf spring set vertically behind

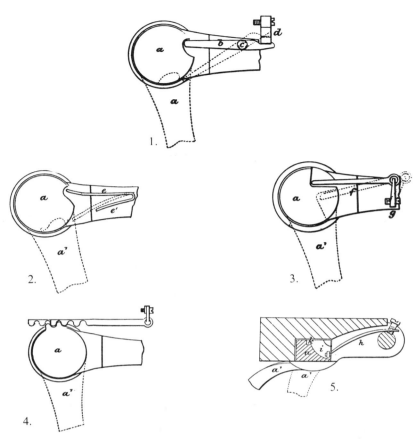

1.

2.

3.

4.

5.

Kirkwood patent no. 3302 of 1866

the standing breech. So that, as the gun is opened, that is when the underlever is turned, this spring is compressed by the movement of the short lever in the action. But, to release the bites of the double grip it is necessary to turn the underlever to such a position that the C shaped depression is beyond the reach of the lever, which now bears on the curved side of the bolting turret. So, despite the spring being compressed, the turret will not turn because the lever has no shoulder to bear on. When the main lever is moved a few degrees back on the closing motion the lever can slip back into its recess, and now bear on a shoulder so that the compressed spring will rotate the bolt.

In the second modification, the short lever is replaced by the longer arm of a V spring, lying with its prongs in a horizontal plane and its bottom to the rear of the gun. The length of the longer arm of the spring is such that the operation is as before.

160

A Westley Richards pinfire in case

Two centre fire Purdey guns used as a pair by James Purdey Jnr. showing first and second pattern

The third model is as the first, but with the lever pivoted on the bottom of the spring, and a different shaped recess in the top of the bolt turret. While the fourth variant is a use of a rack and pinion instead of the recess of the third type.

By contrast, the final mechanism, while it shows the characteristics of the other four, is operated by other means. A curved slot is cut in the vertical side of the turret. In this runs a roller fixed to the free, rear end of a leaf spring, the fixed end of which is shown as being at the front of the action bar above the barrel pivot. The curved slot is so formed and positioned that, as the turret is turned as the gun is opened, the spring is flexed and brought into tension. The over centre condition is achieved, at the top of the curved slot, by the spring and its roller being conveyed onto a horizontal plateau or shelf, so that the downward thrust of the spring is of no avail. However, when the opening lever is partially closed, the roller slips off the shelf and, forcing its way down the curved slot, rotates the turret and bites.

This action is another of those which may have claimed more than its rightful share of space, but it is one that, while basically simple, requires considerable description.

In fact we have considered this patent slightly out of order, firstly to put both Kirkwood designs together, but, more importantly because this arrangement aids the description of the next design in our sub-group. Patented on 17 November 1866, specification No. 3022, was a further attempt at a snapping Henry Jones action. The patentee was another famous arms manufacturer, Thomas William Webley. Here again we can discover something of his history since he became famous, as did Robert Adams, for his revolvers. The shotgun action that is the subject of this patent is very like the Kirkwood but with the important difference that the spring goes over centre at the middle of the travel of the opening lever. So that the first part of motion, be it opening or closing, is stiffened by the spring being compressed. But, as the halfway point is passed, the spring is made to assist the motion, so that the locking bolt snaps either shut or open. This singular facility is possible because a link is pivoted in the bottom of the bolt turret with its rear end connected to the free limb of a V

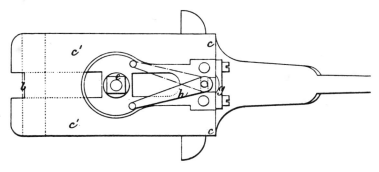

T. Webley patent no. 3022 of 1866

161

spring set upside down in the head of the stock. So, this spring is at its greatest compression when the point at which the link is pivoted to the turret is closest to the action face. This is arranged to be half way between the closed or open position of the lever, the forward part of the link lying to the left of centre when the gun is closed, and to the right when opened.

The patentee of this individual mechanism, for we have now no way of knowing if the name on any patent was in fact that of the actual inventor, was the oldest of the four sons of Philip Webley, who founded the family firm from a variety of origins. He is recorded as being a man of considerable business ability, and undertook promotional trips, chiefly to South Africa. He was a guardian of the Birmingham Gun Barrel Proof House from 1869 until his death in 1904. It was during his time as managing director that Webley's expanded considerably, and took over the important concerns of Tipping & Lawden (1877), W. & C. Scott & Sons (1897) and Richard Ellis & Son (1897). These amalgamations widened the scope of the firm which then became Webley & Scott, and, although no longer an independent organisation, the name is still retained.

Another unillustrated provisional patent was that of John Henry Crane, of Royal Exchange, London, dated 9 May 1868, No. 1526. This contains another attempt to make a snap action out of the inert double screw grip. The method is rather impressively, if not very precisely, described, and involves compressing 'a helical or spiral spring' as the underlever is swung open, and having a catch, which is detailed as a spring loaded rocking lever in the bar of the action, the front end of which is permitted to pop up as the barrels are lifted off the action flats. Thus, the rear end of the lever will depress and engage in a notch in the top of the bolt turret. On closing the gun, the front of the rocking lever would be depressed, and so lift the rear end out of the catch when the underlever could snap shut.

The obvious inconvenience, not to say danger, in the heavy underlever swinging violently round as it shut was anticipated in the specification, and in the last sentence a rack and pinion system with a vertically working lever is outlined to work the double grip turret.

This is another gun to which contemporary references can be found which lead us to believe that it was made, at least in modest quantities although these sources add nothing to our knowledge of this mechanism, which rests therefore entirely with the patent specification.

Though its claim on a place in this sub-section, or indeed in this chapter, could be argued about, we feel that it is only just that we should include, among the attempts to make the Henry Jones double grip inert action snap, the patent obtained on 12 January 1869, No. 92, by the original inventor to a similar end. His new gun was neither a true double screw grip or a true snap, hence our opening remarks. Indeed from our understanding of the patent specification, from which we reproduce the particularly fine drawing, this gun had the curious arrangement of having one bolt snapping and one bolt inert. It is therefore a particularly interesting gun and it is regretted that despite encountering an example, one of the authors (IMC) was neither able to obtain a photograph nor to examine the gun at all closely.

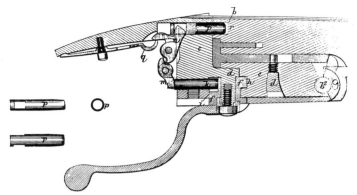

Henry Jones patent no. 92 of 1870

The drawing shows an underlever grip gun in which the rear bite has been sacrificed to work the rest of the mechanism. The single bite that remains on the barrel lumps is further to the rear than on a classic Jones gun, and therefore gives a more secure fastening. The rear portion of the bolt turret is made as a cam instead of a grip, and, as the underlever is rotated, this forces back a rod sliding for and aft horizontally in the action. The rear end of this rod pushes against the lower limb of one of a pair of levers that work together, so that, as the lower limb of the bottom lever is pushed back, so too is the top limb of the top lever. This motion is used to withdraw a round rod bolt, which slides into a hole bored into a solid top rib between the barrels. The upper limb of the top of the two levers has a rearward projecting lip, upon the underside of which bears the forward free end of a leaf spring set under the top strap and fixed at its rear. Therefore the top bolt is always pressed forwards, except when withdrawn as described. Now, since the two levers in the head of the stock, the lower limb of the bottom lever and rod, or the rod and cam, are none of them shown linked together, it would appear that, even if the top bolt could be pushed in by the closing barrels, this motion could not be transmitted to the undergrip which is, as a result, for practical purposes, an inert action. Therefore a most unusual action is produced, to which several modifications suggest themselves, and we wonder whether they were ever incorporated.

It is fitting that the last gun in this group should demonstrate that the double grip could be made to snap completely, and thus that the goal which had eluded the other inventors in this section was indeed attainable. The patent, No. 687, bears another famous name, this time a less famous son of an illustrious father, James Lang.

His father, Joseph, had pioneered the production of the Lefaucheux pin fire breech loader in this country, and his mother was a daughter of James

J. Lang patent no. 687 of 1870

Purdey the elder. At the date of his patent, 8 March 1870, James Lang was presumably working in the family business, as he quotes 22 Cockspur Street as his address on his specification. But later, in 1887, he set up in business for himself at 33 New Bond Street. This eventually became successively J. Lang & Co, Lang & Hussey Ltd, at a variety of addresses, and finally in 1898 amalgamated with the original family business, the combined companies trading as Joseph Lang & Son Ltd from 10 Pall Mall.

James seems to have been the inventor in the family, and was the patentee of a series of designs for hammerless guns, before he established his own business. His hammerless guns, like this snap grip design, are therefore found bearing the name of Joseph Lang and Son.

The secret of his success in persuading the screw grip to snap was to combine it with a sliding bolt, to produce a treble grip. This he worked with a top lever and spindle arrangement, and had a projection from the bolt

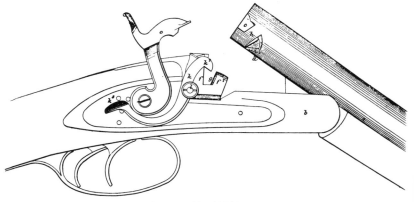

Edge no. 139 of 1865

164

which ran forwards to the grip so that, as the bolt slid forwards it pushed the screw round. The sliding bolt was worked by a transverse lever towards the bottom of the spindle, and below it was another transverse lever which pointed the other way and was connected to the grip by a rod so that, as the vertical spindle was turned to draw back the sliding bolt, the screw grip was rotated in the opposite direction. The screw grip is thus completely governed by the top lever, which is spring loaded by a V under the top strap, and the gun is a true fully snapping action.

There remains a balance of multigrip actions that belong to our period and hence in this chapter, whose only resemblance to each other is the fact that they are multigrip actions. So, no more groups can be assembled and the only logical solution, since they are so few in number, is we feel, to consider them by date of patent.

In 1865, on 16 January, patent No. 139 was obtained by James Simeon Edge, who had the wit to include on his specification that he was 'the elder'. In fact he was the father of the man who, with John Deeley of Westley Richards, invented the falling block rifle action and the forend catch by which the family name is best remembered.

The mechanism that we are concerned with here is distinctive, simple and not particularly practical. What is described, and shown drawn on the patent specification, is an attractive wood bar pin fire gun which, has lugs formed on the extreme outside of both barrels which drop into recesses formed on forward projections from the standing breech. The barrels were held down by two external hook bites pivoted on a transverse spindle through the standing breech, somewhat reminiscent of the Needham action. On the right hand side of the gun a thumb lever is shown curving round to present its thumb piece behind the hammer pivot. The snap spring is a curved leaf in the action, working on the transverse spindle to hold the bites in the shut position. While the heads of the bites are so shaped that the

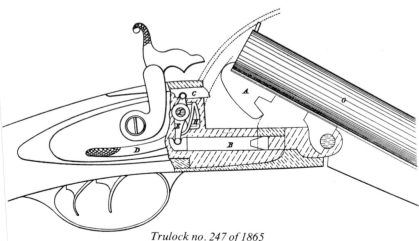

Trulock no. 247 of 1865

descending barrel lugs would displace them and so produce a snap action.

We should have thought it apparent to a sportsman of even slight experience that these external bites would have an almost fatal attraction for all sorts of dirt and obstruction, thus making this gun a most trying implement to use.

A gun in some ways similar to the preceding one was patented but 12 days later, No 247, by Samuel, Richard and William Trulock, whose other inventions we have previously noted. This again uses a transverse spindle in the action but now the locking bolts are internal. In the middle of the action on the spindle is a lever projecting both above and below the spindle which, as with the Edge gun, is worked by a thumb lever behind the right hammer. As this thumb lever is pushed down the top of the lever in the action will move back whilst the bottom swings forwards. It is this motion which is used to work the bolts, the top portion working a sliding bolt, such as we saw over and over again in the single bite snaps, and entering a recess under the top rib. A more ingenious solution had to be found to use the forward opening action of the bottom limb of the lever. This was to make the bite in the front of the rear lump and a sliding bolt, carried round the opening for the lump, which released the barrels as the bolt was pushed forwards. On closing, a cam, formed as a rearward projection of the rear barrel lump, forced back the top bolt, and the bottom one forwards.

A strong claim could be made on behalf of the patent, to which we now turn our attention, for the honour of being the most widely reproduced gun patent specification of our period. The reason for this wide dissemination was not the main subject of the patent, a double bite snap bolting system, but, as we have seen before, a small, almost afterthought of an idea which has proven to be a valuable invention. The patentee was William Rochester Pape, and we refer to his patent, No. 1501 of 29 May 1866, which contained a clear description of how a shotgun barrel was to be choke bored. On the basis of the evidence of the specification, some nine years later, Pape was to be awarded, by a committee assembled by *The Field*, ten guineas donated by a Mr A. J. Lane. As a result of this award Pape was ever after able to claim that he was 'the inventor of the choke bore' and to reinforce his statement by reproduction of his patent specification in his catalogues. While we are certain that so obvious an idea as the choke bore was invented and re-invented many times before Pape it may well have been possible for him to secure considerable financial remuneration on the basis of this specification of 1866. This view is shared by Mr Lane who, in a letter to *The Rod and Gun* in 1902, wrote: 'There have been no end of ramifications of choke boring that have come under my observation, but I have no hesitation in saying there is not one of them that would not have been held to be an infringement of Mr Pape's patent had it not been allowed to lapse . . .'. But there is plenty of evidence that Pape did not appreciate either the potential of his claim or really practically develop it. The most conclusive evidence of this is that he let his patent lapse on 31 May 1873 for non-payment of the £100 fee. Furthermore we have it on G. T. Teasdale Buckell's authority in *Experts on Guns and Shooting* published in 1900 that ... 'when asked in '73 or '74 to do his best, by way of pattern, he (Pape) sent out a weapon that could not put 100 No. 6 shot in the 30in circle at 40 yards. And, having regard to the extreme care with which the cartridges sent to try the gun were loaded, we have every reason to believe he was doing his best.'

And, while his guns took the top two places at the *Field* gun trial of 1866, his winning patterns averaged but 126·2 pellets in a 30in circle from 1oz of No 6 shot, which today would rank his boring as no more than improved cylinder. In spite of this triumph, and second place in the 1866 trial, plus the £10 10s. which, when added to his wins in the previous trials in 1858 and 1859 with muzzle loaders, proved very valuable advertising copy, no one can doubt that Mr Pape would also have liked to have added the royalties on his invention to his bank balance.

But while he failed to reap the financial reward from his idea, it was one of the factors that served to make him one of the great figures of his era. Part of his stature derived from his business, the nature of which can be judged from the following advertisement from *The Field* of 1865, which ran: '. . . being a manufacturer who builds the gun throughout from raw materials our guns will be found unequalled for genuine materials, sound work and beauty of finish with moderation in price. Testimonials and extracts from the Sporting Press and Price Lists on application to the works 36 Westgate St Newcastle.'

We feel that this advertisement should not be taken as holding true for all grades of gun for the duration of the life of the firm. Certainly, evidence from outside our period would suggest that, for the very lowest grade of gun and probably for the middle order as well, these were bought in from makers, principally but not entirely in Birmingham, whose speciality they were.

William Rochester Pape was by any standard a successful business man. The son of a gunmaker, he soon left his father to start in the same business for himself in Westgate Street, Newcastle. In this he evidently prospered for he also found the time to follow his hobbies of gun dogs and falconry. We have previously noted the Newcastle Dog Show of 1859 which, it is said, was almost entirely organised by Mr Pape. He was also famous for his falcons, some of which he supplied to Maharajah Prince Dhuleep Singh. Further evidence of Pape's prosperity are his interests in what today we should call property development. About 1900 he owned the largest block in Newcastle to have been owned by a single individual. He died in 1923, aged 91, probably as the result of being knocked over by a motor car near his Westgate Street works.

The main subject of the patent that prompted these remarks is in fact the distinctive gun from the famous maker, which appeared during a period when so many of the better shotguns were instantly recognisable as being the product of their particular 'houses'. This variety and individuality is

Pape patent no. 1504 of 1866

one of the great charms of this second decade of the breech loader.

The Pape action consisted of two bolts on a common vertical spindle, which terminated on the underside of the gun in a small thumb lever to the right of, and just in front of, the trigger guard. Both bolts are pieces of steel, curved in plan but flat in the horizontal view. The bottom one locks on a bite at the top of the rear barrel lump, the other on the top of a rearward projection between the barrels. The barrel lump is in fact made to project a little further to the rear than usual, and is formed, in side view, as a curve which pushes aside the bolts as the barrels are lowered. The snap spring is a flat leaf set forwards in the action, its free end bearing on a step in the spindle, forcing it, when seen from above, in a counter clockwise direction, that is into the closed position.

An interesting claim that is made for this action is that it is self tightening. So that, as the locking surfaces wore, the bolts could turn further and so compensate for the passage of time. This idea is one which has called forth much ingenuity on the part of designers of shotgun actions down the years. In particular, inventors working for the American market were seeking to build guns which would function faultlessly and stay absolutely tight for many years, despite being shot with heavy loads and perhaps a thousand miles from a competent gun smith. This is a fascinating side turning which, alas, we cannot now explore, belonging as it does not only to another era but to another country as well.

As we can see over a century later, the action provisionally patented 14 January 1869, No. 119, was another herald of future events. It contained a description of a shotgun action which was to be held shut by three bolts. This idea of multiple locking was to be a feature of the next 15 or 20 years, usually, as we remarked earlier in this chapter, using the Purdey bolt as a basis. So, while this specification is another unillustrated and not very precise document, it has an importance greater than some others of a similar nature.

What is described is a train of three separate bolts catching respectively the rear of the front lump, the front of the second lump and the rear of the second lump. The furthermost forward of these bolts was to be worked by a swinging push forward underlever. The bolt, so moved, was in turn, and in a way that is not clear from the specification, to displace the second bolt which in its turn was to act on the third bolt. The patentees of this odd

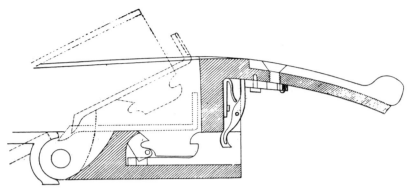

Williams' patent no. 2513 of 1869

sounding set up were Thomas Birkett, gunmaker and Henry Scott, gun action filer, both of Birmingham.

Another provisional specification, although this time we have the advantage of a drawing, is that of John Williams of 25 South Castle Street, Liverpool, No. 2513 of 24 August 1869. This is an ingenious double bite snap with bites on the front and rear of the rear lump. The rearmost one is simple, being exactly as on so many of the single bite snaps with a bevelled lump and bite. The ingenuity lies in the arrangement of the second bite on the single sliding bolt. Made as one piece with the bolt, but projecting forwards under the lump, is a slide. To the front of this is hinged the second bite which has a curved top to it. This fits closely to the curved top of its recess in the action bar so that, as the rear bolt and slide move forwards, the second bolt swings up and back to engage with the bite on the front of the lump. When the bolt assembly is drawn back, it frees the rear catch and the front bite can push back the top of the front bolt, so that the barrels can pivot open.

Russ, Hammond and Hammond patent double bite snap no. 2904 of 1869

The bolt slide is drawn back by the bottom of a vertical lever on a horizontal pivot inside the head of the action. The top of this lever is pushed forwards by a cam worked by a turning top lever, and the snap spring is the free limb of an upside down V fixed to the back of the standing breech, tending always to push back the top of the vertical lever.

Later the same year, on 6 October to be exact, an interesting patent, No. 2904, was taken out by Edwin Russ, Henry Hammond and Edwin Hammond, all of Winchester, for another double bite snap action. The interest of this action lies in the fact that it was undoubtedly a derivation from the very early inert action patented 10 years before by Isaac Hammond, which we described in Chapter 2. This new patent used the same cam bolt across the body of the action, but, in addition to its engaging with a C shaped recess on the front of the rear lump, it also worked a sliding bolt, which was spring loaded and entered a bite in the rear of the same lump. Of necessity the sliding bolt had a slot cut in its forward part to permit the lump to drop through, and it is the two legs or prongs that remain that bear on the transverse cam. The spring, necessary for the forward motion of the sliding bolt and the shutting motion of the cam, is another upside down V in the head of the stock. This patent, as drawn, also featured a means of automatic half cocking, which we will return to in the Gadgetry chapter and a falling block rifle action that is outside our scope.

Another treble grip gun that is well known as a drawing, but not as an actual gun, is the design of George Thackeray Abbey, which was covered by the British patent No. 2218 of 21 July 1869. This unusual state of affairs is simply the result of W. W. Greener using a drawing of it in his *Gun and its Development* to illustrate another form of bolt into a projection from the top rib. Why Greener chose this gun in preference to others very similar we can now only guess, but we feel that it being the invention of an American rather than an English competitor might well be the answer.

Abbey records on his British patent that he was 'of Chicago Illinois' but 'now residing in Birmingham'. Of George Thackeray Abbey very little

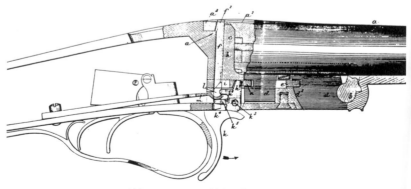

Abbey patent no. 2218 of 1869

seems to be recorded. The sum total of extensive research are the bare facts that he had a retail shop at 43 South Clark Street, Chicago, at which address he was succeeded by one Fred J. Abbey. Why George Thackeray made the long journey to Birmingham in 1869, we can now only speculate. Was it solely to patent this gun or did he wish to study some aspect of gunmaking, to attempt to interest other makers in producing it? We shall probably never know.

The gun we are now concerned with used an action identical to the second pattern thumb hole Purdey, but with a second projection on the lever which worked a bolt which moved vertically up and down in the standing breech. The top end of this vertical bolt entered a slot cut in a rearward projection of the top rib which, in the closed position, lay in a recess cut in the top of the standing breech.

The multi-bite snap actions are surprisingly few, certainly when compared with the plethora of single bite mechanisms. The quest for a sound snap action did not of course come to an abrupt end with the end of our period, but, with a very few exceptions as noted, all single and multi-bites alike were to be swept away by the adoption of the Purdey bolt, when this became public property in 1877. The period that followed was to see a considerable number of attempts to improve on this action, usually with the addition of a connection of some sort between the top of the barrels and the standing breech. But today such actions are used only when exceptional strength is demanded, and it is considered that a well made double bolt is perfectly adequate for guns of ordinary weight shooting standard cartridges.

Surely no greater tribute can be paid to the Purdey action of 1863 than that it looks set fair to be made as long as side by side double barrelled shotguns are made.

Chapter Eleven

BIZARRE ACTIONS

Given so diverse a collection of shotgun breech mechanisms as are to be found in the span under consideration, it is in no way surprising that we are left with a residuum which defies our scheme. We feel that no option exists but to consider these individually, as, in the majority of cases, these are singular designs, and any basis for comparison would therefore be tenuous.

In the preface to this volume we remarked on the difficulty of deciding which gun action to include and which to exclude on the grounds of being either rifle or capping breech loader. We noted that odd guns would be found built on designs which we had excluded, but which nevertheless had been modified to become shotguns using self-contained cartridges.

First in our collection of miscellaneous arms comes a gun which, while it was patented in Great Britain and is therefore included in the present work, shows no evidence of having been produced in this country. It is the Roper repeating shotgun, designed by Sylvester Hayward Roper of Roxbury, Massachusetts, USA, and patented by him in that country on 14 July 1868, No. 79861. On 24 January 1867 John Henry Johnson, acting as agent for the inventor, obtained a British patent, No. 182, for the design. This is shown in the patent drawing as an eight shot rifle, but is more usually seen as a four shot shotgun.

The magazine is a revolving cylinder, turning in an outer fixed cover, and is charged by inserting cartridges through a spring loaded trap door in the outer cover. As each round is inserted it is pushed down counter-clockwise until the last, which remains beneath the trap door and in line with the chamber.

The failing of the design was that the cartridge was not in the chamber when the trigger was pulled. Before it could be fired, the bolt, which was permanently fixed to the hammer, had to push the cartridge into the chamber while simultaneously cocking the firing pin. Then when the bolt was locked, the firing pin was released to finally fire the cartridge.

All this took place *after* the trigger had been pulled making for a long lock time, and it would have inevitably made the Roper a difficult weapon with which to shoot moving targets.

The rest of the firing cycle, that is the extraction of the spent case which remained in the magazine, and the rotation of the magazine, all took place as the lock was manually recocked. So, despite the gun being well balanced for a repeater, it never saw wide use.

The most valuable part of the patent, which is in common use today, is most fully described in the final paragraph of the provisional specification. This idea, of a detachable choke, seems not to have been exploited at the time.

> The second part of this Invention consists in the employment of an attachable and detachable muzzle piece to small shot guns or fowling pieces with a view to varying the scatter of the shot, the muzzle piece being made of a slightly expanded form if intended to scatter the shot, or slightly contracted when the reverse effect is to be produced. By screwing one of these muzzle pieces on to the end of an ordinary fowling piece it may be made to scatter or concentrate the shot as desired.

While this gun was not a success, its designer did not lose interest in repeating arms. His name reappears in British patents as co-designer of the Spencer six shot pump action gun, which was to be sold in limited quantities by Lancaster's in the late 1880s. It is beyond our present scope but interesting in that it was the first repeating shotgun to be sold in any quantity in Great Britain.

It is with some surprise that we note that, in this chapter, we have no less than four specifications in the name of John Henry Walsh. That he, uniquely placed to reconcile the needs of the sportsman with the modifications proposed by inventors from all walks of life, should have gone to the trouble of patenting ideas which, to be a little harsh, should have stayed on the back of the envelopes where they were born, casts some doubt on his judgement. To be fair, he did not trumpet them in the columns of *The Field*, and we can see what his basic ideas were, but we feel that the problems that his 'solutions' created were worse than the difficulties he set out to solve.

These remarks apply with particular force to two of his patents, No. 406 of 14 February, which was only a provisional specification and No. 1923 of

Roper shotgun

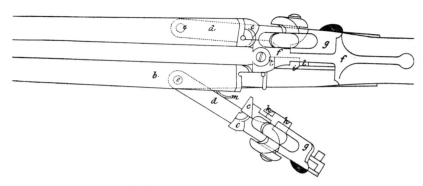

J. H. Walsh patent no. 1923 of 1863

4 August, both of 1863. Both involve having the barrels and stock fixed in relation to each other, like a muzzle loader, and opening the breech by swinging out the breech block/lock assembly. This completely solved all the problems of bolting a drop down or sliding barrel gun, but resulted, if the patent drawing with the full specification is an accurate guide, in an exposed delicate mechanism quite unsuited to anything like rough usage. Not surprisingly these met with less than an enthusiastic response by the gun trade and would be known only as patents were it not for the illustration in Greener's book, *The Gun and its Development*. This, we suspect, was drawn from life and so we believe that at least a prototype once existed. It was therefore with particular enthusiasm that one of the authors (IMC) followed up a lead, from a usually reliable source, that such a gun existed and might even be for sale. The description he was given could only fit this gun, being of a double barrelled gun, in which the barrels were fixed to the stock and did not drop down, and that the 'locks opened to load'. Imagine his disappointment when he was shown a very battered Snider actioned single barrel rifle! However many years ago he saw an actual gun of the true Walsh design but of Belgian make.

The details of the construction of the gun described in the provisional specification are somewhat hazy, but they would appear to be very similar to the second deposition on the subject which is illustrated. What is shown is a well proportioned bar action pin fire with the locks pivoted on not very substantial vertical pivots at their forward ends. By this means the whole of the lockwork, plus the cock and an extension of the lockplate, which is the top of the head of the stock, can swing out sideways to expose the open ends of the barrels. There is shown an inner lockplate to protect the mechanism of the lock, but the tail of the sear has to protrude inwards through this, and no details of any protection for the trigger work are shown.

Curiously, the first specification seems more concerned with a gun using centre fire ammunition, but both have extractors which we will return to later. No details of how the first was to be locked shut are included, but the second has a small thumb lever on the top of each lockplate, just behind the hammer, which turns a button catch which fastens to a downward projection from the underside of the top strap. This latter is continued round and behind the opening for the top of the lockplate, and forms an abutment for it. This is to strengthen the action and is one of the points claimed on the specification.

The third Walsh specification may not belong in this book at all in that it is concerned mainly with the conversion of single barrel muzzle loading rifles to breech loaders, while retaining the facility to load via the muzzle if necessary. Again it is an unillustrated provisional specification; but what is described is an opening system very like the Schneider/Snider that we described in Chapter 7. The chief novelty of provisional specification No. 2322 of 22 September 1864 lay in a hinged 'striker' fixed to the opening lever of the breech block, and extending towards the centre of the gun. The purpose of this was to transmit the blow from the hammer to the pin of a 'Lefaucheux' cartridge, without the former interfering with the user's line of sight.

If the arm was required as a muzzle loader, a steel chamber piece was to be provided to fill the space taken by the cartridge case and the hole for the pin. The chamber piece was to be bored through at its rear to communicate with a channel in the breech block which terminated in a nipple. Upon this a common cap was to be placed and struck by the same striker as was used for the pin fire, and which was made to swivel back the necessary few degrees.

The final patent of the Walsh quartet involves, like the first two, another radical re-appraisal of the breech loading gun. This time it is a drop down gun that is shown, but with the hinge pin directly beneath the action face

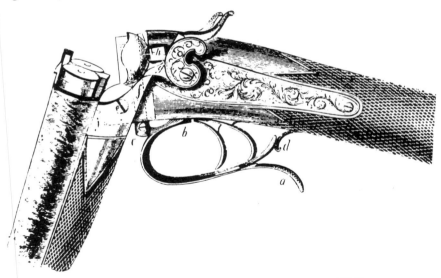

Walsh patent gun with hinge under action face no. 516 of 1866

(Patent No. 519 of 20 February 1866). Beyond our period, Walsh was to pursue this idea further with another patent, No. 5106 of 13 December 1878, for a hammerless version, which is much more widely described in the literature of the day, and was made in at least limited numbers by Blands. We have been fortunate enough to be able to study a prototype of this hammerless gun, which very closely resembles the earlier hammered model. All we know of the latter is the patent specification and the rather nice engraving in *British Rural Sports* (seventh edition of 1867) which we reproduce.

We know from his writings that, at this date, Walsh was convinced of the necessity for a top connection, a form of which was to be the sole bolting on these guns. A U shaped projection from the top rib drops into a recess formed for it in the top of the standing breech. The locking bolt is a vertically sliding rod which enters the projection and locks the gun shut. The bolt is worked by a lever round the trigger guard that has to be drawn up to the stock to pull down the locking bolt. The snap spring is a helix round the bolt. All in all the hammerless gun is a strange and peculiarly awkward gun to use, and such characteristics must have been shared by its hammered forebearer. This might explain why it appears to have been shunned by the gun trade, for its inventor states in *British Rural Sports* that it was available for examination at 'Mr Morris's, Engineer, 21 Rathbone Place, Oxford Street'.

This design had a very important self cocking feature and a less important extractor, which we will return to later.

An idea that obviously harks back to the way a muzzle loader was built, but may well have come down via the success and publicity given to the Dougall Lockfast action, was to have a sliding plug that projected from the action face and entered the breeches of the barrels. That this idea excited some interest we can gauge from the three patents which embody it. Again it is solely as a result of the patent specifications that we know anything of these three guns, as we have been unable to discover any mention of them existing anywhere else. This is not entirely surprising for, despite the idea having the advantage of achieving the very small headspace condition, as described in connection with the Dougall Lockfast, we feel that this trio would not have been the easiest to make, being rather susceptible to wear, and then expensive to tighten.

The first of this little group is the patent of George Edward Lewis, gunmaker, Henry Walker, machinist, and Joseph Blout Wayne, also a machinist, all of Birmingham. Unfortunately no more specific address is quoted, but it is almost certain that this was the G. E. Lewis who founded the famous firm, now in Loveday Street, that turned out some particularly fine and well known work. We reproduce a portrait of the founder, who was, at this time, a talented gun engraver, judging by some of his specimen plates, used when seeking work, which we were privileged to examine by courtesy of his grandson, the present head of the firm. Externally this

176

George Lewis

would have been another gun which would have looked very like a Needham, in that it had a forward facing side lever. We have found several uncommon guns with this style of lever, and would therefore remark that enthusiasts should not dismiss apparent Needhams too lightly, as one first thought to be one such might well turn out to be something very much more unusual.

Shown in the Lewis, Walker and Wayne patent which is No. 2100 of 25 August 1863, is the stripped action of a bar in the wood pin fire with a large standing breech. This latter feature is the result of the need to accommodate the action at this point. The side lever works a stout transverse spindle, cut away to form two cams, which work the plugs when the spindle and lever are partially rotated.

It is of some interest that we note that the next gun in this small subgroup, that of Samuel Mathews, Patent No. 752 of 24 March 1864, uses, in one version at least, the lever work that he protected in his earlier single sliding bolt snap action. Now he proposes to withdraw the plugs from the chambers of a double or single barrelled gun by connecting his top lever to a strong yoke in the standing breech to which the plugs are screwed. This second Mathews patent is again a very long one. It contains another version of a sliding plug locking pivoted breech loader, in which the sliding plugs are controlled by a rocking lever hung on a transverse pivot in the top strap. The front end of this lever carries a curved downward projection which, since the curves are arcs drawn on the same centre as the lever pivots, can enter a curved slot in the standing breech and, in doing so, cam forwards the plugs. These are withdrawn by the rear end of the rocking

177

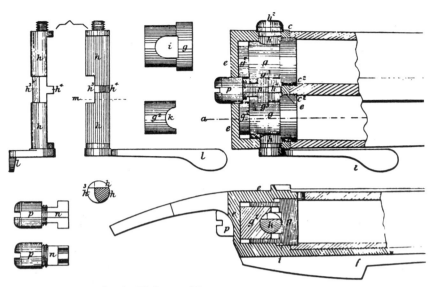

Lewis, Walker and Wayne patent no. 2100 of 1863

lever which, as it is forced down, acts on a curved incline cut in a strong slide under the top strap. This slide in the standing breech branches to become a yoke into which both plugs are screwed. Exactly how the rocking lever was to be worked is not shown in the specification.

Again, like the first patent of Mr Mathews, these two ideas are shown incorporated in what appear to be martial arms, as well as other designs solely for such weapons. If all this were not enough there is a scheme for converting a pin fire breech loader into a muzzle loader with a sort of expanding plug which, when screwed up in the chamber, expands to produce a sealed joint, rather like the device now used to test drains, by which the outfall is sealed, and the system filled with water to test for leaks. The Mathews plug had a nipple that was to go out of the hole for the pin in a

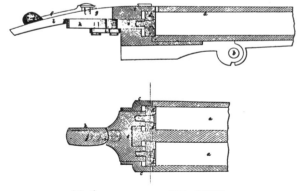

Mathews patent no. 752 of 1864

pin fire barrel, upon which a percussion cap was to be placed. Presumably to be used in conjunction with this device, the patent also protects a telescopic ram rod!

A very much simpler specification is that of Robert Townsend, who gives his address as 13 King Henry Street, Ball's Pond, Middlesex, but no hint of his profession. His patent is No. 922 of 18 March 1868. Again we have plugs, which are to be moved by cams in the standing breech, made as part of a transverse spindle worked by a side lever. There is the slight difference in that the lever is made to curve to the rear round the hammer on the right of a centre fire gun. Also there is the novelty of making the transverse spindle so that it acts on the firing pins in such a way that the latter can only move when the gun is properly closed.

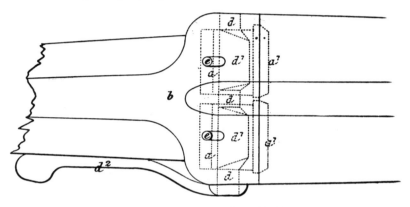

Townsend patent no. 922 of 1868

One further gun of this general type which, while it was not the subject of a patent, was in fact sold in Great Britain, demands inclusion. As to the date of its sale we cannot be certain, but the fact that a description is included in the first edition of J. H. Walsh's *Shotgun and Sporting Rifle*, but ommitted from the second, would seem to indicate a date of about 1859.

This gun differs from those of this class previously described in that the plugs have cut on them male threads, and are made to rotate as they enter the chambers, which are female threads to receive them. The rotation is given to the plugs by a thumb lever on the bottom right of the gun which is drawn up round the action to close. This thumb lever is the projecting portion of a cog in the action, which meshes with teeth formed on the rear enclosed part of the plugs. The specimen we have knowledge of carries the name H. Dickinson, Minories, London, and has Belgian proof marks. It is also of a decidedly continental appearance which would indicate that it was probably totally made in Belgium.

Yet further evidence of the difficulty of drawing a distinct line between the shotgun and rifle actions is a gun that our researches have uncovered.

H. Dickinson gun with screw plugs into chambers

This is simply a single barrel shotgun built on the Alexander Henry patent No. 1071 of 17 April 1865 which we considered in part in Chapters 8 and 12. Some of the history of this gun can be guessed from the fact that, while the gun carries the inscription 'Stephen Grant 67a St James's' on its barrel, under the barrel in small script is 'A H 3803'. Why it was built is more difficult to assess' beyond it being possibly the whim of a rich Victorian.

In some respects it may appear odd that the French seem never to have accepted the pivot opening Lefaucheux gun as the complete answer to the needs of the sportsman. That fixed barrel guns continued to be devised may be in part ascribed to the legacy of the success of the Pauly and Robert guns. We feel this is a possible explanation as to why one Charles Auguste Concalon, a Registrar of 29 Boulevard St Martin, Paris, devised a shotgun

Henry gun patent no. 1071 of 1865

of this description French patent No. 44667 of 22 June 1863, which we now consider by virtue of its being the subject of a British patent No. 677 of 12 March 1863, taken out in the name of William Clark, engineer and patent agent of 53 Chancery Lane. What is described is a gun with a breech block that is pivoted at its rear end between the hammers, hinged back to expose the ends of the barrels. The handle by which the block is to be opened is a spring loaded device that folds into the right hand side of the breech block and looks a very neat little arrangement. The extractor for such a design presents something of a problem, and we will return to this aspect in Chapter 12.

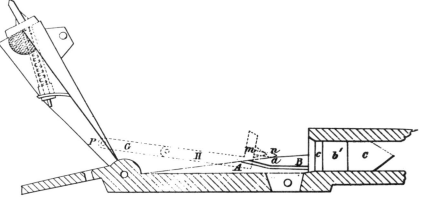

Clark patent no. 677 of 1863

In Chapter 5 we noted the ideas of Henry Allen that were embodied in his patent No. 3097 of 1870 for slide and tilt guns. In fact the main content of this patent concerned a gun, in which the barrels were to be fixed to the stock, and the breech opened for loading by means of a block pivoted at its rear that had to be lifted back to reveal the open ends of the breeches, very like the Concalon gun. In a way that is not clear from the patent drawing, which again is our sole source of information on this gun, the lockwork was to be incorporated in some way in this breech block. The drawing is far more concerned with the way in which the block was to be held shut. This was by the ingenious use of the rear of the opening handle, which was to be pivoted at its front end on the breech block. The back part of this handle was to be so shaped that it filled the angle between the block and the top strap. In this way the block was prevented from moving except when the lever was raised. Further security was to be provided by a projection analagous to a barrel lump that dropped into a recess below and behind the breech face. This patent covers yet further features of extraction and retracting firing pins, and we shall therefore return to it in due course.

This assorted group of ideas thus encompasses all the more sweeping 'revisions' of the sporting gun. We wonder if their inventors could have

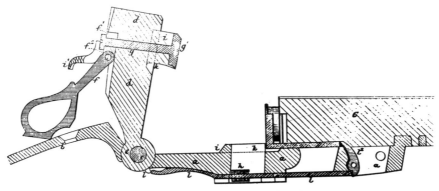

H. Allen patent no. 3097 of 1870

really had very high hopes of them, or did they realise that the longer the
drop down gun bolted by barrel lumps was made and used, so the greater
would be the inertia of sportsmen and gunmakers alike. If an excellent,
cheap-to-make gun, radically different from the Lefaucheux, had appeared
very soon after it, then the whole course of the British shotgun might have
been changed. Perhaps something like the French Darne might have
evolved, instead of the pivot open gun. In the event, the basic virtues of the
Lefaucheux, primarily its ease and safety of manipulation, rapidly
compounded by the sportsman's familiarity, were over-riding, and the
inventors' ingenuity was best employed in solving the teething troubles of a
sound idea, rather than in starting up fresh hares to chase.

Chapter Twelve

THE GADGETRY OF THE CENTRE FIRE

With the resolving, in the Daw versus Eley litigation, as to whether the centre fire system was public property or not, the principle rapidly gained popular acceptance. One of the sources from which we can now gauge this is the list of published results of the live pigeon trap shooting events, which include, with the competitor's name, a note of the make and ignition system of his gun. And, while there remained a considerable proportion of entrants loyal to the muzzle loader, especially for longer range handicaps, it was noticeable by the season of 1869 that the shooters who used a breech loader had almost exclusively adopted the centre fire.

This ever increasing adoption of the new system added further fuel to the furnace of invention. The two essential additional components required by a centre fire shotgun, that is when it is compared with a pin fire, are a firing pin and an extractor. The enormous amount of inventive effort that was expended on these two features was remarkable in itself, and further evidence of the restless character of the period. Yet again we are forced to attempt a classification of these ideas, and once more rigid delineation is not completely possible.

Since, in the sequence of the normal use of a gun, the first of these two additions that is needed is the firing pin, we feel that it is logical to start with a consideration of this. There are three patents which can be regarded simply as attempts to improve the gun Daw was making. The earliest of these is the E. C. Hodges patent No. 3113 of 4 December 1865, which had as its purpose the idea of a striker that moved in the exact axis of the bore and so would deliver, in theory at least, the most advantageous blow to the cap. This was done with a two piece striker, the final horizontal portion being urged forwards by an obliquely set driver that was struck by the hammer. To secure the retraction of the pin and striker, a spiral spring is shown, acting in front of the striker proper.

The William Spinks Riley patent, No. 491 of 16 February 1866, is also concerned with an improvement to firing pins, along with extractors and loaded indicators, which we will consider later. The firing pin was a one piece design, like the Schneider, and, like the latter, delivered an oblique blow. It had the improvement of a large diameter head, which was found to be better able to resist the constant battering of the hammer, and each pin was retained by a small screw set transversely in the standing breech. For retraction a spiral spring was used.

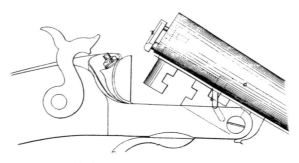

Hodges patent no. 3113 of 1865

Since his provisional specification is without illustration, the modification on this theme patented on 25 June 1866, No. 1691, by Thomas Prosper Saville, is difficult to visualise clearly. But what the inventor, who is best remembered for his latch bolt single bite snap action, seems to be concerned with, is the danger of the firing pins flying out as the gun is fired. To make the centre fire safer, he therefore proposed shields rather like those of a muzzle loader to protect the user from his coil sprung pins, which were to be inserted from the action face and held in place by threaded bosses. The Bissell which had preceded it (Patent No. 1461 of 27 May 1865) had internal strikers, but the firing pins were also disc set and used a peculiar cone shaped spring, formed from a strip of spring steel, looking rather like a clock spring, but working like a compression spring.

The pin fire had provided valuable experience in the design and construction of breech loaders. But we wonder whether, as the change to centre fire was comparatively subtle in contrast with the radical change brought about by the adoption of breech loading, the peculiar problems were not fully appreciated. In a word, the main difficulty was safety, but it manifested itself in a number of ways, and the solutions that were found for the problems reflect yet again the ingenuity of the gunmakers of the period and provide a fascinating series of inventions.

Firstly, there was the difficulty experienced by the sportsman, who had become used to seeing at a glance if his gun was loaded: with a pin fire by the protruding pin, and similarly with the percussion muzzle loader by a capped nipple. The centre fire lacked even these imperfect signs, and looked externally identical loaded or empty. While we today wonder why, particularly with a snap action, the gun couldn't be opened, checked and indeed handled broken, and only shut when it was about to be used. However, popular demand in the 1860s for visible indication of the state of the gun was such that it was bowed to, and a variety of designs were patented as a result.

Not unnaturally, one idea that was pursued was to replace by some means the visible pin on the pin fire cartridge. The first mention in a patent specification is as part of the Alexander Henry design of 1865 which we mentioned earlier. This had a stud that protruded from the action face,

184

which was pushed back when the gun was closed on a cartridge in the breech. The rear end of this stud was bevelled, so that it in turn pushed up another pin on the top of the standing breech. Mr Henry termed this visible pin 'a bolt', and in his patent, which is somehow much more human and less starchy than some, writes: 'the bolt may be made of any bright and distinguishable material so that it may quickly attract the eye of the person in whose hand the weapon may happen to be'. It is an interesting aside that the loaded indicator part of the Scott Spindle patent, No. 2752 of 1865, was the first improvement mentioned therein. This was to be a rigid pin above the firing pin, set so that it protruded from the rear of the standing breech above the firing pin, when a cartridge lay in the closed breech.

Another pin, this time on the barrel, is described in the deposition of William Spinks Riley, gun manufacturer of Birmingham. This was nothing more than a spring loaded pin, set in the top of the chamber, which was pushed up by the cartridge in the breech. This specification is also concerned with extractors which will be considered in due course.

The subject of an entire specification is the idea to the same end patented by James Purdey of Oxford Street. This specification, No. 1464 of 25 May 1866, concerns another pop up pin. Now it is an upturned end of a rocking lever set in the top of the standing breech. The forward end of this lever is automatically pushed back by the rim of a cartridge in the shotgun. Then the rear end of the lever will rise, and the pin become visible above the standing breech.

It was a pair of thumb hole action centre fire Purdeys so fitted that the Prince of Wales chose to replace his pin fire Westley Richards. These guns, now in a derelict condition, have a brass plate let into the stocks, on which it is recorded that they were passed to gamekeepers on the Royal Estate at Sandringham, who wore them out, but that they were returned to their original owner at the instigation of Mr Jackson who was the head gamekeeper at Sandringham, at the end of the nineteenth century.

One of a pair of James Purdey & Sons guns 7712/3 with Purdey patent loaded indicators of 1866. Made for H.R.H. Prince Albert Edward in 1867.

H.R.H. The Prince of Wales in Windsor Great Park in 1867 with one of the pair of centre fire Purdeys

The second group into which the loaded indicators naturally divide are those in which the pseudo pin fire pin is replaced by the word 'LOADED', which is made to appear when a cartridge is in the breech. The first of these to be patented, and in the authors' experience the best known, is another invention of Thomas Horsley. In his patent, No. 710 of 2 March 1868, and on guns built to this design, the top of the standing breech is formed as a simple curve and two curved shutters, one for each barrel, are made to fit over it. The shutter has a stem that is pivoted down in the standing breech. A spring loaded piston, that acts part way up on this stem, protrudes from the action face above the firing pin. When the piston is pushed back by a cartridge in the closed gun, the shutter moves back to reveal the word 'Loaded' inlaid in gold on the standing breech.

A similar idea is also contained in the Hanson patent that embodied the snap action previously described. (Patent No. 2657 of 1868). This time the display was to be on the top rib of the barrels. A spring loaded slide is shown that is pushed forwards by the rim of a cartridge in the breech. The word 'Load' then shows in very small script through an aperture in the rib.

We must infer that the inventors' customers were not very impressed with this idea for, on the few Hanson patent action guns that we have found, while they incorporate a loaded indicator, it is a pop up pin of the Henry type.

The object of a patent on a similar idea was the William Powell design, No. 1055 of 7 April 1869. This time the inscription is on the firing pins, and

186

we have found both actual specimens and a description in *The Field*, all of William Powell guns. These loaded indicators appear on the modification of the lifting lever design, patented in 1864.

We feel that this group can be looked upon as frivolous, to a certain extent, indeed they were not universally applied by their patentees on the guns they made, perhaps showing that at least some sportsmen of the time felt as we do.

Far more serious was the tendency of some of the early centre fires to set off their cartridges as the gun was closed. At least one death resulted from this. Sir Hedworth Williamson and Colonel Harrison of the Indian Army and a party were out shooting on Rimside Moor in the neighbourhood of Alnwick. Sir Hedworth Williamson was showing Colonel Harrison a centre fire gun, made on an improved principle, when it accidently exploded – the contents were lodged in one of the Colonel's legs, which was fearfully shattered. He never rallied. It was proved at the inquest that Colonel Charles Harrison's death was caused by the explosion of a central fire cartridge immediately on locking the gun. There were also many narrow escapes, and even more nasty frights. These unpleasant happenings had a variety of origins. The most fundamental was that it had become very common to reload fired cases, it being far easier with a centre fire than the fiddling process necessary with a pin fire. If the reloader left the caps proud of the cartridge head they might fire as the gun was closed.

It was suggested at the time that Eley's were making their caps unduly sensitive, and, while no proof or rebuttal of these suggestions can now be found, it seems a very plausible idea. There was undoubtedly considerable rivalry, if not actual enmity, between Daw and Eley's over the law suit. Eley's certainly had a period when their caps were more prone to misfire, and so compared unfavourably with the Daw, therefore the theory that they went too far in correcting this sounds very reasonable.

By far the greatest cause of these accidents was the practice of loading with hammers down. What happened was, that, if the firing pins were on the short side and the mainsprings in the locks were relatively weak, in the heat of the moment and the excitement of the shooting field, it was possible to fire the gun, open it, extract the spent case and replace it with a live cartridge. Then in the act of slamming the gun shut, the protruding pins might well fire the cartridge.

To prevent this the obvious answer was to make the firing pins of such a length that, even if the gun were opened with its hammers down, the pins would protrude even further, when the resistance of the cartridge was removed, so that it was impossible to close the breech. If, in addition to longer strikers, the lock mainsprings were made stronger, the firing pins would be driven deep into the caps, and so the only way to open the gun would be to manipulate it correctly, that is half cock the locks before attempting to open the barrels. Then with the pressure off them, if a spiral spring were incorporated with the firing pins, they should then retract behind the face of the breech. Surprisingly this latter concept met with considerable opposition, it being widely argued that the firing pin/spring assembly was liable to clog and rust up. This must presume an almost incredibly slovenly level of gun cleaning, but, when an authority of the standing of Walsh of *The Field* consistently advised that a centre fire only needed cleaning once a season, it is perhaps a fair reflection of contemporary practice.

To make sure that the strikers were retracted, the gunmakers devised various ways in which the firing pins could be mechanically levered back. Yet again the first example is French, in the shape of patent No 2744 of 11 October 1862, granted to the patent agent R. A. Brooman, as a result of a communication from Louis Julien Gastinne of Paris. L. J. Gastinne was the founder of the famous Parisian gunmaking firm of Gastinne Renette, which is still in existence, and which he created in 1835, by marrying the daughter of Albert Renette. The patents describe, in addition to this retracting firing pin, an extractor which we will consider later. The firing pin is of complex shape with a portion that slides in the head of the stock, in a plane parallel to the axis of the barrels, and the rest of the striker projects

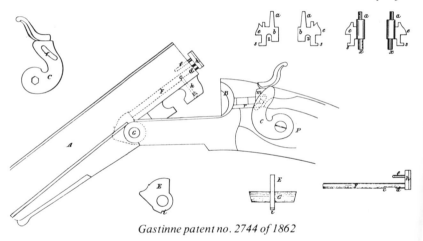

Gastinne patent no. 2744 of 1862

laterally above the top of the lock plates. Here it fits into a slightly curved slot on the inside face of the hammer. By this means the firing pin is both driven forwards as the lock is tripped, and retracted as the cock is drawn back.

The idea of a slot on the inside face of the hammer, which controlled the firing pin, is repeated on other patents, three of which bear close resemblance to the Gastinne. Firstly, there is part of the Purdey patent No. 424 of 1865, which is concerned with the rocking bolt locking system. The Purdey firing pin is simpler in shape, and is the best known part of this patent specification, it being found on sliding bolt snap action guns and not confined to this obscure locking patent.

188

The second patented design was that of Charles Harvey of 27 Pall Mall, No. 1793 of 7 July 1866. Since this is also the address of Wilkinson & Son, gunmakers, who used this invention, we may assume that Charles Harvey was, in some way, connected with the firm, perhaps as an employee.

Harvey patent no. 1793 of 1866. Wilkinson & Son gun with Harvey patent retracting firing pins

Also very similar is the final section of the Hanson patent, No 2657 of 26 August 1868. Once again we are reminded of Walsh's words: 'No law proceedings could possibly separate them.'

The idea of the firing pins linked to the hammers was explored in several other ways. Most basic of all was the design that Alfred Lancaster patented on 3 June 1865, No. 1525. Alfred Lancaster was a son of the Charles Lancaster who founded the famous London business. In 1859, Alfred set up on his own at 27 South Audley Street, and the Lancaster businesses were united in 1890 when H. A. A. Thorn, who had purchased the original business and the right to the Lancaster name, bought this off-shoot.

The concept that concerns us here was to pivot the firing pins on the hammer noses, and then to have the pins act through a cone shaped opening in the standing breech. A glance at the results of *The Field* Trial of 1866 shows several entrants using this gun, whether it incorporated the entire patent, which included an extractor, or merely parts of the patent, the published results do not disclose.

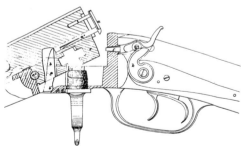

A. Lancaster patent no. 1525 of 1865

A less well known firing pin and hammer combination bears a great deal of resemblance to the one described above. The details of it are contained in another patent of the London maker Frank Emsdorff Walker, No. 981 of 5 April 1866. This time the hammers have rigid points formed on their noses which strike the cap.

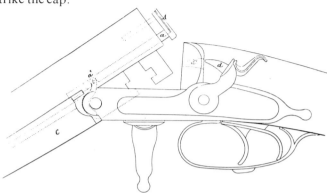

Walker patent no. 981 of 1866

An equally basic idea was that which William Wellington Greener patented on 7 March 1868, No. 800, which was to have horn-like hooks on the breasts of the hammers which drew back the firing pins. These pins had lateral projections to engage with the hooks, and were retained and guided by a slot cut lengthways in the pin, into which projected a small screw set in the standing breech. This type of firing pin, used in conjunction with a slot in the inside face of the hammer, as in the Gastinne patent, while not the subject of a single specification, is one of the most widely encountered systems of retracting firing pins. The illustrated example is on a very early gun by MacNaughton of Edinburgh, but we have also seen guns by Edge of Manchester, and Johnson of Swaffham, so equipped and suspect that it was used even more widely.

Greener patent no. 800 of 1868

MacNaughton gun with retracting firing pins

An idea that was developed in a variety of ways was somehow to retract the firing pins by a lever worked as the lock was half-cocked. Not the first, but perhaps the most basic application of this idea was contained in the Thomas Horsley patent, No 1138 of 17 April 1867. In this the breasts of the hammers had cams formed on them. These cams acted on the ends of two short levers, which were pivoted on vertical pivots, and protruded horizontally from either side of the standing breech. The inside ends of these levers worked the firing pins, and drew them back as the hammers were half cocked. This mechanism was used extensively by Horsley's, usually in association with the pull back top lever single bite snap action, and sometimes with the loaded indicator previously described. Perhaps it is not unworthy of notice that an example of the use of Horsley retracting firing pins has been encountered, is on a gun by Lyell of Aberdeen, and it is the only non-Horsley gun which we have seen using this system. With later Horsleys the system was neatened by moving the levers round towards the bottom of the standing breech, where they were less obtrusive.

A gunmaker who appears to have given considerable consideration to the question of mechanically retracting firing pins was William Rochester Pape. His deliberations resulted in three specifications left with the Patent Office. The first, No. 594 of 2 March 1867, was pursued no further than the provisional stage, and the ideas contained in it were incorporated in the second patent, this time a full specification, dated 3 September 1867, No. 2488. In this the firing pin is worked by a lever pivoted on the outside of the lockplate. The lever and the inside face of the hammer are so shaped that the movement of the hammer, as it is brought to half cock, made the two faces work together to retract the firing pin.

The third Pape patent is No. 752 of 15 March 1870 and describes a lever pivoted inside the lockplate of a bar action lock, up in the angle, where the lockplate curves round the standing breech. This lever is so positioned that, as the lock is half cocked, the tumbler pushes the bottom of the lever forwards, and the top of the lever engages with the firing pin to draw it

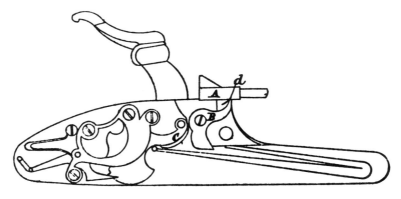

Pape patent no. 752 of 1870

back. Also included in this patent is yet another protection of the Gastinne idea of the slot on the inside face of the hammer.

Furthermore, the idea of the first part of this patent, the internal lever in the lockplate, was not new at the date of the final patent of Pape. It was contained in a patent granted the previous year, on 11 May 1869, to John Hall, gunmaker of Birmingham, No. 1436. This specification describes two internal methods of firing pin retraction. The first involves the use of a rod set almost vertically, from the top limb of the mainspring of a bar action lock to a notch cut in the bottom of the rather large diameter body of the firing pin. The lock appears to be of the rebound type which we will consider in detail later in this chapter. Suffice it to say here that immediately on firing, the lock would return to half cock and the firing pin would be forced back by the top limb of the mainspring.

The other version is more complex, and similar in some ways to the Horsley mechanism, but still totally enclosed. A short lever is hung on a

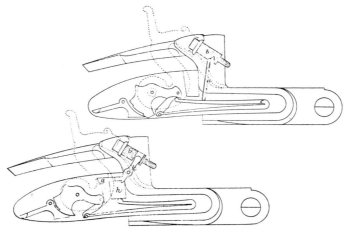

Hall's patent no. 1436 of 1869

192

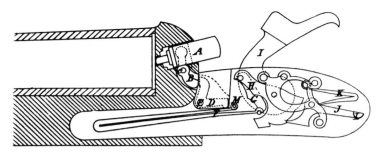

C. Golden patent no. 2980 of 1870

transverse horizontal pivot with its top end in a recess in the firing pin. The lower limb of this lever is pushed forwards by a slide acted on by the front of the tumbler so, as the lock is drawn to half cock, the firing pin is retracted.

The final member of this subgroup, the patent of Charles Golden, No. 2980 of 14 November 1870, can be thought of as a combination of both parts of the Hall patent. Like the first part, it uses a rebound lock, and the firing pin is retracted by a vertical lever on a transverse horizontal pivot in the action, like the second part. The lower half of this lever is pushed forwards by the upright limb of an L shaped lever, pivoted on the lock plate, when the horizontal limb is raised by the top arm of the mainspring on rebound.

Yet another group which, we feel, is a natural arrangement of the retracting firing pin designs, are those in which it is the act of opening the gun, and not the manipulation of the locks, that withdraws the strikers. There are but two of these. One is a modification of the Needham self half cocking action, but the subject of another patent, No. 2709 of 20 October 1865. The modification is very simple in that it involves nothing more than two flats cut on the transverse spindle through the standing breech. The firing pins have shoulders on them by which they are pushed back as the

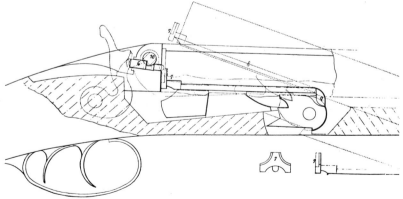

J. Needham patent no. 2709 of 1865

193

opening spindle turns. This action is thus self half cocking and retracts its firing pins in a very neat, controlled way. One of the authors (DJB) well remembers, when he first added an example of this gun to his collection that he was unaware of this feature and that it was not until he worked the action with the muzzles down, and watched the firing pins rise, that he proved its existence.

The other mechanism of this type is the Powell, again a patented modification of an earlier action patent. This new patent is No. 1055 of 7 April 1869. The addition consists of a three pronged slide in the head of the stock. The prongs are parallel and joined at the rear by a cross member. The

Powell patent no. 1055 of 1869

outer two have projections at right angles which engage with the firing pins, while the middle one is pushed back by the swing bolt, which is characteristic of the famous action. It is of interest that the drawings with this specification show modifications of the idea, to enable it to be used with Elliot, and Henry Jones patent guns. While none of these have been uncovered by our researches, we would not discount their probable existence.

The same could not be said of another part of the Allen patent, No. 3097 of 1870, which we include here, for, while it is of this general group, it is of singular design. What are proposed in the specification are moveable hammer heads that first strike the firing pins with a solid part and then, as the final part of the movement of the hammer takes place, the noses pivot slightly, so that the spring loaded pins can slip into a hollow centre of the hammer head, which, while it sounds fine on paper, we have no faith in it in practice.

Another path of development, which was aimed at resolving the danger that resulted from the practice of loading with hammers down, was to make the hammers of pin fire shape, so that they overhung the breeches of the barrels, and forced the user to half cock his locks before he could open his gun. Best known of this type are the Westley Richards guns, made on patent No. 1960 of 28 July 1866, with two piece strikers. To judge from the

194

Moore and Grey gun with internal strikers, patent no. 2743 of 1865

evidence we now have, this style appears to have been the standard Westley Richards type until the firm adopted the rebound lock.

While the idea of the overhanging cock was not the subject of a patent, it is shown in the drawing of F. H. Grey's specification No. 2743 of 24 October 1865. The main feature of this patent was the use of totally enclosed firing pins, which were struck by a suitably shaped tumbler on the inside of the lockplate. The firing pins are shown retracted, either by coil springs, or by an internal stud and curved slot arrangement. In view of the fact that the two guns of this type that we have been able to examine at all closely have been converted muzzle loaders, indeed one going so far as to have engraved on the barrel rib: 'altered to Breech Loading and Rebored by William Moore and Grey, 43, Old Bond Street, London', it is of interest that the patent specification claims: '. . . and to convert the ordinary muzzle loader into a central fire breech loader in a manner that the many parts are protected from the moisture of the atmosphere'. However, those guns known to us differ from the patent drawing to the extent that the locks, which are individually numbered, have free sliding firing pins, not the linked or sprung pattern as described above.

Also very much tied up with the conversion of muzzle loaders to breech loaders is a patent in the name of one of the most publicised exponents of this undertaking, Thomas George Sylven of Bedford Street, Strand. In his patent, which is No. 806 of 19 March 1866, he shows a centre fire gun with cocks of pin fire shape. The firing pins are two piece, the top part being driven directly down and, via an incline, forcing forwards the firing pin proper. Many years ago we were offered a muzzle loading gun by Charles

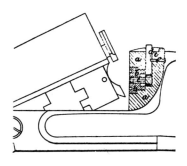

Sylven patent no. 806 of 1866

Lancaster converted in this way, which was priced at what would seem a trifling amount these days, but which, at the time, we thought much too dear.

Finally, before we leave this section, we must remark on the design of J. Jackson, patent No. 847 of 22 March 1866, in which, while the hammers are of pin fire shape, they are not formed to prevent the barrels from opening. The horizontal firing pins, which are again internal, have projections through the lock plates so that it is the breast of the hammers which drives them forwards.

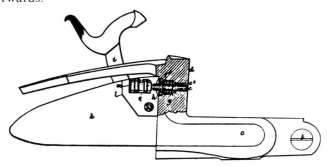

Jackson patent no. 847 of 1866

At this point we feel that it makes sense to detour from our consideration of the various solutions that were devised for the problem of loading with hammers down, and look at an aspect of the breech loader which is greatly tied up with the last set of designs.

The introduction of the centre fire, like the pin fire, and every other radical change in ammunition proposed or actual, before or since, had raised the problem that a user of such a new gun might find himself unable to obtain the ammunition his gun required. For instance, in his *Gun Patents 1864*, which we have previously noted as being largely promotional literature, George Daw includes the following statement: 'With respect to the supply of cartridges for my Central Fire Breech Loader to persons

196

residing out of Great Britain, I am in the process of appointing agents in all the great centres of our colonial empire.'

For those who did not altogether believe such blandishments, there were produced around this period a scattering of guns that would fire both pin or centre fire cartridges. Most surviving examples seem to be Westley Richards guns, and they naturally take the form of the overhanging cock centre fire previously described, and form part of the specification No. 1960 of 1866. This deposition makes the point that the layout of such a gun demands that the pin of a pin fire cartridge, if used, must be struck before the centre fire striker.

However, this was not the first mention in the records of the Patent Office. This distinction belongs to a provisional specification, No. 2030 of 4 August 1865, in the name of Thomas William Webley. This merely claims the idea, with no drawing or practical details. The greatest interest in this specification lies in the description of a species of centre fire cartridge with a dummy pin. This pin served as a loaded indicator, built into a centre fire cartridge, that was only compatible with these rather rare dual ignition guns. We would be very much inclined to consider this as a mere notion included for good measure in a provisional patent specification, were it not for the evidence that such cartridges were in fact made, and advertised in *The Field* of the time.

The idea of using both types of cartridge is also briefly mentioned in the Law and Law patent, No. 2063 of 9 August 1865. This we noted earlier in connection with the idea of using the motion of half cocking one of the locks to work the locking bolt. In addition to this there is the rather bald statement that, by forming the hammers of the appropriate shape and pin slots in the barrels, centre or pin fire cartridges can be used at will.

An ingenious approach to the question of dual ignition is contained in the illustrated provisional specification taken out by William Clark, patent agent, No. 913 of 28 March 1867 on behalf of the gunmaker, Joseph

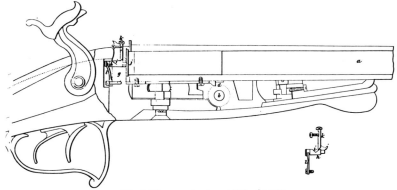

Clark/Brun patent no. 913 of 1867

Auguste César Brun, of 29 Boulevart (sic) St Martin, Paris, French patent

No. 75196 of 22 February 1867. What is shown is a striker that slides for and aft in the plane of the axis of the barrels which has, in its upper part, a V shaped slot formed. Abutting to the forward face of this V is the inclined bottom of a vertical pin so that, as this latter is driven down by the falling cock, the firing pin is driven forwards. The firing pin is to be retracted, and the striking pin raised, by a leaf spring fixed to the rear of the striker, which fixing also serves to maintain the firing pin in its correct position. If it is required to use the gun as a pin fire, the vertical pin has to be removed and could, we would imagine, be very easily lost.

The great drawback to this idea of using both pin and centre fire cartridges in the same gun is that the centre fire case had a far bigger rim than a pin fire, as one of the authors (DJB), who has tried to make pin fire cartridges from centre fire cases, knows only too well.

This point did not escape the notice of commentators of the time who pointed out that to use a pin fire in a chamber formed to accept a centre fire brought with it the risk of burst rims, and hence the fact that such cases could not be reloaded. To which we do not doubt that a practical sportsman would retort that, if he was in an area teeming with game, this was a small price to pay to keep his gun in commission.

In any event such expedients belong to the short period when the centre fire was not widely distributed. Such was the enthusiasm with which the new system was adopted that very soon cartridges for it were as well distributed as those for pin fires, and the need for these dual purpose guns ceased to exist.

To return from the diversion of the dual cartridge gun back to the problem of hammers down loading, another solution that was tried was to lift the cocks to half cock as the gun was opened. This idea does not solely belong to the early centre fire period, and has its roots back with pin fire guns, once again demonstrating that total neat categorisation of our subject is not possible. With a pin fire the advantage of such a system is that speed of use is gained by raising both locks to half cock as the gun is opened.

The best known of this group is the mechanism that forms part of the Needham specification, No. 1554 of 1862. This was originally used on pin fire guns, but was continued, and indeed saw wider use, on centre fires and had the compliment of imitation paid to it in that the same idea is incorporated in later patents of other inventors. The Needham gun, as described in the section on rotating single bite snap actions, has a spindle transversely through the standing breech turned by a forward facing side lever. On the head of this lever, and on the other end of the spindle, lifting cams are formed, which pick up projections on the breasts of the cocks so that, as the spindle is rotated to free the barrels, the cocks are lifted to the safety position. Very similar are the lifters incorporated on the Trulock, Trulock and Trulock gun, patent No. 247 of 28 January 1865, which concerns for the most part a double bite snap action which is drawn as a pin fire, and this equally applies to the W. W. Greener patent No. 2231 of 1863.

Well known as an illustration is the automatic half cocking pin fire that is the subject of Edward Harrison's specification, No. 271 of 1864. This single rotating bolt snap action has a link and lever joined to the opening lever so that, as the latter is pushed down, two rods, one under each cock nose, are pushed up. They lift the cocks clear of the pins and half cock the locks.

In contrast to the well known Needham and Harrison plans are three other means of half cocking the gun, that we know only as patent specifications. The earliest of these is yet another part of the Alexander Henry patent of 1865, no. 1071. This proposed to have two vertical levers, one on each side of the gun, with their lower ends fixed on the spindle that carried the central lever, which drew back the single sliding locking bolt. These external levers were to force back the external hammers as the gun was opened. In fact these external hammers were themselves cocking levers to control the internal tumbler striker works, very like the later Grey gun previously described.

By coincidence, the next automatic half cocking gun in order of appearance is also an internal striker design with external cocking levers. This time the inventor is the gunmaker Thomas Bissell, of 75 Tooley Street, London, patent No. 1461 of 27 May 1865. This trio of internal striker guns, the Henry, Bissell and Grey are considered by some to be the first stirrings of movement towards hammerless guns which was to burst forth in the next decade, but we wonder if this is not an illusion caused by hindsight.

What is shown on the Bissell specification is a double grip action of the Henry Jones type with a projection on the opening lever at the point where this curves away from the bottom of the gun. This projection is a cam to lower the bottom end of two rocking levers. The upper end of the second lever pushes back the tumblers. In fact an example of a gun built on this

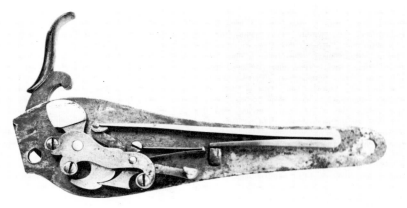

Lock from Bissell gun, to show internal striker patent no. 1461 of 1865

specification is known but it does not incorporate, or show any signs of ever having incorporated, this part of the specification. A clue as to why may be the fact that the head of the stock of this gun was badly shattered, the wood being removed to such a degree in order to accommodate the internal mechanisms that it was seriously weakened. Therefore, we feel it is reasonable to suggest that this half cocking mechanism, which required yet more wood to be removed, was not really feasible in practice.

The final member of this trio of designs is part of the Russ Hammond and Hammond patent, No. 2904 of 1869, for the double bite snap action in which one grip was a rotating cam, the other a sliding bolt worked by the cam. The rear of this bolt is shown bearing against one of a pair of levers, set vertically in the head of the action, and pivoted below the slide. The upper end of the lever acts on a shoulder, or in a slot, in the firing pin so that, as the opening bolt pushes back the lever, the firing pin is withdrawn and this, in turn, pushes back the hammer to the half cock position. Again, with this gun, the only example encountered lacks this part of the patent.

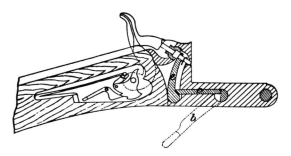

Russ, Hammond and Hammond patent no. 2904 of 1869

Something like a decade later, in the mid 1870s, these designs had an echo in a spate of automatic full cocking mechanisms. These were produced in an attempt to gain the advantage of speed of manipulation that the hammerless gun enjoyed, while yet retaining the external hammers which were a feature that a proportion of sportsmen were loathe to give up.

While various mechanisms we have considered so far in this chapter were effective enough, they were never universally employed. Taking this most acid of tests as our criterion, the complete answer to the danger, inherent in the hammers down loading, lay in the adoption of what is termed, now as then, the rebound lock. In such a lock, the hammer rests at only two positions either full cock or half cock, to which latter position it returns instantly, after striking the firing pin. In view of the mass of inventions we have considered earlier, it is remarkable that so few variants of this idea are found, especially as it became so widely employed. The honour of being the originators of this idea rests, on the basis of their patent, No. 2287 of 6 September 1866, with two Aston men, William Poole Bardell, gun finisher, and William Powell, gun lock maker. The drawing in their patent shows a bar action lock with a heavier than usual sear spring. Pivoted on the inside

200

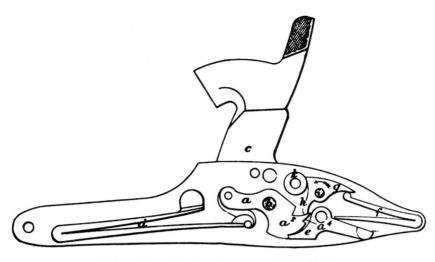

W. Bardell and W. Powell patent no. 2287 of 1866

of the lock plate is a triangular lever hung at its apex and so positioned that, as the tumbler reaches its fired position, it lifts the forward corner of the triangular lever. The rear corner is then forced down onto the top limb of the sear spring which it compresses. This, in reaction, flicks back the tumbler to the extent that the sear nose catches in the half cock bent.

However, the credit for the type of lock that was to see the universal use mentioned earlier, lies with John Stanton, a gun lock maker, who gives his address on his three specifications as 13 Clifton Street, Wolverhampton. His first specification, which is but a provisional, uses an external auxiliary rebound spring which is compressed by a projection on the breast of the hammer and in turn lifts the hammer back to half cock. His specification is No. 49 of 8 January 1867. Just over a month later, on 9 February, he obtained a second patent, No. 367, in which the rebound is brought about by the mainspring of the lock. This spring, in a bar action lock, has a lengthened top limb off which the tumbler bounces. The tumbler has a 'nose' or projection formed on it for this purpose. The idea also applied to back action locks, when it was the lower limb of the spring that effected the rebound. It was this system which was to see such vast acceptance, both on new guns and on existing converted locks. The improvement was of such value and convenience, and the conversion so simple, that this is one of the commonest conversions seen. Some are painfully obvious amid the beautifully made original lock parts. A rough new mainspring and tumbler offend the eye. Others are so well done that it is only when the date of the gun is known by other means that it is realised that they must be conversions. This is one of the classic traps into which it is so easy to fall when attempting to put an exact date to a gun, and it should always be borne in mind.

201

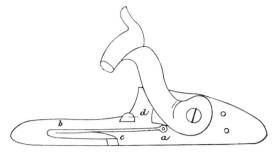

J. Stanton patent no. 49 of 1867

J. Stanton patent no. 367 of 1867

Stanton patent no. 3774 of 1869

Amid this clutch of Stanton patents is a rebound lock patent in the name of Thomas Rigby. This is not a member of the famous London and Dublin gunmaking family but a 'gun lock maker of Bradmore, Nr Wolverhampton'. This provisional specification, No. 332 of 6 February 1867, would appear to be identical to the Stanton patent described above, which it predates by three days, and, if the matter had come to law it would seem to us to have been capable of nullifying the Stanton.

This is but speculation, in fact there is yet another Stanton rebound lock patent, No. 3774 of 30 December 1869. In this the bearings are reversed in that, in a bar action lock, it is the lower limb of the mainspring which causes the rebound, and in a back action lock, the upper. The most noticeable feature of this lock is the curved spring, which terminates as a roller working on a claw of the tumbler. But the rebound is caused by a projection from the tumbler striking the mainspring as the tumbler reaches the fired position. This then is a very distinctive lock and while examples of it are sometimes met with it is nothing like as common as the second patent of 1867. Therefore it is puzzling why it is 1869 which is so frequently quoted in technical literature as the date of the Stanton Patent.

The virtues of the rebound lock, its safety and convenience were perceived almost at once, and favourable notices began to appear in the Sporting Press. For instance, a letter in *The Field* of 30 November 1867 written by a gentleman who signed himself 'Shot' ran '. . . a safer and better principle made by Woodward, late Moore, of St James's', and the next week, in an editorial on *'Accidents with Centre Fire Breech Loaders'* we read of the advantages of the Woodward gun fitted with rebound locks

From these we must infer that it was Woodward's who were the first London firm to recognise the value of the new lock, and presume they were using the second pattern of 1867.

It is, we feel, one of the more remarkable features of our story that so simple a piece of mechanism as a cartridge extractor should have called forth so much thought and ingenuity and that, in the period 1850-70, there should have been no less than 40 patents, or parts of patents, devoted to this single aspect of the gun. As always it is our endeavour to arrange the mass of material in as logical a way as possible, and this is naturally easier if the basic facts and problems are first understood.

The extractor was needed with the centre fire gun because this system, like the pin fire, left a cartridge case in the breech to be removed before the gun could be reloaded. The removal of this case from a pin fire was supposed to be done by grasping the pin and pulling out the spent case. As so often happens, things are not quite as simple as they seem in practice. Neither chamber, nor cartridge dimensions were standardised, and the early cases were much more prone to swell in damp or wet conditions. These factors, both separately and collectively, were a source of endless trouble, with cartridge cases sticking in the breech and resulted in the production of a variety of 'extractors' which the prudent sportsman took care to have with him. There is, however, one design for an extractor for a pin fire gun. It was included as part of the W. W. Greener patent, No. 2231 of 1863. In this a slide, like a saddle, on the top of the barrels is moved to the rear as the gun is opened, and is supposed to engage with the pins of the cartridges and draw them out of the chambers. The slide is worked by a lever between the barrels. This lever is pivoted just below the barrels, and on its lower end carries a rearward facing projection which bears on the action face as the gun is opened. Thus the bottom of the lever is pushed forwards and the top back.

Considering solely British developments, the first appearance of a system integral with the gun was on the Lancaster of 1856. In practice it was found that the boring of the hole through the top of the lump, between the barrel breeches, was an operation of some delicacy. For if the hole strayed and encroached too much on the wall of one barrel, a dangerous weakness was created. One solution to this was to make the stem, or pusher, of the extractor lie outside the barrels, as was done on the Daw gun. Another stratagem was to use only a shallow stem hole and to work the extractor by other means. We have, therefore, divided our mass of material into three sections, long stem, short stem and external stem extractors. In view of the priority of their appearance, we look firstly at the long stem extractors.

With the Gastinne/Bellford/Lancaster gun, it will be recalled that the cam which worked the extractor was a projection from the hinge pin. In our researches on this gun a very important discovery was found, in the remarks contained in the Gastinne/Brooman patent, referring to an improved extractor. It was thus that we learned the date of the assignation to Lancaster of this important invention, as we understand that the records of these assignations have now been destroyed. The Brooman patent, No. 2744 of 11 October 1862, merely has a rigid cam of allegedly improved shape, on the hinge pin. Such a system is also part of the Joseph and George Needham patent, No. 2709 of 20 October 1865. Similarly a rigid cam is also part of the Walker patent taken out on 5 April 1866, No. 981. This time it is formed so that the cam enters a slot in the extractor stem, so that the extractor may be removed for cleaning when the gun is taken apart. In order to simplify taking down the gun one of the first attempts to improve the flat sliding bolt for the forend, which the breech loader inherited from the muzzle loader, is included. This line of development was to be a feature of the 1870s. In the Walker patent this forend catch is a lever set in the side of the forend, which has to be turned through 90 degrees to release a cam bolt from the lug on the barrels, very like the first Hammond action.

Another fixed projection on the hinge pin is shown in the patent of Charles Pryse and Richard Redman, gun manufacturers of Birmingham, No. 1367 of 12 May 1866. The most noticeable feature of this design is the use of an extractor stem with parallel sides and a triangular top, so that it would fit in the angle between the bottoms of the barrels, and so solve the problem of boring a hole.

204

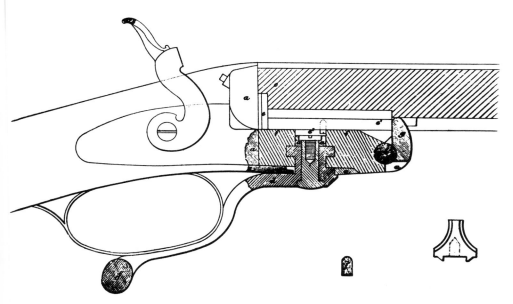

Pryse and Redman patent no. 1367 of 1866

Instead of forming the cam on the hinge pin itself, some inventors opted for a cam of sorts on the rear of the forend iron to work the sliding stem. Such is claimed by William Wheeler Cross in his patent, No. 1300 of 7 May 1866. It is also described in the Woodward and Fellows patent, No. 1489 of 29 May 1866. Thomas Woodward was a gunmaker of 10 Steelhouse Lane, Birmingham and George Fellows claimed his occupation as 'Breechloading Action Filer' and his address was Lichfield Street, also in Birmingham.

Yet another very similar example is the extractor in the Harvey patent, No. 1793 of 7 July 1866. This, like the Walker, has a release for the forend contained in the patent. Again we see a gun action resurrected, this time none other than the forward lever Lefaucheux.

Still in 1866 came a fourth variant, this time in the name of the London action filer, Edwin Charles Hodges. This was his patent, No 2996 of 15 November, for a double lever arrangement in the rear of the forend to work the extractor stem. Instead of siting the operating cam on, or just in front of, the hinge pin, given the spirit of the times, it is probably inevitable that a cam behind the hinge pin would also be tried.

Such was the extractor position on the Alfred Lancaster patent, No. 1525 of 3 June 1865. Here a vertical lever is pivoted in the front lump of a Henry Jones type action, with its top against the rear of the extractor stem, and its bottom, when the gun is closed, projecting just out of the underside of the action. As the gun is opened the lower end of the lever is pushed forwards, as it works in a slot in the bottom of the action, and so the extractor is pushed to the rear.

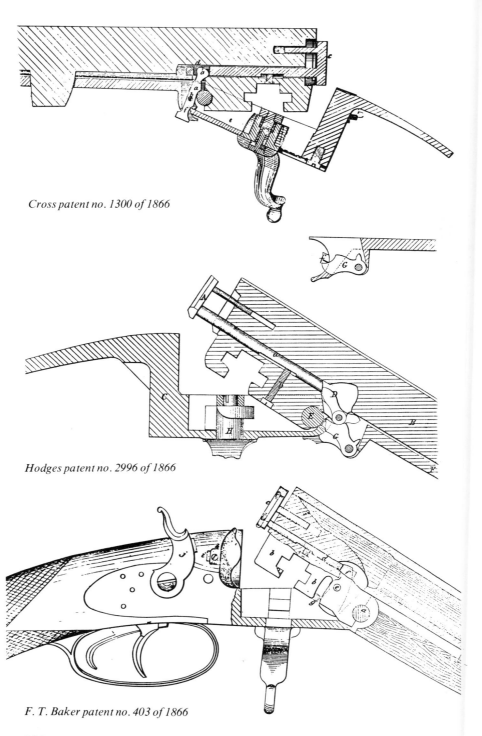

Cross patent no. 1300 of 1866

Hodges patent no. 2996 of 1866

F. T. Baker patent no. 403 of 1866

A feature of most of these patents in this section is the use of the Henry Jones double screw grip action, giving, if such were needed, further indication of the popularity and importance of his invention, which was by now (1865) public property.

One of the few that did not show it was the Stephen and Joseph Law specification, which was mainly concerned with their ideas of working a single swinging snap bolt, by the motion of half cocking one of the locks. The extractor stem they used is perhaps best described as being of medium length, as it is worked by a projection positioned about one third of the way back from the hinge pin.

Rather like the Lancaster is the Frederic Baker patent, No. 403 of 9 February 1866. Again there is a lever pivoted in the front lump of a Henry Jones action which works the extractor, but now the lever is governed by a rod through the action bar, and a slot is formed in the forward lump to receive it.

Belonging to this group is the Tranter extractor, which forms part of patent No. 2113 of 17 August 1866. Here it is the front of the swinging locking bolt which, in the open position, projects upwards, acting as the cam behind the pivot to work the extractor.

Not surprisingly the tip up breech block Henry Allen patent gun, No. 3097 of 1870, required a rather special extractor, but in fact it is not unlike this present group. As the breech block reached the open position a projection on the pivot at the rear pushed forwards a slide along the bottom of the action. This, in turn, pushed forwards the bottom limb of a lever, the top of which pushed back the extractor.

A slightly different approach was to form a slot in the action bar, which acted on a downward projection of the extractor stem in such a way that, as the gun was opened, the extractor was pushed rearwards. This is shown on two patents for long stem extractors that used enclosed stems. Firstly, it appears as a feature of the many part Alexander Henry patent of 1865, No. 1071, and secondly, it is included in E. C. Hodges' specification of the same year, No. 3113.

A very unusual extractor was proposed by T. P. Saville in his provisional specification No. 1691, in which the extraction required a separate movement by the user; a feature which would seem to have ensured its failure, when surrounded by, and preceded by automatic extractors. The proposed scheme was to have the long leg uppermost under the top rib of the barrels, and to fix to the forward end of this a tension spring so that the extractor was drawn shut. The extractor plate was to be formed up as a thumb piece by which the cartridges could be drawn out. A most unlikely arrangement.

Even if this idea was a complete non-starter, the idea was abroad of applying a spring to the extractor, and therefore we see the germ of the concept which became the ejector mechanism, which assumed such importance one or more decades on.

Actually a slightly earlier patent, that of J. Jackson, No. 847 of 22 March

1866, had presaged more accurately the idea of an ejector. What is shown on this drawing is an extractor with both legs of equal length and stoutness. Each limb was fitted into a hole that was deeper than the leg and which contained a fairly short compression coil spring. These springs forced the extractor out at all times. There was a problem with such an arrangement in that, if a tightly fitting cartridge was to be extracted, the extractor was inclined to jam as it lacked the levering out property possessed by the mechanisms so far considered, which has been found to be necessary with true ejector systems.

These remarks also apply, but with even greater force, to a seemingly flimsy little device included in the Harlow patent, No. 2326 of 1866. Here but one spring loaded leg is shown.

In fact, our 20 years included one true ejector patent, registered in the name of Charles William Lancaster, No. 112 of 16 January 1867. This provisional specification is of great interest in view of this firm's early adoption of the Needham ejector, which is regarded as the first successful true ejector. The specification now being considered is very vague and seems to apply more to a bolt action arm, probably a rifle, than a drop down shotgun. But it specified that the spent case be drawn out by an extractor before being flicked up and away by a 'kicker'. But the exact details are obscure.

The second grouping we proposed for the extractors was those which, to avoid the problem of boring a deep hole through the breeches and lumps, used some sort of short stem system.

The first of these may well be the patent obtained in 1858 by Isaac Hammond of Winchester, No. 1451 of 28 June. This is a complete specification, but is again so vague as to be almost meaningless, but we include it here because it speaks of working the extractor from the breech face. This gunmaker took out another patent early in 1859 which we have discussed in Chapter 2, which may shed some light on this.

We get to far safer ground with the Bissell design of 1865, No. 1461. Not only is there a patent drawing, but a battered example of a gun is known, and, indeed has been successfully used by one of the writers. The extractor is worked by a lever shaped like a reversed C, pivoted at its middle and set in the rear lump of yet another Henry Jones action. As the gun is opened, the bottom limb of the C is pushed forwards, and thus the top works the extractor. A minor point which should be made in passing is that this same extractor is drawn, mentioned, but not claimed, as part of the Sylven specification. Indeed it has been used on such converted muzzle loaders that we have found using the firing pin, which is the actual subject of this specification.

In the chapter on the unusual actions we covered the Walsh design with the hinge under the breech face, No. 519 of 1866, Since this gun was intended for centre fire cartridges an extractor is essential and, while this is but briefly described, we can study the hammerless version of this creation

Internal striker and patent extractor on a Bissell patent no. 1461 of 1865, by Maloch of Perth

previously mentioned. This has formed on the centre of the hinge a series of projections, something like the teeth on a sprocket which act on a series of notches on the lower stem of the extractor. In fact it is very like the extractor shown on the centre fire version of Walsh's hinged lock gun, No. 1923 of 1863. Here it is the forward end of the lock plate which is formed as the pinion, and the rack is on the stem of the extractor. There is one system for each barrel.

The final short stem extractor is the Pape, part of the two patents he obtained in 1867, No. 594 of 2 March, which is a provisional, and No. 2488 of 3 September, a full patent. The idea is simply to cut a slot in the action face which, in horizontal section, is T shaped, with the head of the T towards the rear. In this is fitted a flanged rearward projection from the extractor, so that this latter is pulled back as the gun is opened. This could only be applied to the single bite versions of the Pape action but, when used, contributed another very distinctive feature to this already individual design.

The Schneider extractor design, as was made and popularised in England by George Daw, had shown that it was not necessary to weaken the breech lump area by boring holes through it for an extractor and that the two pushers thus necessitated could lie perfectly well on the outside of the barrels. The pushers are of thin rectangular section and lie in shallow slots cut for them in the bar of the action.

Given the success and popularity of the Daw gun, it is not surprising that variants of this idea would turn up patented. The bulk of these, four designs, appeared in 1866. The first is very like the Schneider, and is contained in the Riley patent No. 491 of 10 February. In this is shown a double legged extractor with a short cylindrical guide, working in the position of the usual stem. The two long pushers terminate in thickened pointed pieces, which fit and work in two corresponding slots in the bar of the action so that, as the gun is opened, the extractor is raised.

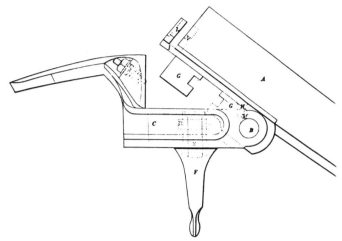

Cole and Melland patent no. 1339 of 1866

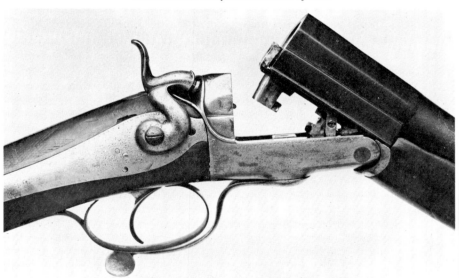

Emme extractor on a single barrel gun by Gibbs, patent no. 1460 of 1865

Two of the other designs are similar to this, and quite incredibly like each other. They are the Cole and Melland patent, No. 1339 of 10 May, and Emme's specification, No. 1460 of 25th of the same month. John Cole and

George Stephen Melland state that they were separately in business in London as gun manufacturers, at Great Portland Street, and Lime Street respectively. While John Emme of Portland Street, Soho, also in London was a breech loading action maker. Of these two the Emme is fairly well known, while the Cole and Melland is known to us solely from the patent specification. But, so similar are the mechanisms that the latter may be mistaken for the former, and is a point worth checking in a detailed examination of a gun fitted with an extractor of this design. Both have two legs that slide under the breech. The forward, down-turned, ends of the legs enter corresponding slots in the action bar. These are so shaped that the extractor is raised as the gun is opened, and drawn back as it is closed. Both specifications make the point that it is not the face of the action which pushes back the extractor. The differences are that the Emme has a short central guide rod, and the extractor is fixed in position by a screw, between the two legs, that works in a slot cut in the forward lump. The Cole and Melland has neither of these features, and is thus removeable by hand for cleaning.

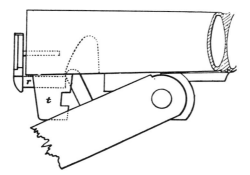

Turner and Siddons patent no. 2227 of 1866

The final design of 1866 is that of Thomas Turner Junior, gun manufacturer, and William Siddons Junior, gun lock maker, both of Birmingham. Their patent, No. 2227 of 29 August, contains a variety of extractors which have the common failing that the cam that works them is a bar projecting up from the point where the action lever of a Henry Jones gun pivots. This prong enters a slot cut between the barrels, and the short external legged extractor has a cross piece or, in another version, a slot that bears on the prong. These are the main emphasis of the patent but a version is mentioned with a hole bored through the rear lump to take a short leg extractor working in the same way.

Earlier in this chapter we described the design of Joseph Brun, which was patented in the name of the patent agent, William Clark. This was patent No. 913 of 1867, and appeared in the section on dual ignition. An additional feature of this gun was an external legged extractor very like the

Schneider or Riley type, but with the distinction of having a separate arrangement for each barrel.

Once again, as with all our other attempts to classify the designs, we are left with a residue that bears only the most tenuous resemblance to the bulk, and we feel that these designs have to be considered separately. By coincidence, the first of these is part of another French design patented in this country by the patent agent William Clark. Now we are concerned with the extractor on the lift up breech block gun of Charles Concalon, No. 677 of 1863. This part is pivoted on the underside of the breech block, just above the main pivot, so that the extractor is drawn back as the block is lifted.

Another extractor which evades our scheme is embodied in the Purdey specification, No. 424 of 1865. It adapted the slide forward Bastin style gun to centre fire cartridges. Pivoted just below the action bed, and in front of the action face, is a small spring loaded catch, over which the head of the cartridge rides as the gun is closed but which then pops up and retains the rim as the barrels slide forward. An interesting feature that is shown is to make a projecting tail on the bottom of each extractor so that, by pushing this forward, a loaded cartridge would not be extracted as the gun was opened.

Our final extractor is perhaps the oddest of all. It was the subject of patent No. 1061 of 14 April 1866, taken out in the name of the agent Henri Adrien Bonneville, a Frenchman from Vincennes, by the name of Charles Victor Plumerel, French Patent No. 76399 of 1866. What is proposed is a moveable chamber that contains the entire cartridge, and it is opened on a longitudinal hinge to remove the spent case. By this means 'the obstruction of the breech is prevented and consequently the length of time during which the arm may be fired without cleaning is increased'!

With this curious device we come to the end of an admittedly long and tedious collection of inventions. They are remarkable if only for their number and the subtle variations that were felt to be worthy of patent protection. Practical experience dealt severely with this unwieldy group and what, in fact, was most widely adopted was a long stem extractor opened by a cam on the forend or hinge pin and closed by the action face, very like the Gastinne/Lancaster prototype. And within two decades all the rest were forgotten.

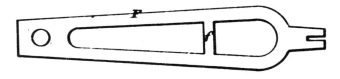

Purdey patent no. 3118 of 1870

Before we finally close this chapter of the gadgetry of the centre fire two more inventions must be considered. The first is a safety so contrived that a breech loading gun could not be fired until it was properly shut. This was another Purdey patent, No. 3118 of 28 November 1870, and is shown on the drawing, applied to a second pattern thumb hole gun. This, it will be recalled, used a bifurcated mainspring that lay on each side of the trigger work. The clever idea involved in this patent was to have a connection, between these two limbs, through a slot in the trigger blades. This slot is of such a shape that, if the snap spring is not in the fully up position, as it is when the bolt is completely forward, then the triggers are locked.

A more widely seen safety on the early breech loaders, which was in fact a device borrowed from the muzzle loaders, is the 'grip safety'. This means that the triggers are bolted, and only released when a lever under the hand of the stock is squeezed up to the stock, as in the act of firing.

In the closing days of the span of this book, on 13 December 1870, a little device was patented No. 3257 which has become so widely used that it is a pity that its inventor has been forgotten by the majority of those who use it. The invention was the snap cap, which permits the locks of a gun to be fired 'dry', that is without a live cartridge in the breech and the inventor was Alexander Henry of Edinburgh. Given that this maker was so involved with, and famous for, his rifles, the fact that he formed his cap in the shape of a rifle cartridge is not surprising. In addition to saving the lock, this cartridge had another use. By suitably impregnating the porous material of the body, both wood and paper are mentioned, it was claimed that the bore would be preserved from rust and corrosion. At the time of writing, 1976, the recent extensive advertisement of just such a cartridge proves once more the truth of this often misquoted passage from Ecclesiastes:

> The thing that hath been, it is that which shall be, and that which is done is that which shall be done and there is no new thing under the sun.

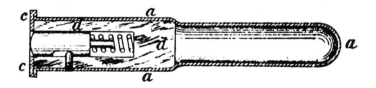

Henry snap cap patent no. 3257 of 1870

Chapter Thirteen

THE HAMMERLESS ACTIONS

It has been our deliberate intention to retain for this last chapter those gun actions which we, looking back, now regard as pointing the way in which the British shotgun was to develop. At their inception their potential was no doubt dreamed of by their inventors, for every patentee, no matter how bizarre his invention, must dream that his brainchild will achieve wide usage and he will thereby make his fortune. The Needham needle fire was considered earlier, both because of its very early production and its use of a special cartridge. For the rest, they form the one group of guns in this period that were covered in anything like adequate detail by Greener in his works. His likely reason for so doing was that they was the precursors of the then relatively new hammerless guns his firm were making. In view of this importance, and with regard to later, events there arises the question as to where the inspiration for these guns came from. Greener, writing within a few years of their production, gives us no clue, neither do the patent specifications. But it is the view of the authors that some credit for this must go to the Robert and Chateauvillard guns described in Chapter 1. One version of the Robert, it will be noted, used pin fire cartridges, thus disproving W. W. Greener's remarks about the success of the pin fire being a hindrance to the acceptance of the hammerless.

While trying to clarify this, to us interesting, question by research we came upon seemingly contradictory statements made by various contemporary authors. On the one hand, V. J. Majendie, in his description in *The Illustrated London News* of 31 August, to which we have previously referred, assures us that hammerless guns were in general use in Prussia at the date he wrote (1867). While a German author claimed that the hammerless gun was an English invention. In fact, it is our belief that both statements are in their way, correct and that the German sportsman used the early hammerless guns in some numbers, while it was the English inventors who evolved the hammerless gun as we know it today.

The first English example of a hammerless sporting gun cited by Greener is the one he describes as 'introduced by Mr Daw about 1862'. Walsh, in *The Modern Sportsman's Gun and Rifle,* also refers to an early Daw hammerless, and goes so far as to say that it was patented in 1862. It is however not mentioned in Daw's patent, No. 1594 of 27 May 1862, which is his only specification for that year. No mention is to be found in Daw's *Gun Patents* which was published in 1864 either. Its omission from this work

'Daw Hammerless' gun

may, however, be due to the fact that, in Walsh's words, 'it was a clumsy piece of mechanism and never attained any degree of popularity'.

Extensive research has not completely cleared this point. Coming back to the *Illustrated London News* passage, this highlights one of the features of the research for this book, and indeed research of all sorts that, in the pursuit of an answer to one question, so often, far from that question being solved, others are posed. Captain Majendie definitely claims that the hammerless gun, used in Prussia, was the invention of Prince Pless. Extensive enquiries among some of today's most eminent arms experts have proven totally fruitless. No one it seems has so much as heard of Prince Pless as a gun designer. The description of 'his' gun is such that we believe it could well be the gun we know simply as 'The Daw', and so we conclude, on the basis of the evidence available, that this was in fact what was in common use in Prussia and that, in some way or for some reason Majendie was misled. It is interesting that the sole example, conforming to Greener's illustration, we have been able to discover was made in Prussia.

In fact the first hammerless gun for which we have found a patent was the design of Adolphe Jean Victor Marcet, which was also the subject of a French patent, No. 59126 of 22 June 1863. In England it was patented by the agent H. A. Bonneville, No. 1752 of 13 July 1863. Overall this gun, if it were made as per the specification, which again is our only knowledge of this creation, would be something less than a really practical sporting piece. But, having said that, it contains many points of interest. The chief claim of the text is that the gun shall be hammerless or, as the rather quaint translation more accurately puts it, 'suppress the hammer or cock'.

The action is worked by a forward facing underlever which terminates at its forward end in a catch. Freeing the catch and drawing down the lever both releases the barrel bolt and,because the head of the lever has a second

215

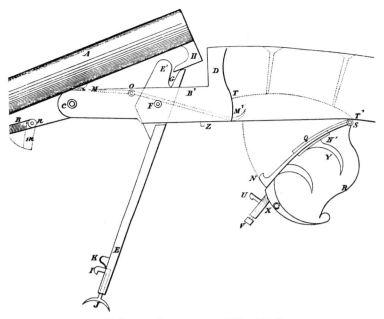

H. Bonneville patent no. 1753 of 1863

lower limb, raises the barrels as well. The travel of the lever and barrels is such that the lever and barrel lumps do not part company so that, on raising the underlever, the upper limb of the head bears down on the hook shaped barrel lump and draws the barrels back onto the action. The less practical part of this gun is that it requires a special cartridge which will fire when struck on the rim at right angles to the long axis of the cartridge. Details of this are not shown, except for a mention of a cartridge with two opposing pins, like very short pin fire pins, one of which sounds as if it is a dummy and used solely as a loaded indicator, while the other actually fired the charge. The striker is a spring with a 'head' on it, combing sear and striker, and cocked by means of an outside 'winch', whatever that may mean. The spring/striker also carries a stud, which projects beyond the bottom of the action when the gun is cocked.

The final feature of this gun, which has claimed more than its share of space, due to the mass of ideas claimed for it, is the safety arrangement, which is to have the trigger work pivoted at the rear of the guard, and with a catch at the front, so that it can hang away from the gun as a means of making the piece safe.

The probability that the hammerless shotgun found popular favour earlier on the continent of Europe is reinforced by the discovery of another British patent for a gun of this type taken out by two Belgians, Oscar Oelkers and Frederic Spengler, from Liège. The actual specification is however in the name of one René Louis Martin of Saarbruck.

216

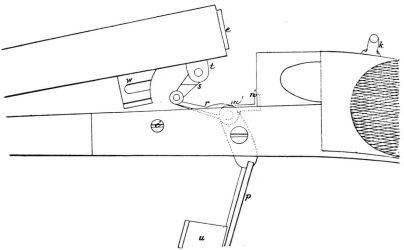

Oelkers & Spengler patent no. 3356 of 1866

The gun that was the subject of this patent, No. 3356 of 20 December 1866, has a range of features, some of which, from our present stance, we now regard as harking back at least a decade. Also this design poses another problem for our system of classification, for it is both a hammerless gun and one in which the motion of the barrels is 'slide and tilt', but we consider it here as we attach more importance to the fact that it is of the concealed hammer group.

The drawing, and again this is our only knowledge of the gun, shows a forward facing underlever which has to be pulled down and back to open the gun. The underlever is pivoted in the bar of the action, just forward of the action face, and carries on its head a double link which is joined to the rear barrel lump. The effect of this link is to move the barrels forwards until they are free of the various locking bolts, when they pivot open. The bolting of this gun is at two sites. The breeches of the barrels each have a circular projection which enters the breech, and the barrel lump has a slot cut in its rear into which slots a pin fitted across the bar of the action. To permit the back and forth movement of the barrels, the hinge pin works in a slot in the forward barrel lump.

The double link by which the underlever is jointed to the barrels allows the barrels to be closed by simply pushing up the underlever. First the barrels have to be shut by hand, and then the lever is raised, thus forcing the barrels back. In this movement the linkage is aided by a wedge, shaped as an upward projection from the lever, which acts on the front of the rear lump.

The lock work of this gun is shown as a trigger plate type with strikers pivoted to the heads of the tumblers, and it is cocked by a rod running up and back from the underlever, to which it is pivoted just forward of the main bearing. So, if the lock has been fired, the gun is cocked as it is opened.

217

This gun, as drawn, has yet two more points of interest; a safety set on the top strap which has underneath it a stop, which prevents the movement of the tumblers. This stop is put in place or removed by a quarter turn of the external lever which is shaped rather like a wing nut. An interesting claim is made for this feature, that it will impede the sight of a user of the gun should an attempt be made to fire the gun, at 'safe'.

The cartridge shown with this gun is yet another special type and is a species of centre fire with a deep rim to fit in the recess cut in the standing breech to receive the backward sliding barrels. The claim for this is that the breech is thereby made perfectly gas tight. On this point it would seem that the designers of this gun had ignored the advances made by other inventors and produced an archaic creation, Yet their lockwork would stand comparison with that in use a decade later.

An excellent example of one of the problems that confronted the authors in the preparation of this work, that of what to include and what to exclude, is the next design that we come to consider. It is one of the group that Mowbray Walker, who described himself as an engineer, and Lieutenant Colonel George Henry Money patented in 1868 on 8 January, No. 70. A study of the specifications and the drawings would lead unhesitatingly to the conclusion that the subjects were rifles, and military ones at that. This view was supported by the fact that one of the patentees was a military man. Indeed, a Money Walker rifle was included in the final short list of 10 drawn up by the Select Committee on Breech Loading Small Arms in 1868, whose deliberations were to lead to the adoption of the Martini Henry rifle for the British Armed Forces. The Money Walker failed the exposure tests and was therefore eliminated by the committee.

However this view is totally overturned by the existence of a double barrelled sporting shotgun built to one of these patterns. Nothing, unfortunately, is known of the provenance of this particular gun, but it is tempting to speculate that it was built for one of the patentees.

There are four distinct guns described in this specification but the one which we have to consider would seem to have been, in the inventors' view, the most significant of the quartet. They describe it as having a 'balanced breech' which is an illustrative term for it. It will be apparent from the photograph that the top of the breech has two chutes or channels formed in it, rather like a double Martini action, and that to open the breech the forward ends of these are depressed, again like the Martini. But, unlike the latter action, this is accomplished by lifting a lever which, when the breech is shut, lies along the top of the 'hand' of the stock. The breech mechanism thus pivots, very much like a seesaw, hence its name. It is the act of opening that also serves, if necessary, to cock the action. The bottom face of the breech block, as it rotates, forces back the hammers until the latter engage with sears formed as part of the trigger blades. The motion of the breech block also works the extractor which can be thought of as a capital letter U of angular form. This is pivoted at the bottom of the right hand limb and

218

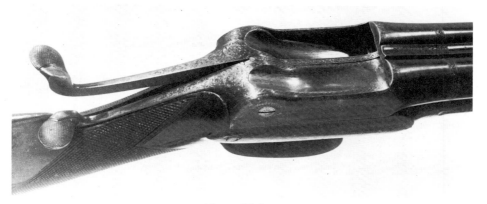

Money Walker

the whole is set at an angle in the gun action so that, as the breech block is lowered, it forces down this right hand limb and so extracts the cartridge from the chamber.

Inevitably, this is a somewhat cumbersome action, expecially as a double barrelled shotgun, which may explain why the example we have encountered was built as a 20 bore.

By an odd coincidence, the next patent registered at the Patent Office for a hammerless breech loader was also the work of a military gentleman, one Lieutenant Francis Bacon of the Royal Marine Artillery. He had a relatively short service career, mostly spent aboard HMS *Magicienne,* a second class steam frigate serving, at the period when Bacon was likely to have been with her, in the Mediterranean. It is tempting to wonder whether he may have decided to leave the sea to devote his energies to the gun with which we are now concerned. His father was Rector of Wymondham, near Oakham, and Bacon returned to live with him after he left the Navy. Lt Bacon adopted the unusual strategem of handling the promotion and distribution of his invention himself. Exactly why he did so is yet another of those points on which we must speculate. Was this his original intention or did he first offer his unusual gun to the trade and, finding no one willing to back it, decide to go it alone? What is certain is that he arranged for his gun to be made in Birmingham; again there is a tantalising blank in that we have no means of now knowing by which firm; a minute examination of existing examples gives no clue. All we can suggest is that it was probably one of the larger, more mechanised makers, as the price of finished guns was quoted in the £18–£20 bracket. To sell these guns he arranged a chain of distributors up and down the country, an advertisement in 1872 lists the following:

> Blissett of Holborn, Grant of St James's, Holland of Bond Street, Kerr of King William Street, Murcott of The Haymarket, Reilly of Oxford Street, Richards of Liverpool, Conway of Manchester, Dobson of

Louth, Hetherington of Nottingham, Gibbs of Bristol, Webb of Oxford, Hast of Colchester, Norfolk of Bury St Edmunds, Henry of Edinburgh, Playfair of Aberdeen, Truelock and Harris of Dublin, Richardson of Cork

Guns have been found bearing some of these names, and yet other specimens have no maker's name at all. These may have been retailed by some of the outlets, or may have been guns sold direct by the inventor himself for he advertised that he would send guns on approval 'against the usual references'.

The object of all this energy is a most distinctive design, being a double bolt action and the subject of two patents, No. 1260 of 17 April 1868 and No. 3242 of 10 December 1870. The former is principally, but not entirely, concerned with a single barrel version which would seem to bear out the fact that the Bacon gun was originally conceived as a rifle, presumably with an eye to service use. Indeed a Bacon was included, along with the Money Walker previously described, in the short list of the Select Committee on Breech Loading Small Arms. However, it achieved the undesirable distinction of prematurely discharging a defective cartridge, which event reinforced the committee's view of the inherent danger of all bolt action arms and so all guns of this class were eliminated from the trial. Then, when

H.M.S. Magicienne *from* The Illustrated London News

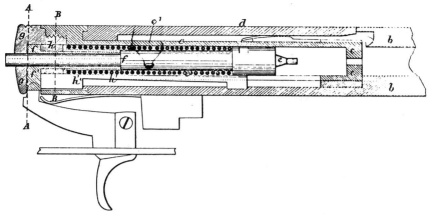

Bacon single barrel patent no. 1260 of 1868

it failed to gain official acceptance, the inventor concentrated on the 'siamese twin' version, which we know as a sporting shotgun. In this the bolt handles are at the extreme rear of the action and have to be lifted a quarter of a turn before the bolt can be drawn back. If the lock in question has been fired this motion also serves to cock it. As the handle is rotated, two inclined faces near the breech force back two projections on that inner part of the bolt which carries the striker. By this means, the striker is moved backwards and the spiral mainspring is compressed, until the sear at the rear engages. When the lock is cocked, the tail of the striker projects from the rear of the bolt. It is the first part of the bolt's rotation that cocks the lock, the final part disengages the two locking lugs at the rear of the bolt and so permits it to be drawn back. On the backward travel the bolt is guided by four surfaces, one on each side of the top piece, which is made the same shape as the outer surface of the barrels, and two more bearing surfaces on the underside. So there is very little wobble even on a well used specimen. The rearward travel of the bolt also serves to withdraw the cartridge from the chamber. A spring loaded hook on the head of each bolt catches on the cartridge rim and, when fully extracted, the cartridge, live or spent, falls through the port cut in the bottom of the stock, this being the most noticeable difference between the two patents.

The safety arrangements are a sliding catch between the tails of the bolts which, in its rearward position, prevents the movement of the lifters which work the sears.

Assembly of the barrel/bolt part of the gun with the stock/trigger work part is necessarily unusual. The undersides of the barrels have two projecting lugs, the forward one which receives a conventional flat forward sliding bolt, and a stouter one at the rear, which takes a round bolt. Both bolts slide transversely. To locate more accurately the barrels there are two studs, one either side of the rear lump, which fit into recesses in the underside of the barrels.

221

Externally it is a somewhat ungainly creation, and it suffers, as do all bolt actions, from the extra length that such a mechanism imposes on it. It is also a rather awkward and inevitably slow mechanism to use. For instance, a correspondent who called himself 'Scott' told, in a letter published in *The Field* in January 1872 of how he had a Bacon on approval and took it out shooting, when the party he was with killed over 300 head of game. His neighbour was using a snap action Purdey, and was reckoned to be able to load at twice the speed he could. He barked his knuckles a couple of times into the bargain.

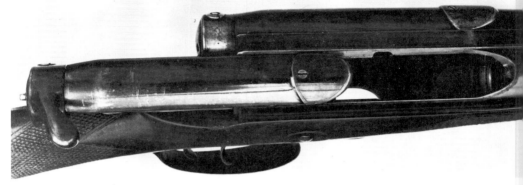

Bacon shotgun patent no. 3242 of 1870

In view of these defects, it is perhaps surprising that it received the patronage it did, for examples are now encountered commonly enough to suggest relatively wide usage. Evidently some users were well satisfied, for, in the correspondence referred to above, we find a Mr J. B. Younge of Otterbourne, nr Winchester writing: 'I have used the Bacon gun for four years and very much prefer it to any other for ease and speed of loading, hard hitting and the great advantage of the barrels being independent of each other'.

The heyday of the Bacon gun is but a few years in the very early 1870's. In 1871 his father died and he therefore had to leave the rectory at Wymondham and he moved, first to Grafham, nr Guildford, in 1872, and then to Cholsey, nr Wallingford in 1873. But in 1874 the gun was advertised by an agent, and very soon afterwards ceases to be advertised, probably a reflection of the decline in popularity caused by more conventional hammerless guns which were then gaining an ever greater share of the market. It may well be that the success of these later guns was due in some measure to the publicity gained by the Bacon gun, so that, while it was itself short lived, it helped prepare the way for the next decade.

From the evidence available it is the authors' opinion that several hundred of these guns may have been made, which represents a creditable effort on the part of Lieutenant Bacon to popularise an unconventional gun.

The final gun in this series bears out most fully our remarks at the beginning of this chapter. Although it was not a commercial success, and indeed in all our collecting and researching we have never encountered a single specimen, it most surely pointed the way ahead. This was the hammerless gun that was patented in 1868 by W. C. Green, No. 2716, dated 3 September. It was to be the prototype for the next decade, when a series of guns appeared, all of which, as Greener points out, used features borrowed from it.

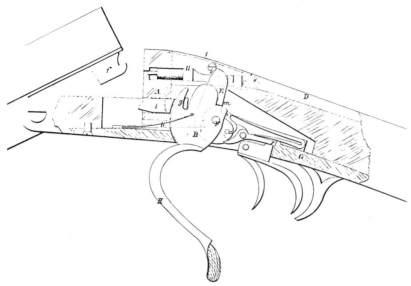

W. C. Green's hammerless gun, patent no. 2716 of 1868

Of the patentee, William Charles Green, virtually nothing seems to be traceable, and it is not known if he was part of the family of gunmakers of the same name who had businesses in Cheltenham and Gloucester. The hammerless gun he designed was cocked and opened by a push forward underlever, which was also the trigger guard. His patent drawing shows two distinct forms, one of which is also shown as a pistol. There are, in addition, two forms of safety mechanism. In both actions the lockwork is built on the trigger plate. The locks are of simple design, each being composed of a tumbler, a sear and spring, which does duty as both sear and mainspring. In the two variants of this gun the tumblers are forced back to full cock by the rear of the upper portion of the underlever. In one version, the axis on which the underlever pivots is the same as that of the tumblers. In the other these axes are separate, and the one for the lever is below and in front of the tumbler spindle. There are also shown two methods of withdrawing and forcing forward the single bite barrel locking bolt. In the version with the common centres for tumbler and lever, there is a curved slot, formed vertically in front of the top part of the underlever, which engages with a slot in the bolting lug and cams this back and forth as the lever is pushed down or pulled up. The other method has the bolt and lever hooked together as shown in the drawing. In both forms there is the spring, as shown, to lift the underlever back to its up position.

There are two sites for a safety catch, one to bolt the firing pins, the other the tumblers. Both catches are spindles set transversely in the standing breech with portions cut out so that, in one position the movement of the member is blocked, but, when the safety is rotated, the pin or tumbler can move. Both, it would seem, showed the dangerous fault that, if the sear were displaced from its bent and this fact were not noted, the gun could fire as the safety was removed.

What appears to be a variant of the above gun is described in a provisional specification, No. 3589 of 11 December 1869, also in the name of William Charles Green. This specification was declared void, 'the Patentee having neglected to file a specification in pursuance of the conditions of the Letters Patent'. As far as can be judged from this document, the gun is a minor variant of the type described above, in which tumblers and opening lever shared a common centre.

These few internal hammer guns, and the small group of what we can regard as intermediate designs, those with internal strikers but external cocking levers formed as hammers, are the seeds from which were to spring forth, in the next decades, yet another flowering of British invention, necessarily different from what we have been considering, in some ways more subtle, and yet, because they hide inside the guns where sportsmen are less disposed to probe, undeservedly less known. We feel that, in comparison with the lively interest and curiosity shown in the more obvious attractions of the hammered gun, these mechanisms, though every bit as fascinating, have suffered from a lack of appreciation. We therefore hope to stimulate a keener awareness of their qualities with our next volume.

Appendix 1

Small Arms at the 1851 Exhibition, London

GREAT BRITAIN

59 – W. Greener, Birmingham; double guns and rifles, harpoon guns, rocket gun and lines for use in shipwrecks, patent stanchion gun for wild fowl shooting, military musket and rifle; laminated steel, etc.

200 – Wilkinson & Son, 27 Pall Mall; gun, with spiral recoil spring, for wild fowl shooting, fowling pieces, rifle, etc.

203 – Witton, Daw & Co, 57 Threadneedle Street; rifles for India and Africa, fowling piece, duelling pistols.

205 – Hawker, Col P., Longparish House, near Whitchurch, Hants; a stanchion gun, with improved waterproof ignition, forged and stocked on a new principle, models of two-handed punts containing gun, gear, etc., for wild fowl shooting.

206 – Brazier, J. & R., Wolverhampton; specimens of gun manufacture; double gun-tube locks; double rifle locks, musket percussion locks, etc.

207 – Potts, T. H., Haydon Square, Minories; double barrel guns, with improved breeches, bolted triggers, etc.

209 – Moore & Grey, 78 Edgware Road; double fowling pieces, two grooved rifles and pistols.

214 – Robinson, A., 41 Whitcomb Street, Haymarket; best Damascus gun barrels.

215 – Gibbs, G., Clare Street, Bristol; improved reg. double barrel gun, with protector against wet.

216 – Beattie, J., 205 Regent Street; two-groove rifle, double gun, duelling pistols, etc.

217 – Manton & Son, 6 Dover Street, Piccadilly; double guns, double rifle, duelling pistols, etc.

218 – Needham, W. & J., 26 Piccadilly; patent self-priming gun, self-priming musket, to use the military flange cap; safety stop-lock gun, game registers, double and single guns to load at the breech, self-loading carbine.

219 – Boss, T., 73 St James's Street; a central fire double and other guns.

220 – Beckwith, H., 58 Skinner Street, Snow Hill; fowling pieces, blunderbusses, and other fire arms.

221 – Bentley & Son, 12 South Castle Street, Liverpool; double patent central fire percussion guns.

222 – Trulock & Son, 9 Dawson Street, Dublin; double bar guns, centripetal double gun, pistols, etc.

223 – Deane, Adams & Deane, 30 King William Street, EC; patent spiral raised rib rifles, patent safety stop lock guns, patent gun locks, fowling pieces, Indian and African rifles, pistols, etc.

224 – Parker, Field & Sons, 233 Holborn; fowling and rifle guns, pistols, air-gun musket, fusil, carbine, etc.

225 – Eley, W. & C., 38 Broad Street, Golden Square; illustrations of the manufacture of patent wire cartridges and percussion caps, gun wadding.

226 – Lang, J., 7 Haymarket; guns, rifles, pistols and revolvers, patent walking stick gun, with rifle and shot barrels, etc.

228 – Golding, W., 27 Davies Street, Berkeley Square (Joe Manton's old shop); double sporting gun with improvements.

230 – Woodward, J., 64 St James's Street; fowling piece with detached waterproof lock.

231 – Yeomans & Sons, 67 Chamber Street, Goodman's Fields; an assortment of muskets.

232 – Egg, H., 1 Piccadilly; self-priming and barrel copper cap fowling pieces.

233 – Fairman, 68 Jermyn Street; double cross-eyed gun, double gun in soft state, single gun, single rifle, two grooved, etc.

234 – Osborne, C., 1 Lichfield Street, Birmingham; improved central fire double guns with chain-twist barrels, bar slide, double and single guns, tube single gun, large single gun with Colonel Hawker's improved ignition, improved alarm gun, pistols, etc.

235 – Goddard, S. A., Birmingham; fowling guns, American ducking gun, pattern and common African musket, Californian protector gun, invented by the exhibitor.

236 – Rigby, W. & J., 24 Suffolk Street, Dublin; guns and rifles, double and single. rifle and revolving pistols, etc.

237 – Reilly, E. M., New Oxford Street; improved guns, rifles, pistols, air guns, etc.

238 – Davidson, D., Captain, Bombay Army; rifles and pistols with telescopic sights and bored for grooved bullets.

238A – Watkins & Hill, Charing Cross; rifle with telescope.

239 – Bull, J., Bedford; double-barrel gun, with the modern improvements.

240 – Richards, Westley & Son, Birmingham; rifles, double tiger guns, punt gun, pistols, etc.

241 – Cooper, J. R. & Co, 24 Legge Street, Birmingham; patent self-cocking pocket pistol, revolving pistols, ladies' pistols, etc.

242 – Walker, R., Graham Street, and Broad Street, Birmingham; specimens of percussion caps, metallic gun wadding, etc.

243 – Townsend, J., 11 and 12 Sand Street, Birmingham; improved rifle and walking-stick air guns.

245 – Hart, H., 54 New Canal Street, Birmingham; guns and pistols; specimens of gun barrel manufacture in every state, from the old horse-nail stubs of earliest period to the latest improvements.

246 – Brooks & Sons, 28 Russell Street, Birmingham; fowling pieces, rifles, revolving gun, military guns, South American (Buenos Ayres) and Spanish carbines, African trading guns, Dane guns, pistols, etc.

247 – Tipping & Lawden, Birmingham; illustration of gun barrel manufacture, rifles, guns, pistols, air guns, etc.

249 – Powell & Son, Carr's Lane, Birmingham; double-barrelled rifle and gun; pistols, improved safety trigger guard, pair of lock actions, etc.

250 – Winton, H., 53 Cleveland Street, Birmingham; improved safety guns.

252 – Hoskins, J., 31 Frith Street, Soho Square; double guns with safety, on a new

and simple principle.

253 – Davis, J. 1 Duke Street, North Parade, Bath; soldier's musket, substituting the blade of the bayonet for the ramrod.

255 – Fletcher, T., 161 Westgate Street, Gloucester; patent safety gun, with various improvements.

256 – Forsyth & Co, Leicester Street, Leicester Square; patent safety gun, etc., original percussion gun as invented by Forsyth, containing a reservoir of powder.

257 – Erskine, J., Newton Stewart, Scotland; two guns, newly invented to prevent accidental discharge, with complete waterproof for the cap.

258 – Rippingille, E., 87 Albany Street, Regent's Park; an improved gun lock with stock.

259 – Haswell, R., 12 Upper Ashley Street; air pistol on a new principle.

260 – Needham, H., 4 Vine Street, Regent's Park; self-priming fowling piece.

261 – Brider, J., 4 Clifton Cottages, Denmark Street, Camberwell; telescopic loading rod for firearms.

262 – Brider, L., 30 Bow Street, Covent Garden; rifle mallet for hot climates.

263 – Baker, T. K., 88 Fleet Street; improved patent gun lock for preventing accidents from fire-arms.

264 – Golden & Son, Huddersfield; Bentley's patent double gun with improved locks, etc.

265 – Webster, W., Hampstead Road; fuzee musket.

267 – Mortimer, T. E., 97 George Street, Edinburgh; double rifle, fowling piece, Highland pistols, improved conical and other balls, etc.

269 – Hodges, R. E., 44 Southampton Row; patent application of india-rubber to projectile purposes.

270 – Parsons, W., Swaffham, Norfolk; improved double guns, etc.

277 – Joyce, F. & Co, 57 Upper Thames Street; improved anti-corrosive water-proof gun caps percussion tube primers, chemically prepared gun waddings, patent wire cartridges, etc.

278 – Grainger, J. Wolverhampton; tube and bar-action gun and rifle gun locks.

280 – Gardner, W. T., 22 Mead Row, Lambeth; model of a ship's gun loaded at the breech.

281 – King, T. J., 16 Whiskin Street, Des.; pistols inlaid with gold and silver.

284 – Walker, Sarah, & Co., 12 Legge Street, Birmingham; percussion caps and patent metallic gun waddings.

287 – Squires, W., Cottage Grove, Mile End; new rifle calulated to project a ball to a great distance with a small charge.

288 – McGettrick, F., 81½ Philip Street, Kingsland Road; model of a war engine able to fire 10,900 charges of ball cartridges in 10 minutes.

297 – Cherrett, D., Grosvenor Mews, Berkeley Square; an improved two-groove rifled pistol, with invisible lock. Throws a ball 250 yards, and can be used as a pistol, or from the shoulder.

AMERICA

236 – Allen, G. F., Utica; telescopic rifle.

307 – Pecare & Smith, New York; self-locking and repeating pistols, with stocks of ivory and rosewood, mounted with steel and gold.

321 – Colt, S., Hertford; specimens of fire-arms.

328 – Robbins & Lawrence, Windsor; Vermont rifles with their various parts made to interchange.

347 – Palmer, W. R. New York; specimens of two rifles.

AUSTRIA

112 – Meyer & Co, Innsbruck; a Tyrolese rifle, exhibited for its superior qualities and cheapness.

116 – Kehlers Nephew, Prague; a pair of pistols for shooting at a target.

118 – Schamal, F., Prague; an air pistol.

119 – Micheloni, G., Milan; double barrelled fowling piece.

BELGIUM

143 – Ancion & Co, Liège; guns, muskets, pistols, rifles and other weapons.

144 – Thonet, J., Liège; gun, ornamented with gilt silver; a pair of Scotch pistols, incrusted.

145 – Lepage, Liège; complete collection of fire-arms, double-barrelled guns, rifles, holster pistols, duelling pistols, pocket pistols.

146 – Plomdeur, N., Liège; guns and pistols.

147 – Malherbe, L., Liège; double-barrelled and other guns, rifles, pistols, etc.

148 – Ledent, M., Liège; a lock for all sorts of guns.

149 – Doutrewe, F. J., Liège; a 'needle' gun.

150 – Bernemolin, N., & Brothers, Liège; double-barrelled gun and pistols.

151 – Lardinois, N. C., Liège; rifle, with accessories, Swiss style, double-barrelled with accessories, made except the barrel and locks by Mr C. Lenders.

152 – Tinlot, M., Liège; a double-barrelled gun with stock carved style Louis XI.

153 – Dehousse, Liège; guns and pistols.

154 – Falisse & Rapmann, Liège; arms and percussion caps, fire-arms, rifles, guns, pistols.

155 – Tourey, H., Liège; collection of fire-arms.

158 – Montigny & Fusnot, Brussels; three infantry guns (Montigny system).

DENMARK

14 – Jensen, N. S., Naval Arsenal, Copenhagen; a rifle with an oval barrel, to discharge a conical ball, specimen of cartridge.
(The oval bore is mentioned by Col Beaufoy, 'Schloppetaria', 1808; it was also adopted by Capt Berner, in Brunswick, 1855; and Lancaster oval bore percussion rifles were issued to our sappers and miners, about 1856).

FRANCE

58 – Bertonnet, Paris; guns of several kinds, damasked and carved rifle guns, drawing room pistol; pistol with carved barrel, etc.

166 – Devisme, Paris; muskets, various fire and side arms, patented.

215 – Flobert, Paris; guns, muskets and pistols, patented.

418 – Berger, F., St Etienne; fancy fowling pieces of various kinds.

491 – Dandoy-Maillard, Lucq, & Co, Mauberge; military weapons.

509 – Fontenau, F., Nantes; percussion gun, with under box and a safety hammer.

519 – Gevelot & Lemaire, Paris; percussion caps.

618 – Mathieu, L., Paris; fire-arms.

947 – Peigne, V. J., Nort; new self-priming gun.

1133 – Caron, A., Paris; a Parisian and other guns and pistols.

228

1158 – Claudin, Paris; guns and pistols of a new construction.

1251 – Goddet, A., Paris; pistol and fowling piece with two and four barrels.

1308 – Lefaucheux, Paris; different sorts of guns.

1364 – Moutier le Page, Paris; guns, carbines, pistols, swords, etc.

1451 – Ronchard-Siauve, St Etienne; double-barrel gun, 15 shades.

1546 – Beringer, B., Paris; five fowling pieces of various prices.

1547 – Bernard, L., Passy; Damascus gun and pistol barrels.

1611 – Gastinne-Renette, Paris; guns, carbine, unfinished gun barrels, pistols (for practice) in their cases, and small fancy pistols; model of a machine to load pistols and serving as a meter.

1628 – Houiller, B., Paris; a box of pistols.

1681 – Prelat, Paris; brace of pistols with carved and chased gold mountings, five-barrelled pistols (charges fired separately).

1712 – Duclos, J., Paris; six guns and 12 pistols.

1724 – Lagreze, Paris; five guns.

GERMANY

60 – Gehrmann, T., Berlin; priming pin rifle gun, rifle, double-barrelled gun.

61 – Ludlich, Posen; rifle.

62 – Ohle, E. F., Breslau; shot tubes made by the hydraulic press (tinned inside and outside).

63 – Grzybowski, H., Potsdam; rifle in rosewood.

64 – Kehl, J. C. Berlin; pistols in box.

478 – Schaller, C., Suhl; rifle, with cast-steel barrel, iron trimming; gold hunting piece (engraved) with iron spring lid – it is loaded at the stock and has a contrivance for pointed bullets (Spitz-kugeln).

479 – Sauer & Son, Suhl; a double gun and single rifle, a single rifle ornamented with silver.

481 – Pistor, G. & W., Schmalkalden; rifle gun with barrel of German cast steel.

638 – Dreyse & Collenbusch, Sommerda; percussion caps.

677 – Krupp, F., Essen; steel gun, six-pounder complete, steel cuirass and one tried by being fired at with six different bullets.

678 – Teutenberg, L., Huesten; rifle with seven barrels, which can all be fired and loaded at once, particularly applicable for shooting wild fowl, etc.

698 – Anschutz, R., Zella; gun and rifle barrels of common wire and flower damask, of fine Paris and fine Flower (Turkish) damask, of fine chain damask, of Laminette and Gotha damask, of fine steel wire and iron damask; the iron for the steel is made in Zella of sparry ironstone, obtained from the district of Schmalkalden.

699 – Brecht, A., Weimar; rifles with fine damask barrels and walnut-tree stock, ranged for pointed and round balls, etc; the iron employed is from Thuringia, the barrels from Lutsorh.

701 – Konig, C. G., & Sons, Coburg; pair of octagon pistols inlaid with gold in the Gothic style, the stocks of elm (Ulmus campestris) inlaid with silver.

702 – Sauerbrey, L., Zella Blasii; double rifle of solid cast-steel. Both barrels are bored in a converging direction, to one aim, in such a manner as to direct the balls to the same mark; it carries pointed and also round balls, etc.

801 – Blancke, E., Naumberg; double barrelled gun, joint bullet rifle.

855 – Schilling, Suhl; pair of fine target pistols.

887 – Gleichauf, B., Bockenheim; a needle pistol with 12 barrels.

229

20 – Heinlein, C. V., Bamberg; a rifle, highly finished, carved and ornamented in the old German style.

21 – Kuchenreuter, T. J., Regensburg; two pairs of rifle pistols in rosewood cases, highly finished and carry 240 yards.

15 – Royal Gun Manufactory, Oberndorf; gun for infantry rifle with bayonet, and common rifle; made of cast-steel.

32 – Thuerigen, F. T., Meissen; a gun with double barrel on a new percussion principle.

6 – Weber & Schultheis; single and double-barrelled rifles.

18 – Dichore, A., Giessen; rifle, 4ft 10in long, inlaid with gold and silver.

3 – Tanner, C. D.; brace of pistols in case; gun with two double barrels, in case; rifle in case.

5 – Fischer, Carl August; guns, double-barrelled rifle with case, fowling piece, and rifle.

2 – Schmidt, J., Güstrow; three guns.

Appendix 2

PART ONE

The Programme of the Field Gun Trial (1858)

The following Rules will be strictly enforced:

RULE 1. The two kinds of guns (all double-barrelled) to be first separately arranged in sets, according to bore and weight, as follows, the muzzle-loaders being ranged under the letter M, and the breech-loaders under the letter B.

Class 1. 12 bore wt. not exceed 7½lb, barrels not more than 32in.
Class 2. 13 bore wt. not exceed 7¼lb, barrels not more than 32in.
Class 3. 14 bore wt. not exceed 7 lb, barrels not more than 32in.
Class 4. 15 bore wt. not exceed 6¾lb, barrels not more than 30in.
Class 5. 16 bore wt. not exceed 6½lb, barrels not more than 30in.

RULE 2. The exhibitors of each kind of gun to choose by vote six inspectors but if the exhibitor is not present, the Editor of *The Field* to vote for him by proxy. The duties of these inspectors to be as follows viz: One of each side to be placed at each target, and as soon as each shot is fired to take the quire of paper down and attach their initials, after which it is to be put on one side for future inspection. The other four to superintend the loading of all the guns, and more especially the firing of those charges which are only meant to test the amount of recoil after the gun is fouled by them.

RULE 3. Four targets to be fixed, so as to allow of shooting without delay and each to be inspected according to Rule 2. The targets to be composed of a quire of brown paper, placed on a foundation of boarding and to be arranged in pairs, each 50 yards from the centre of the tent, and protected from the wind. The guns to be shot from fixed rests and levelled by the exhibitors, or those whom they may appoint – excepting such shots as are not aimed at the target, as presently to be described.

RULE 4. All the guns belonging to the classes M1, M2, M3, M4 and M5, to be shot at the two western targets, a shot from each being made at 40, 50 and 60 yards respectively but preceded by a shot with the meter attached to register the recoil when clean. Then each to be fired in the open, 24 times, and finally a shot to be taken from the meter again to register the amount of recoil when foul. The inspector to note the effect on the targets according to Rule 2.

RULE 5. All the guns belonging to the classes B1, B2, B3, B4 and B5, to be in like manner shot at the two eastern targets, preceding and following each by the measure of the recoil as specified in Rule 4 and the targets being likewise inspected and noted in the same manner.

RULE 6. All the guns to be loaded by parties appointed by the Editor of *The Field* from powder and shot furnished by him, and in the presence of the inspectors. The charges not to exceed $2\frac{3}{4}$ drachms of powder for the muzzle-loader and 3 drachms for the breech-loader with $1\frac{1}{4}$oz of shot for each. The cartridges also to be furnished by the Editor of *The Field*.

RULE 7. Every exhibitor to forward (carriage paid) the gun or guns which he intends to be tried, to the office of *The Field* on or before the day of trial or produce it on the ground. In either case the sum of 10s 6d must be paid with each gun or notice in order to cover the expense of ground, ammunition, rests, targets, etc. the balance if any being repaid after the expiration of one week from the day of trial.

RULE 8. As soon as all the classes M and B have been thus tried apart and the targets examined the best one from each class respectively to be shot three times at 40, 50 and 60 yards respectively in competition with the selected one of the corresponding class in the same way as under Rules 4 and 5 the recoil being also measured as before. By this method the trial between the two kinds will be more fair than if a small number of either kind were allowed to be shot against a larger number of its opponents, when it might be expected that from superiority in numbers alone an advantage might result to the latter side.

RULE 9. The whole of the shots to be recorded by the Editor of *The Field* or those whom he may appoint, and published as soon as possible in that paper. The power of penetration and the recoil being readily capable of measurement, there can be no dispute about these points; and if there is any doubt of the comparative regularity of the discharge between two guns, the face of the target to be photographed and engraved for publication.

RULE 10. As the ground at Ashburnham Park is not suited to the testing of rifles if any are sent in, they shall be tried elsewhere on Saturday 10 April, the exhibitors themselves, or those whom they may appoint shooting from the shoulder at 100 and 200 yards respectively.

RULE 11. The proprietors of *The Field* will be responsible for the safe custody of any guns intrusted to them except from injury in shooting during the trial, in which, however every care shall be taken of them.

RULE 12. The proprietor of the ground to be allowed to admit the public at a fixed charge, so long as they do not disturb the proceedings of the trial. Each exhibitor to have a ticket for himself free of charge.

Dated 19 March 1858 – Field Office, 2 to 5 Essex Street, Strand, London WC.

FIELD TRIAL RESULTS: 1858

			NAME OF OWNER	MAKER
CLASS I	1.	M.	Prince, 138 New Bond St, London	Prince ....
	2.	M.	Pape, Newcastle-on-Tyne....................................	Pape............................
	3.	M.	Pape, Newcastle-on-Tyne....................................	Pape............................
	4.	M.	Greener, Birmingham	Greener.......................
	5.	M.	Bolton, The Hyde, Stourbridge	Moore & Harris ....
	6.	M.	Penryn Aston, Cross St, Golden Sq, London	P. Aston ....
	7.	M.	A. Henry, Edinburgh	A. Henry ....
	8.	M.	O. Smith, Derby...	O. Smith......................
	9,	M.	J. R. Kedward, Exley Court, Hereford................	E. Ladmore...............
	10.	M.	Reilly, New Oxford St, London	Reilly ....
	11.		Col Astley, Guards Club	Lancaster ....
CLASS II	12.	M.	Dunbar, Brawl Castle, Thurso, N.B.	Pape............................
	13.	M.	A. Henry, Edinburgh	A. Henry ....
	14.		Hon Capt Talbot, 27 Chesham Pl, London	Ad. Jansen ....
	15.	M.	Reilly, London...	Reilly ....
CLASS III	16.	M.	Bolton...	H. Fear ....
	17.	M.	Ollard Upwell	Culling.......................
	18.	M.	Reilly, London...	Reilly ....
	19.	M.	Pape, Newcastle-on-Tyne..................................	Pape............................
	20.	M.	Greener, Birmingham	Greener.......................
	21.	M.	Reilly, London...	Reilly ....
	22.	M.	Reilly, London...	Reilly ....
CLASS IV	23.	M.	Horton, Birmingham	Horton.......................
	24.	M.	Greener, Birmingham	Greener.......................
ABOVE WEIGHT (not classed)				
	25.	M.	Fletcher, Gloucester...	Fletcher ....
	26.	M.	A. Henry, Edinburgh‡..	A. Henry ....

NO. AFFIXED AT TRIAL	DESCRIPTION OF GUN	BORE	LENGTH OF BARREL	WEIGHT lb oz	CHARGE OF POWDER drms	CHARGE OF SHOT oz
11	M/L	12	30	7 4	$2\frac{3}{4}$	$1\frac{1}{4}$
6	M/L	12	30	7 $2\frac{1}{4}$	$2\frac{3}{4}$	$1\frac{1}{4}$
7	M/L	12	31	7 $3\frac{1}{4}$	$2\frac{3}{4}$	$1\frac{1}{4}$
9	M/L	12	30	7 0	$2\frac{3}{4}$	$1\frac{1}{4}$
5	Fr B/L*	14	30	7 8	3	$1\frac{1}{8}$
1	Fr B/L*	12	30	7 6	3	$1\frac{1}{4}$
8	M/L	12	30	7 0	$2\frac{3}{4}$	$1\frac{1}{4}$
10	M/L	12	30	6 15	$2\frac{3}{4}$	$1\frac{1}{4}$
2	Fr B/L*	12	30	7 8	3	$1\frac{1}{4}$
12	M/L	12	31	7 0	$2\frac{3}{4}$	$1\frac{1}{4}$
5a	B/L†	14	30	7 $7\frac{1}{2}$	$2\frac{3}{4}$	$1\frac{1}{8}$
15	M/L	13	31	7 $1\frac{1}{2}$	$2\frac{3}{4}$	$1\frac{1}{4}$
14	M/L	13	30	7 0	$2\frac{3}{4}$	$1\frac{1}{4}$
16	Belg as Fr	14	30	7 4	3	1
13	M/L	13	30	6 12	$2\frac{3}{4}$	$1\frac{1}{4}$
21	M/L	14	30	6 0	$2\frac{3}{4}$	$1\frac{1}{4}$
23	M/L	14	30	6 12	$2\frac{1}{4}$	$1\frac{1}{8}$
25	Fr B/L*	15	30	6 12	3	1
24	M/L	14	30	7 0	$2\frac{3}{4}$	$1\frac{1}{4}$
22	M/L	14	30	6 9	$2\frac{3}{4}$	$1\frac{1}{4}$
20	M/L	14	28	6 12	$2\frac{3}{4}$	1
	Fr B/L*	14	30	7 0	3	1
28	M/L	15	30	6 12	$2\frac{1}{2}$	1
27	M/L	15	30	6 8	$2\frac{1}{2}$	1
29	Fr B/L*	12	30	7 12	3	$1\frac{1}{4}$
30	M/L					

No.	40yd R	40yd L	50yd R	50yd L	60yd R	60yd L	40yd R	40yd L	50yd R	50yd L	60yd R	60yd L	TOTAL ON FACE OF 6 TARGETS	TOTAL THROUGH 6 TARGETS
	NO. OF MARKS ON FACE OF TARGET						NO. OF SHOTS THROUGH TARGET							
1.	51	60	39	51	21	9	1	0	4	3	6	3	231	17
2.	47	38	24	27	22	6	5	1	17	15	8	2	164	48
3.	28	57	24	25	27	15	3	0	0	5	14	4	176	26
4.	55	46	33	23	14	20	0	0	0	5	0	0	191	5
5.	43	42	11	29	24	23	1	0	0	5	0	17	172	23
6.	53	45	20	19	25	18	0	0	15	0	8	4	180	12
7.	51	44	23	18	14	19	0	0	3	0	7	6	169	16
8.	46	49	30	18	10	8	3	0	1	2	6	2	161	14
9.	38	43	15	19	15	18	3	0	1	1	3	4	148	12
10.	34	32	17	11	20	6	0	0	1	0	8	3	120	12
11.	18	25	23	14	14	23	0	0	0	0	4	6	122	10
12.	40	50	15	48	20	18	0	0	10	6	8	11	191	38
13.	25	37	23	44	24	24	0	0	0	14	18	15	177	37
14.	30	36	14	28	4	12	3	2	0	0	0	2	124	7
15.	41	15	29	11	5	11	0	0	3	1	0	0	112	4
16.	50	63	29	22	21	27	0	7	12	5	15	23	212	62
17.	53	51	§	§	26	17	0	0	§	§	15	3		
18.	46	52	19	22	12	13	4	6	6	1	11	11	194	39
19.	49	42	15	23	25	21	0	3	4	8	15	12	175	42
20.	45	34	23	22	26	10	0	2	0	0	8	6	160	16
21.	38	36	22	26	12	14	0	0	12	2	7	0	148	21
22.	30	24	18	14	6	10	2	5	0	0	4	9	102	13
23.	36	13	23	21	24	12	7	0	2	2	20	4	129	35
24.	43	13	18	11	10	11	0	1	1	3	10	3	106	18
25.	33	36	32	19	16	22	0	2	12	4	11	14	158	43
26.														

*Used with French cartridges
†Used with Lancaster cartridges
‡Mr A. Henry's third gun was overweight and could not therefore be classed. It was shot, but the targets being exhausted no correct record was kept
§§Mr Ollard's gun was mislaid and could not be found until all the 50yd targets were exhausted; the average is thus taken of the middle distance

Targets all made of extra stout brown paper, 28in wide by 11in high: those used at 41yd 40 thicknesses weighing 2¾lb; at 50yd 30 thicknesses weighing 1lb 13oz; at 60yd 20 thicknesses weighing 1lb 6oz.
Powder – Lawrence's No. 2.
Shot No. 5.

235

Appendix 2

PART TWO

The Field, Saturday 16 April 1859

The three essentials for the shot gun we hold to be:
1. Regularity and proper closeness of pattern.
2. The utmost extent of penetration consistent with the first condition.
3. An absence of unpleasant recoil.

RULES FOR SHOTGUNS
1. The guns (which must be all double barrelled) to be arranged in the following classes, each class including any description or variety which may be sent in of the bore, weight, and length specified below. Any gun of a bore between 12 and 14 to be placed in Class 1 and between 14 and 16 in Class 2. And if in a gun whose bore is suitable, the weight or length is too great for the 2nd or 3rd class respectively, it shall be placed in that one which will admit it, according to the undermentioned conditions relating to those particulars:-
Class 1. 12 bore wt not exceed 7½lb barrels not exceed 32in.
Class 2. 14 bore wt not exceed 7lb barrels not exceed 32in.
Class 3. 16 bore wt not exceed 6½lb barrels not exceed 30in.

2. Each target to be composed of a single sheet of paper thirty inches in diameter, having in the centre another twelve inches in diameter, which shall be either of 40 thicknesses for 40 yards or 20 for 60.

3. The targets to be inspected by gentlemen appointed on the ground to the satisfaction of the competitors, and to have the initials of the inspector appended to each, so as to guarantee that it belongs to the gun which it represents.

4. Each barrel to be shot at the above targets at 40 and 60 yards once, from the shoulder, with the aid of a rest if required; and then to be shot from the recoil machine, and the measure of the recoil recorded in pounds according to the index on the scale.

5. Every gun to be loaded on the ground by a person appointed for that purpose by the Editor of *The Field*, and to be fired by the exhibitor or any person whom he may appoint.

6. The powder used for all the guns to be Lawrence's No. 2 and the shot No. 6. The charge of powder not to exceed 3 drachms for the breech-loader and 2¾ drachms for the muzzle-loaders. The shot not to exceed 1¼ for each. In the third class, the charge

of powder to be $\frac{1}{4}$ drachm less for each respectively, and the shot only $1\frac{1}{8}$oz. The cartridges for the breech-loaders be forwarded with each gun empty, and to be loaded on the field. Greased felt wadding to be used and to be forwarded with each gun.

7. Every exhibitor to forward (carriage paid) to *The Field* office 346 Strand, the gun or guns which he intends to exhibit, on or before the tenth day of June, or to give notice on that day of his intention of so doing in time for the trial. In either case the sum of 10s 6d must accompany the gun or notice, and if the latter is sent must specify breech-loader or muzzle-loader.

8. The whole of the shots to be recorded in the manner above described in the columns of *The Field*, as soon as possible after the conclusion of the trial.

FIELD TRIAL RESULTS: 1859

	NAME OF MAKER	KIND OF GUN
1.	Pape, Newcastle-on-Tyne	M/L ....
2.	Prince & Green, London	M/L ....
3.	Pape, Newcastle-on-Tyne	M/L ....
4.	Egan, Bradford	B/L* ....
5.	Prince & Green, London	B/L ....
6.	Pape, Newcastle-on-Tyne	B/L ....
7.	Pape, Newcastle-on-Tyne	M/L ....
8.	Needham, London	B/L† ....
9.	Egan, Bradford	M/L ....
10.	Culling, Downham Market	M/L ....
11.	Reilly, London	B/L ....
12.	Elliot, Birmingham	B/L ....
13.	Needham, London	B/L ....
14.	Hast, Colchester	B/L ....
15.	Reilly, London	B/L ....
16.	Elliot, Birmingham	B/L ....
17.	Francotte, Liege	B/L‡ ....
		Averages ....
18.	O. Smith, Derby	M/L ....
19.	Culling, Downham Market	M/L ....
20.	Dougall, Glasgow	M/L ....
21.	Joe Manton, London§	M/L ....
22.	Culling, Downham Market	M/L ....
23.	Reilly, London	B/L* ....
24.	Lang, London	B/L* ....
25.	Reilly, London	M/L ....
26.	Prince & Green, London	B/L* ....
27.	Prince & Green, London	M/L ....
28.	Hast, Colchester	M/L ....
29.	Reilly, London	B/L* ....
		Averages ....

BORE	BARREL in	LENGTH OF GUN lb oz		WEIGHT OF POWDER dr	CHARGE OF SHOT oz	CHARGE OF at 40yd R	L	NUMBER OF MARKS ON FACE OF TARGET at 60yd R	L
12	30	6	11	$2\frac{3}{4}$	$1\frac{1}{4}$	158	118	63	60
12	30	7	6	$2\frac{3}{4}$	$1\frac{1}{4}$	148	98	52	65
12	$29\frac{1}{2}$	6	8	$2\frac{3}{4}$	$1\frac{1}{4}$	116	129	46	40
12	30	7	8	3	$1\frac{1}{4}$	144	90	32	58
12	30	7	2	3	$1\frac{1}{4}$	103	93	60	62
12	30	7	0	3	$1\frac{1}{4}$	132	93	55	38
13	30	7	0	$2\frac{3}{4}$	$1\frac{1}{4}$	117	71	47	61
13	29	6	10	3	$1\frac{1}{8}$	65	135	24	54
13	28	6	14	$2\frac{3}{4}$	$1\frac{1}{8}$	113	113	24	46
12	$29\frac{1}{2}$	6	10	$2\frac{1}{2}$	$1\frac{3}{16}$	106	103	35	31
16	30	7	4	3	$1\frac{1}{4}$	95	105	50	31
16	28	7	4	$2\frac{3}{4}$	1	73	99	22	42
13	$28\frac{1}{2}$	7	4	3	$1\frac{1}{8}$	97	95	31	20
12	31	7	8	3	$1\frac{1}{8}$	100	77	32	28
12	30	7	4	3	$1\frac{1}{4}$	88	91	37	31
13	28	5	4	3	1	90	87	20	28
14	$29\frac{1}{2}$	7	8	3	$1\frac{1}{8}$	60	48	31	40
—	—	—		—	—	106	97	33	43
15	30	6	14	$2\frac{3}{4}$	$1\frac{1}{8}$	101	121	48	55
14	$28\frac{1}{2}$	6	11	$2\frac{1}{4}$	$1\frac{1}{8}$	147	85	42	48
14	27	5	14	$2\frac{1}{2}$	1	130	92	30	60
16	31	6	12	$2\frac{1}{2}$	1	122	86	36	57
14	29	6	0	$2\frac{1}{4}$	$1\frac{1}{8}$	101	103	30	55
15	30	6	14	3	$1\frac{1}{4}$	105	106	63	26
15	29	6	8	3	$1\frac{1}{4}$	129	57	45	52
14	29	6	4	$2\frac{3}{4}$	$1\frac{1}{8}$	99	99	34	42
15	30	7	0	3	1	77	100	41	31
14	30	7	0	$2\frac{3}{4}$	1	71	92	52	27
15	$30\frac{1}{2}$	6	8	$2\frac{3}{4}$	$1\frac{1}{8}$	83	55	44	24
15	28	6	4	$2\frac{3}{4}$	$1\frac{1}{8}$	83	101	34	7
—	—	—		—	—	104	92	42	40

239

	NUMBER OF SHEETS PIERCED at 40yd		NO. OF SHOTS THROUGH 20 SHEETS at 60yd		TOTAL ON FACE OF 4 TARGETS	TOTAL THROUGH 4 TARGETS	GROSS TOTAL	RECOIL OF EACH BARREL IN POUNDS	VARIATION FROM AVERAGE RECOIL FOR 2 BARRELS	FINAL RESULTS
	R	L	R	L						
1.	28	33	5	2	399	68	467	68–62	3 under	470
2.	28	22	1	2	363	53	416	66–65	2 under	418
3.	25	28	1	1	331	55	386	68–64	1 under	387
4.	28	30	0	2	324	60	384	untested	—	384
5.	24	31	2	4	318	61	379	untested	—	379
6.	26	33	2	3	318	64	382	70–68	5 over	377
7.	29	37	4	8	296	78	374	untested	—	374
8.	29	39	0	1	278	69	347	64–62	7 under	354
9.	23	34	0	1	296	58	354	68–68	3 over	351
10.	22	32	0	0	275	54	329	59–61	13 under	342
11.	20	27	2	0	281	49	330	untested	—	330
12.	30	40	0	1	236	71	307	64–66	3 under	310
13.	22	26	0	0	243	48	291	65–61	7 under	298
14.	33	25	0	0	237	58	295	72–69	8 over	287
15.	22	27	2	1	247	52	299	76–73	16 over	283
16.	20	31	1	0	225	52	277	64–68	1 under	278
17.	25	23	0	0	179	48	227	74–68	9 over	218
	26	30	1	1½	285	59	344	67–66	—	344
18.	38	22	3	5	325	68	393	63–58	8 under	401
19.	24	19	0	0	322	43	365	53–54	22 under	387
20.	25	27	2	0	312	54	366	65–63	1 under	367
21.	27	28	2	0	301	57	358	64–62	3 under	361
22.	21	25	0	1	289	47	336	60–44	25 under	361
23.	29	33	6	1	300	69	369	69–76	16 over	353
24.	20	28	0	3	283	51	334	64–60	5 under	339
25.	32	27	0	8	274	67	341	68–74	13 over	328
26.	33	26	5	0	249	64	313	71–73	15 over	298
27.	20	29	0	0	242	49	291	69–64	4 over	287
28.	28	29	5	0	206	62	268	68–67	6 over	262
29.	18	28	0	0	225	46	271	68–72	11 over	260
	26	27	2	1½	277	56	334	65–64	—	334

*Lefaucheux's
†Needham's
‡Bastin's
§Breeches by Trulock and Harris of Dublin

240

FIELD TRIAL RESULTS: 1866

		EXHIBITOR	MAKER
CLASS I: 12 bore	1.	Mr Pape	Pape, Newcastle
	2.	Mr Pape	Pape, Newcastle
	3.	Mr W. W. Greener	W. W. Greener, Birmingham
	4.	Drawn Steel Co	Drawn Steel Co, City Road, London
	5.	Mr Pape	Pape, Newcastle
	6.	Mr Henry	Henry, Edinburgh
	7.	Mr Pape	Pape, Newcastle
	8.	Mr Henry	Henry, Edinburgh
	9.	Mr Crane	Crane, Royal Exchange, London
	10.	Mr Henry	Henry, Edinburgh
	11.	Drawn Steel Co	Drawn Steel Co, City Road, London
	12.	Cogswell & Harrison	Cogswell & Harrison, Strand
	13.	Mr Hillen	Berry, Woodbridge
	14.	Mr Erskine	Erskine, Newton Stewart, N.B.
	15.	Major Hinchcliffe	Cogswell & Harrison, Strand
	16.	Mr Dobson	Thompson & Son, Edinburgh
	17.	Mr Melland	Melland, Lime Street, London
	18.	Mr Hasdell	Hasdell, Clerkenwell, London
	19.	Mr Dobson	Thompson & Son, Edinburgh
	20.	Mr Elliot	Elliot, Birmingham
	21.	Mr Hill	Harlow, Birmingham
	22.	Mr Crane	Crane, Royal Exchange, London
	23.	Mr Wilson	Wilson, Horncastle
	24.	Mr Fletcher	Fletcher, Gloucester
	25.	Mr Hasdell	Hasdell, Clerkenwell, London
	26.	Cogswell & Harrison	Cogswell & Harrison, Strand
	27.	Mr Joynson	Williamson & Son, Bridgnorth
	28.	Mr Joynson	Williamson & Son, Bridgnorth
	29.	Mr Fletcher	Fletcher, Gloucester
	30.	Mr Hasdell	Hasdell, Clerkenwell, London
	31.	Mr Tolley	Tolley, Birmingham
	32.	Mr Hast	Hast, Colchester
CLASS II: 16 bore	1.	Mr. Pape	Pape, Newcastle
	2.	Mr Elliot	Elliott, Birmingham
CLASS III: 8 bore	1.	Mr. Elliot	Elliot, Birmingham

Description and Weight of Gun			Price
Lefaucheux Breechloader, with pin cartridge; $7\frac{1}{4}$lb	Laminated steel	30″	£30
Lefaucheux Breechloader, with pin cartridge; 7lb 1oz	Laminated steel	30″	£35
His patent wedge fast B/L, with pin cartridge; $7\frac{1}{4}$lb	Laminated steel	30″	33gs.
A. Lancaster's patent B/L with C/F cartridge; 7lb 2oz	Drawn steel	30″	35gs.
Lefaucheux B/L with P/F cartridge; 7lb 1oz	Laminated steel	30″	£40
His patent B/L for C/F or P/F cartridge, shot with C/F; 6lb 10oz	Damascus	30″	35gs.
His patent B/L with C/F; 6lb 15oz	Damascus	30″	£40
Same as No. 6 but with P/F	Damascus	30″	35gs.
A. Lancaster's patent B/L with C/F cartridge; 6lb 11oz	Damascus	$29\frac{3}{4}$″	35gs.
His patent B/L with C/F; 7lb 3oz	Damascus	30″	35gs.
A. Lancaster's patent B/L with C/F cartridge 7lb 2oz	Drawn steel	30″	38gs.
Their patent self-cocking B/L with C/F cartridge; 6lb 15oz	Damascus	30″	35gs.
Lefaucheux B/L with P/F cartridge; $7\frac{1}{4}$lb	Damascus	30″	35gs.
His improved Lefaucheux B/L with P/F; $7\frac{1}{4}$lb	Damascus	30″	£20
Dougal's patent Lockfast B/L with pin; $7\frac{1}{4}$lb	Damascus	30″	35gs.
A. Lancaster's patent B/L with C/F; 7lb	Damascus	30″	28gs.
A. Lancaster's patent B/L with C/F; 7lb 1oz	Damascus	29″	35gs.
Lefaucheux B/L for P/F or C/F shot with C/F; 7lb	Damascus	30″	£35
Lefaucheux B/L with P/F; 7lb	Damascus	30″	25gs.
His patent snap-action B/L with P/F; 6lb 14oz	Damascus	30″	£25
His patent wedge-bolt B/L with P/F; 7lb	Damascus	30″	£23
A. Lancaster's patent B/L with C/F; 6lb 13oz	Damascus	29″	35gs.
Lefaucheux B/L with P/F; 6lb 13oz	Damascus	30″	£28
His patent snap-action B/L with P/F; 6lb $15\frac{1}{2}$oz	Damascus	30″	£26
Lefaucheux B/L for P/F or C/F, shot with P/F; 7lb	Damascus	30″	£35
Their patent self-cocking B/L with P/F; 7lb	Damascus	30″	35gs.
Lefaucheux B/L with P/F; $7\frac{1}{4}$lb	Damascus	30″	£30
M/L; 7lb 2oz	Foreign iron	32″	£25
His patent snap-action B/L with P/F; 7lb	Damascus	30″	25gs.
A. Lancaster's patent B/L with C/F; $7\frac{1}{4}$lb	Damascus	30″	35gs.
Lefaucheux B/L with P/F; $6\frac{3}{4}$lb	Damascus	30″	8gs.
A. Lancaster's patent B/L with C/F; 7lb2oz	Damascus	30″	23gs.
Lefaucheux B/L with P/F; 6lb 15oz	Laminated steel	29″	£35
His patent snap-action B/L with P/F; $5\frac{3}{4}$lb	Laminated steel	30″	£35
His patent snap-action B/L with P/F; $14\frac{1}{2}$lb	Laminated steel	36″	£50

242

PATTERN
(six shots from each barrel)

	CHARGE OF POWDER		1 R	1 L	2 R	2 L	3 R	3 L	4 R	4 L	5 R	5 L	6 R	6 L	AVERAGE	
1.	3dr.	No.6	140	158	146	144	130	47	132	106	135	159	104	126	131.1	123.2
2.	3dr.	No. 6	134	52	94	156	138	129	165	157	110	73	163	135	134	117
3.	3dr	No. 5	114	130	124	80	115	127	110	137	158	118	125	122	124.2	119
4.	3¼dr.	No. 5	141	113	101	131	109	102	125	150	114	133	106	72	116	116.5
5.	3dr.	No. 5	46	152	153	148	116	116	128	111	103	127	61	149	101.1	133.5
6.	3dr.	No. 6	117	117	40	92	74	164	133	119	145	153	141	117	108.2	127
7.	3dr.	No. 5	152	68	139	97	108	136	127	121	136	141	93	66	125.5	104.5
8.	3dr.	No. 6	105	104	126	130	91	110	124	129	94	101	137	119	112.5	115.3
9.	3dr.	No. 3	99	103	127	141	72	96	133	125	95	144	85	107	101.5	119.2
10.	3dr.	No . 6	132	67	129	120	97	64	68	116	143	120	141	78	118.2	94.1
11.	3¼dr.	No. 5	88	100	113	87	85	105	74	135	100	102	132	113	98.4	107
12.	3¼dr.	No. 3	104	90	126	93	99	126	95	117	37	109	98	111	93.1	107.4
13.	3½dr.	No. 3	100	103	83	99	104	122	103	105	72	101	97	113	93.1	107.1
14.	3dr.	No. 3	73	91	117	128	89	84	61	109	87	110	97	102	87.2	104
15.	3¼dr.	No. 3	77	117	105	99	59	59	106	121	118	103	99	108	94	101.1
16.	3¼dr.	No. 6	78	118	63	97	112	61	120	100	116	129	71	89	93.2	99
17.	3¼dr.	No. 5	57	114	93	98	110	89	99	79	112	106	96	112	96.3	99.4
18.	3dr.	No. 5	87	127	100	84	114	123	65	103	107	81	95	91	94.4	101.3
19.	3¼dr.	No. 6	87	92	112	108	128	56	118	78	82	50	118	89	107.3	78.5
20.	2¾dr.	No. 3	104	125	70	82	69	106	67	99	84	100	86	104	80	102.4
21.	3¼dr.	No. 3	44	123	82	74	110	100	101	51	75	113	94	98	84.2	93.1
22.	3dr.	No. 3	114	107	118	104	89	73	88	102	98	63	63	72	95	86.5
23.	3dr	No. 5	118	144	79	111	47	61	127	90	32	100	104	78	84.3	97.2
24.	3dr.	No. 3	94	83	92	62	103	73	89	92	96	65	110	96	97.2	78.3
25.	3dr.	No. 5	104	114	113	93	90	70	85	86	92	81	68	56	92	83.2
26.	3¼dr.	No. 3	88	68	48	108	49	102	114	48	97	111	56	111	75.2	91.2
27.	3¼dr.	No. 3	97	106	73	82	97	88	62	90	106	78	41	96	79.2	90
28.	3dr	No. 3	94	56	87	109	55	72	109	95	83	70	94	76	87	79.4
29.	3dr.	No. 3	80	74	58	56	102	77	99	103	88	85	86	57	85.3	75.2
30.	3¼dr.	No. 3	97	82	81	72	61	78	42	73	88	46	106	84	79.1	72.3
31.	3¼dr.	No. 3	87	75	61	92	83	69	57	48	60	48	81	76	71.3	68
32.	3½dr.	No. 3	82	55	73	78	43	74	87	48	61	34	57	54	67.1	57.1
1.	2½dr. 1oz shot	No. 5	135	127	129	122	122	117	97	130	51	128	69	88	100.3	118.4
2.	2¼dr. 1oz shot	No. 3	93	50	74	65	88	80	61	54	60	80	93	78	78.1	67.5
1.	6dr. 1½oz shot	No. 3	143	89	62	90	111	106	101	118	142	91	107	141	111	105.5

MEAN OF 2 BARRELS		PENETRATION (six shots from each barrel)												AVERAGE		MEAN OF 2 BARRELS	TOTAL FIGURE OF MERIT
	1		2		3		4		5		6			R	L		
	R	L	R	L	R	L	R	L	R	L	R	L				
127.1	23	24	27	25	27	20	26	23	31	27	27	27	26.5	24.2	25.4	305.4
125.3	24	20	23	32	23	23	26	27	22	20	26	22	24	24	24	299
121.4	26	23	19	30	31	26	18	27	26	26	28	26	24.4	26.2	25.3	294.2
116.3	23	26	29	24	26	23	30	26	29	28	26	21	27.1	24.4	26	284.4
117.3	22	20	27	24	25	27	25	22	21	26	21	21	23.3	23.2	23.3	281.5
117.4	30	23	17	20	23	20	19	25	26	23	25	27	23.2	23	23.1	281.4
115.2	23	24	24	23	20	25	22	30	27	25	22	15	23	23.4	23.2	277.2
114.1	23	21	22	26	25	21	17	22	22	21	21	20	21.4	21.5	21.5	271.5
110.4	25	22	31	32	22	20	25	25	21	21	21	19	24.1	23.1	23.4	268.3
106.2	22	24	23	24	26	26	29	24	27	23	24	24	25.1	24.1	24.4	261.5
102.5	28	20	21	28	32	26	27	31	26	24	32	32	27.4	26.5	27.2	260.1
100.3	24	29	24	23	24	23	27	25	16	30	27	28	23.4	26.2	25	250.5
100.1	25	25	20	27	27	30	26	24	24	22	24	26	24.2	25.4	25	250.2
95.4	25	27	25	32	24	23	33	18	38	24	25	30	28.2	25.4	27	245.2
97.4	29	25	28	24	27	15	25	27	25	28	18	27	25.2	24.2	24.5	244.5
96.1	28	33	28	23	27	25	23	20	21	27	22	26	24.5	25.4	25.3	242.5
98.1	17	24	23	22	29	25	24	24	19	23	25	22	22.5	23.2	23	242.2
98.1	25	24	30	20	19	21	20	20	21	22	19	16	22.2	20.3	21.2	239
93.1	19	24	20	22	26	20	21	29	25	17	32	23	23.5	22.3	23.1	232.4
91.2	28	27	20	24	27	20	20	30	25	25	26	19	24.2	24.1	24.2	231.1
88.5	24	26	28	30	25	23	33	21	25	32	27	25	27	26.1	26.3	230.4
91	21	23	24	32	32	24	22	21	23	18	21	18	23.5	22.4	23.1	228.2
91	24	21	22	25	18	16	21	18	19	28	26	25	21.4	22.1	21.5	225.4
87.5	25	23	22	18	27	29	22	24	23	20	21	27	23.2	23.3	23.3	222.4
87.4	23	26	19	17	22	22	25	22	27	26	17	22	22.1	22.3	22.2	220
83.2	30	24	25	26	25	33	24	26	21	25	22	33	24.3	27.5	26.1	219
84.4	28	23	27	24	27	28	25	20	22	23	19	24	24.4	23.4	24.1	217.4
83.2	36	19	23	25	26	22	28	24	22	21	32	24	27.5	22.3	25.1	217
80.2	19	26	20	22	28	27	27	22	35	26	20	27	24.5	25	25	210.4
75.5	27	31	27	30	27	30	31	26	26	23	24	23	27	27.1	27.1	205.5
69.4	32	26	13	18	18	11	20	13	27	19	21	29	21.5	19.2	20.4	180.4
62.1	32	24	23	20	15	21	23	18	17	15	15	17	20.5	19.1	20	164.2
109.4	15	22	29	23	19	26	24	26	20	28	20	22	21.1	24.3	22.5	264.5
73	21	18	22	21	22	26	20	17	23	20	23	23	21.5	20.5	21.4	188.4
108.2	27	24	23	29	27	23	24	30	25	31	38	34	27.2	28.3	28	272

Appendix 3

Patent Law and Patent Specifications

The value of the patent specifications as a source of information to students of arms development would be hard to overestimate. These official documents represent a factual account that has no parallel, indeed without them much of the story of arms evolution would be unintelligible.

In the hope of making Appendix 4 of even greater interest, we have written the following short résumé on what a patent was. These brief notes are in no way a primer on patent law, which is a large and specialised subject in its own right. They are rather directed to the enthusiast using the patents as a source of information.

A patent is a grant of a monopoly, in theory at least, by the sovereign, to an inventor, so that he has the control over his invention for a period of time in which to realise its potential. In return for this privilege the inventor has to fulfil certain conditions. From our point of view two are important. Firstly, he had to pay the prescribed fees, indeed the span of his monopoly depended on this, as will be explained later. Secondly, he had to deposit a complete specification, which fully described his invention in such a way that it was intelligible to a skilled worker in the trade to which the invention applied. It had to be a complete specification in the sense that a worker, as envisaged above, could have made use of the invention in the best manner known to the original inventor without the worker needing to invent further for himself.

This insistence on a complete description, with the allied requirement of a clear statement of what was claimed as original, is what makes these documents of such immense value to the researcher. The inventor was also obliged to submit his name, address and a statement of profession, all of which can give a lead on him. The accuracy and validity of the description of the invention are the hunting ground of the patent lawyer and have very important bearings at certain points in our story. For instance in the Eley v Daw law suit.

Of more general interest are the costs and hence the period for which a patent was maintained. While the cost of drafting and drawing a specification would obviously depend on its length and complexity, we have been unable to discover an exact scale of fees but are led to believe that the drafting and drawing would have cost the average inventor in the 1860s some £10. In addition to this he would have had to meet the fee of £15 for the first three years of the actual patent.

It should be explained that a provisional specification was a more general statement of what was claimed as new, which was left with, and kept secret by, the Patent Office for a period of six months. During this period it was required that the inventor desposited his complete specification as detailed earlier.

After three years the inventor or owner of the patent could extend it for a further four years on payment of a fee of £50, and then, at the end of this again, prolong its life to the maximum length of fourteen years by a payment of £100.

The Gunmakers' triumphal arch erected on the occasion of Queen Victoria's visit to Birmingham in 1858

Appendix 4

BRITISH SHOTGUN PATENTS 1850–1870

DATE	NUMBER	NAME OF PATENTEE	DESCRIPTION
28/6/1858	1451	I. Hammond	Extractor
24/9/1858	2149	Westley Richards	Inert action top lever & rib extension
4/12/1858	2778(P)	Smith, Townsend & Williams	Inert, two lumps side by side
26/1/1859	236	I. Hammond	Inert action, extractor & special cartridge
2/2/1859	300	J. R. Cooper	Inert side opening gun
20/7/1859	1703	J. Erskine	Inert slide & tilt (two actions)
7/9/1859	2040	H. Jones	Inert double bite with under lever
14/11/1859	2583	H. J. Daniell	Inert sliding bolt action
3/2/1860	285	R. Adams	Inert under lever hook bite
10/4/1860	899	J. Rigby & W. N. Norman	Inert laterally moving barrels
26/4/1860	1056	W. Harvey	Inert sliding action
7/5/1860	1128	J. D. Dougall	Inert slide & tilt
10/5/1860	1153	W. E. Gedge (agent for Humbertjean & Matthey)	Single snap bolt in barrel lump French patent No. 43163 dated 27/2/1860
24/5/1860	1291	W. F. Prince	Inert screw up & down on quick thread
25/7/1860	1808	W. Rose	Inert, bolting by bolt on laterally swinging arm
13/2/1861	368	T. T. Lawden & T. Jones	Inert laterally moving barrels or breech
18/4/1861	950	H. Jones	Inert under lever, double grip, assisted closing
11/6/1861	1487	F. E. Schneider	Snap under lever action centre fire French patent No. 46957 dated 4/10/1860
15/6/1861	1538	S. Grant	Inert under lever, double grip
31/7/1861	1904	H. J. Holland & W. Payten	Inert slide & tilt
4/9/1861	2203	F. E. Schneider	Centre fire cartridge & machinery for manufacture.
2/1/1862	22	G. Jeffries	Laterally moving barrels, inert action
12/2/1862	374	T. Horsley	Single sliding bolt snap lever in trigger guard
29/3/1862	873	Y. Palfrey	Inert sliding barrel
22/5/1862	1544	J. Needham	Side lever snap, half cocking, slide & drop, slide forward & extractor for needle fire
27/5/1862	1594	G. H. Daw	Improvement on No. 1487 of 1861
31/5/1862	1648	T. T. Lawden	Single bite inert action
8/7/1862	1966(P)	J. Rigby	Inert laterally moving action
22/7/1862	2079	P. F. Cassegrain	Single bite tilt & slide forward French patent No. 54002 dated 3/5/1862
29/8/1862	2395	H. Jones	Inert slide & tilt, two bite, under lever
11/9/1862	2506	Westley Richards	Sliding top lever snap
11/10/1862	2744	R. A. Brooman (agent for L. J. Gastinne)	Retracting striker & extractor French patent No. 53844 dated 22/4/1862
9/12/1862	3300	G. Jeffries	Inert laterally moving barrels
31/12/1862	3485	J. W. P. Field	Single bolt snap
14/2/1863	406(P)	J. H. Walsh	Hinged Lock loading
14/2/1863	411	F. E. Walker	Double bite inert action
12/3/1863	677	W. Clark (agent for Concalon)	Hinged breech block French patent No. 44667 dated 22/6/1863

2/5/1863	1104	J. Purdey	Double bite snap
23/6/1863	1585	E. Brooks	Inert sliding barrels
8/7/1863	1696	J. Gibson & S. R. & W. Trulock	Inert slide & tilt
13/7/1863	1752	H. A. Bonneville (agent for A. J. V. Marcet)	Hammerless snap, safety & indicators French patent No. 59126 dated 22/6/1863
16/7/1863	1782	H. Elliot	Single bolt snap
23/7/1863	1847(P)	W. Horton	Slide & drop inert action
4/8/1863	1923	J. H. Walsh	Hinged lock loading & extractor
25/8/1863	2100	Lewis, Walker & Wayne	Retracting plugs into chambers
29/8/1863	2139	A. Agnew	Single bite snap
10/9/1863	2231	W. W. Greener	Top connection with top rib
28/9/1863	2380	J. T. & E. Harlow	Bolt from lump to standing breech
1/10/1863	2410	T. Horsley	Sliding top lever, single bite snap
6/10/1863	2441	S. Mathews	Pivot top lever, single bite snap
8/10/1863	2468	J. D. Dougall	Lockfast "punt" or "camel" gun
19/10/1863	2554	W. Fletcher	Under lever snap hook bite
21/10/1863	2580	J. Hinton	Snap top hook bite
7/12/1863	3072(P)	R. Richards & S. C. Willetts	Single snap action, slide action
14/12/1863	3159(P)	T. Wilson	Single snap action
16/12/1863	3171	J. Smith	Side lever or lateral bolt, single bite snap
30/1/1864	259(P)	R. Brazier	Single bite snap
1/2/1864	271	E. Harrison	Push forward under lever, single hook bite, half cocker
4/2/1864	297	T. Newton	Slide forward top lever, single bite snap
24/3/1864	752	S. Mathews	Plugs into chambers
7/4/1864	866(P)	W. Hill	Snap with top & bottom bites
7/5/1864	1163	W. Powell	Top lever single bite snap
19/5/1864	1269	J. Frazier	Under lever single bite snap
14/6/1864	1465	E. Pope	Side lever, two bites, inert
22/6/1864	1559	T. P. Saville	Press button latch bolt snap
14/7/1864	1760(P)	J. Needham	Various actions
29/7/1864	1888(P)	R. Redman & D. Kirkwood	Snap actions, double & single bites
8/8/1864	1967	W. Collins & W. Pountney	Single action latch bolt snap
22/9/1864	2322(P)	J. H. Walsh	Hinged breech block
19/10/1864	2585	T. Turner	Lever behind guard, snap bite
22/10/1864	2623	W. Richards	Pivot top lever snap
22/11/1864	2912	J. Snider	Lateral rolling block. American patent No. 69941 dated 15/10/1867
1/12/1864	3001(P)	T. Wilson	Various actions
14/1/1865	124(P)	W. Ansell	Single bite snap
16/1/1865	139	J. S. Edge	Snap action locking by hooks to studs outside barrels
28/1/1865	247	S. R. & W. Trulock	Half cocker, two bites, one in lump, one between ribs
14/2/1865	424	J. Purdey	Single rocking latch, top stud or under lever snap, & extractor for slide forward barrels
14/2/1865	425	B. Thompson (agent for C. E. Sneider)	Inert slide & tilt American patent No. 47755 dated 16/5/1865
23/2/1865	506(P)	W. H. Aubin	Single bite snap action
17/4/1865	1071	A. Henry	Single bite snap, circle joint, internal strikers, cocking indicator.
24/4/1865	1136(P)	de Fontaine Moreau (agent for du Liege de Puychaumeix)	Inert slide & tilt, extractor French patent No. 58837 dated 4/4/1865
9/5/1865	1276(P)	S. & J. Law	Single bite snap action
10/5/1865	1293(P)	P. O'Hagan	Pivoting barrels & curved breech horizontal & vertical pivot

248

19/5/1865	1382(P)	S. Ebrall	Single bite snap action
25/5/1865	1433(P)	E. Paton	Single snap actions
27/5/1865	1461	T. Bissell	Internal striking, half cocking & extractor
3/6/1865	1525	A. Lancaster	Extractor & firing pins
4/8/1865	2030(P)	T. W. Webley	Pin fire for centre fire
9/8/1865	2063	S. & J. Law	Single swinging bite action, opening at half cock & extractor
20/10/1865	2709	J. & G. H. Needham	Retracting striker
24/10/1865	2743	F. H. Grey	Internal striker
25/10/1865	2752	W. M. Scott	Spindle lever & two bites & loaded indicator
4/12/1865	3113	E. C. Hodges	Two piece striker & extractor
9/2/1866	403	F. T. Baker	Extractor & striker
16/2/1866	491	W. S. Riley	Striker, extractor, half cocking & loaded indicators
20/2/1866	519(P)	J. H. Walsh	Single bite snap, hinge under action-face, half cocking
19/3/1866	806	T. G. Sylven	Two piece striker
22/3/1866	847	J. Jackson	Striker hit by breast of cock & extractor
5/4/1866	981	F. E. Walker	Striker solid with cock & extractor
11/4/1866	1033	J. Crofts	Top lever snap action with cam bolt
16/4/1866	1061	H. A. Bonneville (agent for C. V. Plumerel)	Extractor French patent No. 70399 dated 1866
19/4/1866	1101	E. Wilson	Inert, conical joint pin & single bite
7/5/1866	1300	W. W. Cross	Extractor
10/5/1866	1339	J. Cole & G. S. Melland	Extractor
12/5/1866	1367	C. Pryse & R. Redman	Extractor
25/5/1866	1460	J. Emme	Extractor
25/5/1866	1464	J. Purdey	Loaded indicator
29/5/1866	1489	T. Woodward & G. Fellows	Extractor
29/5/1866	1501	W. R. Pape	Single bite snap action & choke
25/6/1866	1691(P)	T. P. Saville	Firing pins & extractors
7/7/1866	1793	C. Harvey	Striker connected to cock & extractor
28/7/1866	1960	W. Richards	Dual ignition, pin fire or centre fire
17/8/1866	2113	W. Tranter	Single bite snap & extractor
25/8/1866	2196(P)	E. Brooks	Laterally moving barrels
29/8/1866	2227	T. Turner & W. Siddons	Extractors
6/9/1866	2287	W. P. Bardell & W. Powell	Rebound lock
10/9/1866	2326	E. Harlow	Various actions & extractors
15/11/1866	2996	E. C. Hodges	Extractors
17/11/1866	3022	T. W. Webley	Under lever double bite action, spring assisted open & close
15/12/1866	3302(P)	D. Kirkwood	Spring return for various levers
20/12/1866	3356	R. L. Martin (agent for Oelkers & Spengler)	Slide & tilt hammerless
4/1/1867	28(P)	P. Dagnall	Action fastening & strikers
8/1/1867	49(P)	J. Stanton	External spring rebound lock
16/1/1867	112(P)	C. W. Lancaster	Extractor & ejector
24/1/1867	182	J. H. Johnson (agent for S. J. Roper)	Roper shotgun American patent No. 79861 dated 14/7/1868
25/1/1867	191(P)	W. J. Hill	Single bite snap action
6/2/1867	332(P)	T. Rigby	Rebound lock
9/2/1867	367	J. Stanton	Rebound lock
2/3/1867	594(P)	W. R. Pape	Extractor & firing pins
28/3/1867	913(P)	W. Clark (agent for J. A. C. Brun)	Pin fire or centre fire & extractor French patent No. 75196 dated 22/2/1869
11/4/1867	1075	S. Smith	Single bite snap opening by cocking right lock
17/4/1867	1138	T. Horsley	Withdrawing striker
7/5/1867	1339(P)	W. W. Greener	Single bite & cross bolt
18/6/1867	1785(P)	J. Lang	Locking & use as muzzle loader

29/6/1867	1904	S. R. & W. Trulock	Inert slide & tilt
5/7/1867	1971	J. MacNaughton	Slide & tilt
25/7/1867	2168	G. L. Barens &	Single bite snap & forend catch
		J. F. Ladougne	French patent No. 77147 dated 18/7/1867
5/8/1867	2263	G. Schneider	Single bite snap, retracting firing pin & adjustable hinge pin
3/9/1867	2488	W. R. Pape	Action, extractor & striker
8/1/1868	70	M. Walker & G. H. Money	Hammerless action
14/1/1868	121	W. E. Gedge (agent for Benoit-Dulin)	Inert action slide forward barrels
2/3/1868	710	T. Horsley	Loaded indicator
7/3/1868	800	W. W. Greener	Striker & action
18/3/1868	922	R. Townsend	Action & plugs into chambers
17/4/1868	1260	F. Bacon	Single barrel bolt action
9/5/1868	1526(P)	J. H. Crane	Double bite snap action
16/5/1868	1612	C. Golden	Single bite snap action
14/7/1868	2222(P)	W. Payton	Rotating barrels
26/8/1868	2657	G. Hanson	Action, striker & loaded indicator
3/9/1868	2716	W. C. Green	Hammerless action
16/10/1868	3173	C. Churchill (agent for W. H. Miller)	Single bite snap action American patent No. 59723 dated 13/2/1866
14/1/1869	119(P)	T. Birkett & H. Scott	Multiple bolting
3/4/1869	1017	F. Boyd (agent for F. E. Boyd & P. S. Tyler	Lateral rolling action American patent No. 88540 dated 6/4/1869
7/4/1869	1055	W. Powell	Action, retracting strikers
1/5/1869	1342(P)	J. Mackie	Snap action slide and drop
11/5/1869	1436	J. Hall	Retracting strikers
21/7/1869	2218	G. T. Abbey	Treble snap bolt action
24/8/1869	2513	J. Williams	Double bite snap action
6/10/1869	2904	E. Russ, H. & E. Hammond	Double bite snap & retracting firing pins
15/10/1869	3003	J. Mackie	Snap action slide & tilt
11/12/1869	3589	W. C. Green	Actions, patent void for want of final specification
27/12/1869	3750(P)	W. Adams	Single bite snap action
30/12/1869	3774	J. Stanton	Rebound Lock
12/1/1870	92	H. Jones	Double bite action
4/2/1870	324	J. Thomas	Single bite snap action
8/3/1870	687	J. Lang	Triple grip top lever snap action
15/3/1870	752	W. R. Pape	Striker
27/6/1870	1829(P)	W. R. Lake (agent for C. E. Sneider)	Action
14/11/1870	2980	C. Golden	Striker retracting on rebound
25/11/1870	3097	H. Allen	Breech mechanisms & extractors
28/11/1870	3118	J. Purdey	Safety
10/12/1870	3242	F. Bacon	Double barrel bolt action
13/12/1870	3257	A. Henry	Snap cap
24/12/1870	3376	W. R. Lake (agent for C. E. Sneider)	Single bite snap top lever action American patent No. 85252 dated 22/12/1868

Bibliography

Abridgements of Patent Specifications
Birmingham Trade Directories
A brief history of the Westley Richards firm, 1812–1913   Leslie B. Taylor
Cartridge Manual: an illustrated digest by W. A. Bartlett and D. B. Gallatin
Catalogue of the Greener Collection of important firearms; the property of W. W. Greener Ltd (Sotheby, Wilkinson & Hodge – auctioneers)
The Causes of Decay in a British Industry   Artifex & Opifex
A Century of Guns   H. J. Blanch
The Complete Specification   Haseltine, Lake & Co
Gun Patents 1864   G. H. Daw
Deane's Manual of the History and Science of Firearms   J. Deane
Études sur les Perfectionnements apportés aux armes et sur les différents systèmes qui ont précédés le modèles en usage actuellement   Fauré Lepage
Experts on Guns and Shooting   G. T. Teasdale-Buckell
The Field 1853–1953   R. N. Rose
Forsyth & Co: Patent Gunmakers   W. Keith Neal and D. H. L. Back
The Golden Age of Shotgunning   Bob Hinman
The Gun and its Development (4th & 9th editions)   W. W. Greener
Gunnery in 1858   W. Greener
Guns and Shooting – A Bibliography   Ray Riling
Hart's Army List
Hints on Shooting and Fishing   Christopher Idle
Instructions to Young Sportsmen   Col P. Hawker
An Introduction to the Field Sports of France   R. O'Connor
Kelly's Directories
Kings of the Rod, Rifle and Gun   Thormanby
The Mantons: Gunmakers   W. Keith Neal and D. H. L. Back
Manual of British Rural Sports   J. H. Walsh
Modern Breech Loaders, Sporting and Military   W. W. Greener
The Modern Sportsman's Gun and Rifle   J. H. Walsh
Nouvel Manuel complet de l'Armurier, du Fourbisseur et de l'Arquebusier   Paulin-Desormeaux
The Revolver   A. Taylorson
Shooting, its Appliances, Practice and Purpose   J. D. Dougall
Shooting Simplified   J. D. Dougall
The Shotgun and Sporting Rifle   J. H. Walsh
The Sporting Cartridge published by F. Joyce & Co
The Sportsman in France   F. Tolfrey
The Webley Story   W. C. Dowell
Weller and Dufty Sale Catalogue No. *11205*

PERIODICALS
Arms and Explosives; Bell's Life in London; Birmingham Post and Mail; The Commissioners of Patents Journal; Daily Telegraph; The Field; Glasgow Herald; Illustrated London News; The Ironmonger; Journal of the Arms and Armour Society; Land and Water; Newcastle Journal; Reading Chronicle; The Times; Yorkshire Herald

Index

Conversions; breech loaders to muzzle loaders; 178: muzzle loaders to breech loaders; *54, 56,* 125, 126, 129, 146, 175, 195: to rebound locks; 201
Cooper, J. R.; gun; 97
Conway; 219
Correspondence to *The Field*; 25, 29, 32, 38, 40, 41, 42, 46, 49, 107, 109, 110, 112, 203, 222
Crab joint; 132
Crane, J. H.; gun; 162
Crofts, J.; pat. 1033/1866; 149, *150*
Cross, W. W.; pat. 1300/1866; 205, *206*
Crystal Palace; 26
Curious; 38

Dangers; of early centre fire guns; 184, 187, 188, 194, 198
Daniell, Col. H. J.; pat. 2585/1859; *54, 56*
Davies, J.; 26
Daw, G. H.; advertisements; *102, 106*: caps; 6: guns; 35, 40, 46, 67, 94, Chap. 7, 109, 131, 134, 183, 187, 196, 197, 209: hammerless; 214, *215*: headstamp; 6 : pat. 1594/1862; *102*: trade label; *102*: versus Eley; 35, 106, 183, 187
Deane, Adams & Deane; 56
Deane, J.; 15
Deeley, G. D.; 131: J.; 131, 165
Demondion, A.; patent agent; *19, 24*
Dickens, C.; 51
Dickinson, H.; gun; 179, *180*
Dobson; 219
Dolphin, The; 15
Doll's head; 131–133
Dougall, J. D.; and guns; 28, 41–43, 65, 73, *75, 76, 77*: pat. 2468/1863; *77,* 78, 80, 82, 129, 176
Dual ignition; 197, 198

East India Company, Honourable; 104
Ebrall, S.; 118
Edge, J. S.; pat. 139/1865; *164*–166, 190
Edward VII, H.M. King; 156
Egan; 43
Egg, C.; *89:* D.; 15, 16: H.; 90: improvement; *89*
Ejectors; 31, 207, 208
Eley Bros.; 35, 41, 105: advertisement; *106*: caps; 187: headstamp; 6: versus Daw lawsuit; 35, 106, 183, 187
Elliot, H.; pat. 1783/1863; *143,* 144, 149, 194: of Wigan; 43
Ellis, R. & Son; 162
Emme, J.; pat. 1460/1865; *210, 211*
Enfield Rifle; 104
Erskine, Col. K.; 78
Erskine, J.; pat. 1703/1859; *71, 73,* 81
Exhibitions; The Great, 1851; 22, Chap. 2, Appendix 2: London International, 1862; 76: Paris, 1834; 20: Paris, 1867; 136: Reading Industrial; 118: The Workman's 1870; 96
Experts on Guns and Shooting; 167
Expiry of patents; 50, 166, 224
Extraction: of pin fire cartridges in slide forward

gun; 84
Extractors; 31, 36, 70, 71, 84, 98, 100, 101, 103, 183, *203–209*
External stem extractors; 209

Fane, V.; 132
Fellows, G.; and Woodward patent extractor; 205
Field, J. W. P.; pat. 3485/1862; 120, *121*
Field, The; 25, 27, 29, 32, 35, Chap. 3, 71, 74, 76, 78, 83, 90, 95, 106, 107, 109, 112, 117, 120, 131, 139, 144, 146, 151, 152, 166, 167, 173, 188, 197, 203, 222: Trials, 1858; Chap. 3: Rules; Appendix 2, 231–232: Results; Appendix 2, 233–235: 1859; Chap. 3, 47, 49, 56, 85: Rules; Appendix 2, 236–237: Results; Appendix 2, 238–240: 1866; 144, 146, 167, 189: Results; Appendix 2, 241–244
Firing pins; 68, 98, 103, Chap. 12
First modern British breech loader; 27
Fixed barrels; *14–16, 19,* 22, *174,* 175, *181,* 212
Fletcher, T.; 56, 145: W.; pat. 2554/1863; *145*
Fontaine Moreau, P. A. le Comte de; gun; 70
Forend fastenings; 119, 204, 205
Forend fixed to stock; *66–73*
Forsyth, Rev. A. J.; 13, 15, 156
Francotte; 85
Frazier, J.; pat. 1269/1864; 113, *114*
French crutch gun; 48
French patentees; Beringer; 20: Brun; 198: Chaudun; 44: Concalon; 181: Gastinne; 32: Houllier; 21, 44: Lefaucheux; 16: Marcet; 215: Pauly; 13: Plumerel; 212: Pottet; 18: Robert; 19

G.M.; 29, 40
Gamekeeper in Windsor Great Park; *55*
Garibaldi, Gen.; 105
Gastinne, L. J.; 32, 66, 71, 100: pat. 2744/1862; *188,* 190, 192, 204, 212
Gastinne Renette; 188
Gedge, W. E.; patent agent; pat. 121/1868; *89, 90,* 128
Gevelot; 41
Gibbs; guns; *28, 129, 210*
Gibson, J.; and Trulock, Trulock and Trulock pat. 1696/1863; 79, *80,* 8ł
Glasgow Gunmaker; pseudonym of J. D. Dougall
Golden, C.; pat. 1612/1868; 115, *116*: pat. 2980/1870; *193*
Grant, S.; pat. 1538/1861; *59,* 60, 180, 219
Greaves & Smith, patentee; *98*
Green; 43
Green, W. C.; pat. 2716/1868; *223,* 224
Greener, W.; 44, 73, 88, 89
Greener, W. W.; 31, 32, 34, 43, 51, 96: pat. 1339/1867; 124, *125*: pat. 2231/1863; *132,* 133, 158, 170, 174: pat. 800/1868; *190,* 199, 214, 215, 223
Grey, F. H.; pat. 2743/1865; *195,* 199
Grip safety; 36, 213
Gun and its Development; 32, 51, 96, 170, 174

256

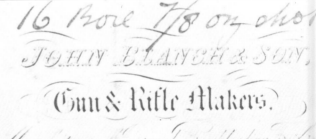

16 Bore 7/8 oz shot

JOHN BLANCH & SON,

Gun & Rifle Makers.

Manufacturers of improved Breechloading Guns

29, GRACECHURCH STREET.

London

E.C.

George Gibbs,

GUN-MAKER,

29 Clare Street,

BRISTOL.

Single & Double Barrelled Rifles, on an improved principle.